A HISTORY OF THE ROYAL COLLEGE
OF PHYSICIANS OF LONDON

I. Thomas Linacre, Founder, President and Benefactor of the College

A History of
THE ROYAL COLLEGE
OF PHYSICIANS
of London

VOLUME ONE

SIR GEORGE CLARK, F.B.A.

CLARENDON PRESS · OXFORD
for
THE ROYAL COLLEGE OF PHYSICIANS
1964

Oxford University Press, Amen House, London E.C.4

GLASGOW NEW YORK TORONTO MELBOURNE WELLINGTON
BOMBAY CALCUTTA MADRAS KARACHI LAHORE DACCA
CAPE TOWN SALISBURY NAIROBI IBADAN ACCRA
KUALA LUMPUR HONG KONG

PRINTED IN GREAT BRITAIN AT
THE UNIVERSITY PRESS
ABERDEEN

PREFACE

THE long history of the Royal College of Physicians of London is so rich in incident and in significance for medical science, education and practice that the reader should be told which of its many aspects are treated in the present work. The central theme which I have followed does indeed lead on to all the others, and I hope my plain tale may serve as an introduction to all or any of them. I have traced the purposes which the College as a body set before itself, its efforts to fulfil them, the ways in which it was helped or hindered by other institutions, in short its place in English social history.

The invitation to write this book for the College was conveyed by its former President, Lord Moran, and throughout its progress I have owed to him such advice and stimulation as no one else could have given, but I must not close this sentence without adding the name of Lady Moran, whom I cannot sufficiently thank for her hospitality. Lady Franks, as on some former occasions, has generously relieved me of much of the burden of research. Dr. H. A. T. Robb-Smith most kindly read the first twelve chapters in typescript and made valuable comments. Mr. Leonard Payne, Librarian of the College, has read the whole and, while I have been working, has ungrudgingly allowed me to draw on his great knowledge of the College records and of medical history and bibliography in general. These, with my perpetual debt to my wife's companionship and encouragement, are my chief obligations. The names of some others to whom I owe thanks will be found on another page.

It is unnecessary to state, though as a matter of form perhaps I ought to write it, that the Officers of the College have done everything that was possible to smooth my way, keeping nothing secret from me but never exercising any censorship or even seeing what I have written.

This first volume carries the story down to the Revolution of 1688, which was also a revolution in the affairs of the College, except for one omission. The account of the preliminary steps, from 1675 onwards, which led to the opening of the famous Dispensary in 1696 has been reserved for publication in a second volume, continuing the story to the Medical Act of 1858. In one matter I must ask the reader's indulgence: the present volume has no index. After much consideration it has been decided that the advantages of a single index for the two volumes will outweigh the temporary inconvenience of having none for the first. The full table of contents and the cross-references in the footnotes should partly make good the deficiency. The second volume will include some Appendixes relating to both volumes.

All Souls College, Oxford   G.N.C.
    6 March 1964

ACKNOWLEDGEMENTS

IN the Preface and other places I have mentioned some of those who have helped me with information and advice, and among the others I ought to express my sincere gratitude to the Officers and Staff of the Royal College of Physicians, especially two successive Presidents, Sir Robert Platt and Sir Charles Dodds, two Registrars, the late Sir Harold Boldero and Dr. K. Robson, the Harveian Librarian, Dr. Charles Newman, the library staff, especially Mr. M. J. de C. Hamilton and Miss Hazel Short, and the Secretary, Miss Ina Cook; the Trustees of the British Museum and Miss H. M. Wallis of their Map Room; the Librarian and staff of the Guildhall Library; the Curators of the Bodleian Library and Dr. Richard Hunt; the Society of Apothecaries, Dr. W. S. C. Copeman, Past Master, and Mr. Ernest Busby, their Clerk; the Wellcome Historical Medical Library, especially the Director, Dr. E. Ashworth Underwood and the Librarian Dr. F. N. L. Poynter; Professor T. S. Ashton, the late Dr. W. J. Bishop, Dr. J. M. S. de Guilleuma, Dr. Philip Jones, Mr. P. I. King, Miss A. Lothian, Dr. R. S. Roberts, Professor Rubera, Mr. John Sparrow, Warden of All Souls College, Professor R. Weiss and Dr. Gweneth Whitteridge.

TABLE OF CONTENTS

III Thomas Linacre

IV The Foundation of the College of Physicians of London

V The First Phase, 1518–55

VIII   THE ELIZABETHAN COLLEGE, 1572–1603

XII JACOBEAN PLANS, 1614–20

XIII THE COLLEGE HOLDS ITS OWN, 1621–40

XV Doubtful Prospects, 1621–40

XV Revolutions and recovery, 1640–60

XVI HARVEY

XVII FROM THE RESTORATION TO THE FIRE OF LONDON, 1660–6

XIX From the Popish Plot to the Revolution Settlement, 1679–89

Appendixes

LIST OF PLATES

NOTE ON DATES

Most of the dates in this volume are English, and are therefore given in the Old Style used in this country down to 1752, but for dates between 1 January and 25 March, from which latter day the new year was reckoned, the double year-date is given. The few foreign dates are given as in the authorities from which they come, but they do not relate to transactions between England and foreign countries in which the sequence of dates is of any importance, and so those of them which are in New Style cannot cause any confusion.

I: THE HEALING ARTS IN EARLY TUDOR ENGLAND

IN the year 1518, when King Henry VIII granted a charter to the College of Physicians of London, the continuous history of English physicians as an organized profession began. It did not, however, begin quite suddenly from nothing, and in order to explain the origin of the College it is necessary to describe how illnesses and injuries were dealt with in the preceding period. If we were dealing with a modern country, even a very undeveloped country, we should begin such a description with an account of the medical services, with a list of institutions, statistics of the various kinds of practitioners and so forth. For the England of 1518 that approach is possible, though it involves research, since at the time there were no directories and no one kept lists of medical men, or suffered any inconvenience from the lack of them. But nothing of that sort would be suitable as a beginning for our survey. To see the medical services of that simpler England in proper perspective we must begin not with the trained services, such as they were, but with home medicine. Nowadays we think of the medical art as something known and practised by doctors. Housewives and children's nurses deal with minor ailments, cuts and bruises and so on, for which it is not worth while to trouble the doctor; but they try to do as the doctor would wish them to do, and they often attend classes which the professionals teach. They take for granted the presence of numerous, active, trusted professional practitioners. In Tudor times most people had to rely on themselves and their neighbours for much more serious attentions. Most of them were country-dwellers and they doctored one another as they doctored their farm animals. Home medicine was not only more in demand than it is now; it was also proportionately more highly esteemed. So far from being confined to a residue of trivial cases it constituted the main provision of therapeutic service.

It was needed equally in all ranks of society, and if some villagers could only gather medicinal herbs in the hedgerows, the rich and well-educated cultivated them in physic-gardens beside their manor-houses and monasteries. They exchanged information and ideas. Laurent Joubert, chancellor of the university of Montpellier, one of the famous physicians of the century, is said to have complimented his mother on her salve, ointment and 'wine of absinthe' exactly as he might have praised the recipes used in her kitchen.[1] Masses of recipes and rules for health have survived from those times singly or in greater or smaller collections. At first sight they seem to be merely a chaotic mixture of sense and nonsense, but successive generations of modern scholars have sorted them out into a coherent arrangement.

To begin with there was a body of inherited good sense for which we can no more detect a specific origin than we can for intelligence or good manners. From time immemorial people had understood more or less clearly that cleanliness, exercise, temperance and a suitable diet were healthy, just as they knew that some plants were poisonous and some drinks intoxicating. They did not know the reasons for these things, and when they tried to explain them and to apply their explanations to inventing new remedies or health rules they often went lamentably astray, but, for all that, the tradition somehow carried the race along. It did not consist simply of a few rules and proverbs and instincts. In three of its branches, although the tradition included many things which have since been set aside as futile or positively harmful, it rendered social service and engendered a sense of responsibility and discipline. The first was nursing. For the lady who dressed the wounds of the unhorsed knight and equally for the ploughman's wife there was a difference between skilled and unskilled nursing then as now. One of Shakespeare's characters said: 'I will attend my husband, be his nurse, diet his sicknesse for it is my Office.'[2] The second branch also, midwifery, was a women's occupation. Little can be known about the daily work of midwives over the country as a whole, but there are some signs that it was regarded as a public, not merely a domestic function.[3] Obviously of public concern was the third branch, sanitation.[4] Manorial courts in the villages enforced rules for the

---

[1] In the prefatory matter before his *Chirurgia Magna Guidonis de Cauliaco Restituta*, but not in the copy of the 1585 edition which I have consulted.

[2] *Comedy of Errors*, v. i. 98.

[3] It appears to have been in the sixteenth century that the Guild of Birmingham granted one of its houses rent-free to 'the common midewyffe': J. Toulmin Smith, *English Gilds* (Early English Text Society, 1870), p. 249. See also the Note on the Licensing of Midwives at the end of c. IV below.

[4] Sir William Holdsworth, *History of English Law*, iii (1923), 279.

removal of refuse; in the boroughs there were by-laws against nuisances, and others for precautions against infectious diseases.

Some of the scholars who have explored the practice of this popular medicine have been impressed to find that many of them were identical with those of other countries in the remote past, with those of primitive peoples studied by anthropologists and with those of the more primitive inhabitants of modern European countries. They pointed out, truly enough, that in the contemporary West, and not only in isolated rural places, there exists side by side with the officially accepted system of therapy another which works with entirely different means but has at least as many permanent or occasional adherents. This unauthorized system confidently applies its remedies without any definite notion of how they work. It recognizes a very limited number of diseases, and it takes very little trouble over diagnosis; but it has been strangely uniform over wide areas and through long periods of time. It reminds us of primitive religious beliefs, especially animism. Its main idea about sickness is to ascribe it to an intruding evil being. This applies to many afflictions, from possession by evil spirits to the ravages of real or imaginary worms. The system has two famous principles. The principle of sympathy underlies cures which use some object associated with the causation of an injury or disease. The principle of signatures provides a clue to finding efficacious herbs by some resemblance of shape or colour to the affected part or to the symptoms, and this resemblance serves as an explanation of their remedial power. Thus arise exorcism, whether heathen survival or skimmed over with a Christian varnish, cures by sympathetic magic, the sacrificial killing of small birds and animals with proper incantations, and above all herbal remedies. Comparative folk-lore suggests that this system of 'instinctive' healing has been handed down, mainly by oral tradition, from very distant times and belongs to the deep sub-soil of civilization.[1]

It is however true that both its principles and many of its details are written down in manuscripts of the sixteenth, fifteenth and earlier centuries, and this implies that the system was transmitted partly in writing and not only by word of mouth. It also implies

---

[1] An attractive statement of this view, written by a catholic priest before modern psychology brought in new criteria for judging the irrational, is in J. Schrijnen, *Nederlandsche volkskunde* (?1918), ii. 302–11. O. von Hovorka and A. Kronfeld, *Vergleichende Volksmedizin*, 2 vols. (1908–9) is a sort of encyclopaedia of the subject at the same stage, less full for western than for central and eastern Europe.

that in those days it was current among the lettered minority as well as among the illiterate many. When these manuscripts have been printed during the last hundred years scholars have indeed sometimes thought that the language of the recipes and of the rhymed English health-maxims was more racy of the soil than that of sophisticated literature. Further consideration has modified this view. A good example of medical self-help is in a manuscript volume written out, perhaps copied or perhaps compiled, by a Yorkshire country gentleman, Robert Thornton, in 1422–54. His family seem to have kept it by them and it would not be in any way surprising if they were still using it in 1518. In other parts of the volume he copied out romances, sermons, mystical writings, and religious lyrics. The medical part contains some prescriptions which are attributed to named authorities. There are about twenty in English and one in Latin from the rector of Oswaldkirk: these are erudite and not naïve. One, for deafness, comes from Master William of Exeter, who was physician to Queen Philippa in 1336–44,[1] and two presumably from the Franciscan William Appleton, physician to John of Gaunt from 1371. The fourteenth-century plague-tract often ascribed to John of Bordeaux is transcribed: forty English fifteenth-century manuscripts of this tract survive.[2] There is a list of hot ingredients for medicines, which the learned editor compares in parallel columns with those of the great ancient writer Galen and the great medieval writers Avicenna and Guy de Chauliac. But along with these pieces of dignified origin there is a miscellaneous collection of recipes and charms, typical of the medieval tradition. The charms are of various kinds, from straightforward prayers, for instance for use by childing women, to the famous square of letters

$$
\begin{array}{ccccc}
S & A & T & O & R \\
A & R & E & P & O \\
T & E & N & E & T \\
O & P & E & R & A \\
R & O & T & A & S \\
\end{array}
$$

where the same words are found by reading in four different directions, with magical effects if the proper procedure was followed.

[1] C. S. Emden, *Biographical Register of the University of Oxford*, i (1957), 659–60.

[2] H. S. Bennet, *Chaucer and the Fifteenth Century*, Oxford Hist. of English Literature, vol. ii, pt. 1 (1947), p. 196. For other notices of the medical works of the time see ibid. pp. 102, 158, 164–5, 256–7, 264.

Like the whole medical part of the manuscript this collection looks like a jumble, and in a sense it is a jumble. The compiler seems unable to distinguish better materials from worse either by any test of quality, or by their venerable antiquity, or least of all by their being up to date. Yet the editor is able to write in the light of accumulated knowledge that 'the material contained in these late vernacular collections is more stereotyped than has usually been recognised', and that from the point of view of language what we have here is not 'setting down of the details of folk-procedure in a kind of spontaneous language which does not appear in ordinary literary prose'.[1] As in other departments of culture much that has been mistaken for untaught popular wisdom had in fact filtered down, degenerating as it came, from the greatest masters of earlier times. And in the early sixteenth century the medical literature which was written for and even by men with no medical training stood high in reputation. The most esteemed poet of the fifteenth century, John Lydgate, was a Benedictine monk. He wrote verses about many subjects, among them medicine. There were eighty-one lines of verse called 'Medicina Stomachi' following the thirty-two prose pages of his *Governayle of Helthe*. Caxton printed this little book about 1489, and from that time the flow of medicinal books for the household has never ceased, though the books themselves have changed as much as everything else in the medical world. Educated men in general read the standard medical books in which medical science was embodied. Medical studies were primarily literary and only in the second place practical; there were medical books in many libraries, and men who could understand their language did not consider themselves debarred from acting in accordance with what they read.

There were limits to what even the most diligent amateur of remedies could hope to accomplish. He or she might acquire a reputation for skill by any means from common sense to witchcraft, and might be resorted to by neighbours who might give some fee or some reward in kind, but besides home-healing there were services rendered by people who depended on them for a livelihood and laid claim to special skill. Such people were to be found in the towns. In the whole of England and Wales—which probably had a total population of some three or four millions—there were between

---

[1] Margaret S. Ogden in her excellent edition of the *Liber de Diversis Medicinis* (Early English Text Society, 1938), pp. xxv–xxvi.

six and seven hundred boroughs and market towns. They lay much closer together in the busy and populous parts of the country than in the less prosperous regions like the north and west, but there were enough of them almost everywhere to enable the countryman to do his necessary selling and buying with no more than a day's journey there and back on foot or on horseback. Most of the towns were very small. London was by far the largest, with something in the neighbourhood of 50,000 people. About thirty towns seem to have numbered from 5,000 to 10,000; Coventry, which was probably one of the twenty-five most populous had 6,601 in 1520.[1] Among the shopkeepers in many of these little settlements there were apothecaries, and their trade had been recognized as a distinctive occupation for centuries. They sold medicaments and the materials from which they were made for internal and external application, especially, of course those which were less easy to come by. These ranged from dried herbs to imported drugs and portions of human mummies and corpses of animals, birds and fishes. The trade was slowly becoming differentiated from the selling of spices and other such commodities which were not perishable, but there cannot have been many places where it was possible to make a living from pharmaceutical goods alone. Thus there are few records of the apothecaries' activities at this time; but it is inconceivable that they refrained from giving advice about their wares. When they recommended one rather than another and explained how it was to be used, they gave more or less rudimentary medical advice. It may be taken for granted that their customers sometimes paid for the advice as well as for the medicine. The Royal household included a 'yeoman potycary' who, in addition to providing medicines and ingredients, had the duty of fumigating the king's clothes to prevent infection.[2] Other great households also employed or dealt with apothecaries, sometimes paying them considerable sums. In London they were numerous enough to be organized as a body, but even there they were not a separate company but formed a component of the Company of Grocers.[3] In other towns they were associated with some other group of shopkeepers.[4]

---

[1] *The Coventry Leet Book,* ed. Mary D. Harris, iii (1909), 675.

[2] A. R. Myers, *The Household of Edward IV* (1959), pp. 118, 125 ; T. Vicary, *Anatomie* ed. F. J. and P. Furnivall (Early English Text Society, 1888), pp. 99 ff.

[3] A charter of 26 Henry VI extended the Grocers' control and oversight to druggists, apothecaries and confectioners.

[4] In Worcester, for instance, at a later date they were members of the mercers' company. See the entries relating to Dr. John Colbatch in the Annals of the College of Physicians, 8 May and 3 July 1696.

Besides the apothecaries there were surgeons in the towns. The use of surgical instruments may be supposed to have lain outside the range of any except the most enterprising amateurs, and for a long time past the barber-surgeon had been a familiar figure. There was nothing incongruous in the ancient combination of these two crafts which have since drawn so far apart. There was something in common between the two. They both required good hands, and the line between the remedial and the cosmetic is never absolutely definite. For some emergencies surgery was the only recourse, but in that simple society there were very few places where surgeons could find enough work to subsist by it alone. With the aid of barbery they maintained themselves in considerable numbers and much more is recorded of them than of the apothecaries. Both they and their patients must have regarded it as natural that in addition to using their instruments they should give advice to their patients about internal remedies.

Our information about them comes chiefly from the craft associations in which they were enrolled. All over western and central Europe in the later Middle Ages, as in many other places and times, it was usual for the shopkeepers and craftsmen of the towns to belong to such bodies, which are commonly called 'guilds'. Their members had an exclusive right, conferred by the municipal authorities, of making or selling some particular kind of goods in the civic market and within a specified distance from it. They had the right to make and enforce regulations to keep up standards of quality in their goods; they controlled the hours and conditions of work and the numbers of the journeymen whom masters might employ; they supervised the numbers, enrolment and training of apprentices. It was their function to stand up for the interests of their craft, and this included checking what was regarded as unfair competition among themselves and seeing that the consumer had reasonable treatment at their hands. Like all medieval institutions they showed an infinite variety of detail within their broad uniformity of type, but everywhere they provided a setting for the social activity and enjoyment for their members. They had banners and processions, banquets and services in church; the richer among them had common halls; they all had some degree of corporate spirit. There were lively antagonisms within and between them, within them for instance about elections and voting arrangements, between them about the demarcation of their respective spheres.

In some places they came to excerise power in municipal government, driving into a corner the older, oligarchical associations or
other bodies which originally controlled it. In France, Italy and
the Low Countries they rose up against feudal lords and civic
tyrants. So partly from their nature and partly from their history
the name of 'guild' has gained richly coloured associations. It calls
up the vision of a free, democratic, equitable, self-governing urban
society which was extinguished in the early sixteenth century or
thereabouts by the rich, or the New Monarchy or the Reformation,
or all three.

This all helps to explain the tendency of some medical historians
to ascribe too much importance to the companies of barber-surgeons
One writer calls them 'a powerful state medical service',[1] and another
less wide of the mark, 'the early nurseries of general practice'.[2] To
some extent these writers were misled by economic historians who
transferred some of the romance of the guilds from the Continent
to England, where their history was altogether more modest.[3]
Even their use of words was tinged with this mistake. In England
in the fifteenth century the word 'guild' was used much more
commonly for religious, social and quasi-municipal organizations[4]
than for craft-organizations. We do sometimes find a body with a
name like 'guild of carpenters', but generally we find a craft, fellowship or mystery (distinguished by modern scholars as 'mistery').
For the surgeons in London it is sometimes 'the faculty'; but that
has nothing to do with 'the faculty' as a vague description of doctors
in general: it is only a synonym for 'craft'. About the year 1534 a
writer with notions of reform, dealing with every kind of trade, or
as he put it 'mystere craft and faculty' wanted to see 'every man in
his craft and faculty to meddyl wyth such thynge as perteyneth
therto, and inter meddyle not wyth other'.[5] Some writers however
prefer to call all medieval trade-associations 'guilds' or, with a more

---

[1] G. Parker, see below, p. 10 n. 4.
[2] J. J. Keevil, ' The Seventeenth Century English Medical Background ' in *Bulletin
of the History of Medicine*, xxxi (1957), 20.
[3] See for instance J. Toulmin Smith, *English Gilds* (1870) and L. Brentano's Introduction to it. On p. 259 the English Guilds are said to have been 'annihilated' in the
reign of Edward VI.
[4] By quasi-municipal I mean such bodies as the *gilda mercatoria*, for which the
best translation seems to be not 'guild merchant' but 'market-guild'. Occupational
guilds whose heads were called aldermen existed from the time of Henry II to that
of Edward IV when the charters of livery companies, with masters or wardens,
began in London.
[5] T. Starkey, *England in the Reign of Henry VIII* (E.E.T.S., 1871), pp. 157-8.

old-world appearance 'gilds'.[1] Some refer to the medieval universities as guilds of teachers, but this is another instance of the use of the word for any kind of self-governing body. The masters in the universities did not sell goods or services to outside customers, and no apprentices were bound to them as individuals. The companies of barber-surgeons belonged to the humbler sphere of those who traded, took apprentices and employed journeymen.

There were itinerant surgeons who moved from one fair or market to another, just as there were no doubt pedlars who sold apothecaries' wares; and even among the settled practitioners in some of the towns organization was not highly developed. There never was any law in England compelling every craftsman to belong to the guild of his craft. The law of 1363 (3 Edward III, c. 6), which is sometimes said to have had this effect, merely says that no one is to belong to more than one such body. In a few specified crafts there were laws in later times which compelled all masters to belong to the appropriate bodies, but in general such compulsion as there was rested on municipal ordinances in each place, and the strength of the system was that it was the interest of the masters to associate. There were pirate masters who refused to obey a company's orders or even tried to break its monopoly, but they were only an inevitable by-product of the associative system. For special reasons some occupations, the most notable of which were those of masons and other workers in the building trades, never came into the network. The advantages of being in it were so great that workers were often packed together without any logical classification of callings. On the Continent there are many records of companies of barber-surgeons. Where they were too few to form a company of their own, they were allowed to combine with others who might have very little in common with them. In Amsterdam in the sixteenth century the surgeons were in the guild of the makers of wooden shoes.[2] There are instances of the same practice in England. In Kendal in Westmorland in 1578 the tenth

---

[1] Toulmin Smith, p. 259, line 6, writes in the name 'gild' for mysteries or crafts.

[2] The physicians and apothecaries went in with the stall-keepers. (P. L. Muller, *Onze gouden eeuw*, 2nd edn. (*s.a.*, ?1908), p. 356. The wooden shoemakers' guild obtained its charter in 1551 and included other minor trades (*Bronnen tot de geschiedenis van het bedrijfsleven en het gildewesen van Amsterdam*, ed. J. G. van Dillen, i(1929), no. 364). The Amsterdam barbers' guild, which included barber-surgeons, was in existence in 1508, and a charter was granted to a surgeons' guild in 1552, but there were still barber-surgeons after that (ibid. 1320, 376, 494).

in order (probably the order of seniority in age) among the twelve companies, combined the surgeons with scriveners, barbers, glovers, skinners, parchment, and point-makers.[1] In Newcastle-on-Tyne the barber-surgeons went along with the wax-chandlers, an allied occupation since wax was used for embalming.[2] In Oxford their associates were the waferers (confectioners) and the makers of 'singing bread' for Holy Communion. At Kingston-upon-Hull they were united with a craft closely allied with barbers, namely the peruke-makers, but in Salisbury they were brigaded with the silk-weavers.[3] It seems likely that something of the same sort happened elsewhere, so that the absence of a barber-surgeons' or surgeons' company does not mean that there was no organization for them. Where they were provided for in this way their traces may very well have escaped notice. In one place they may have passed unnoticed for another reason. Norwich shared with London the privilege that, whatever company men belonged to, they might pursue any trade. In London, as we shall see, this is probably not important as concealing the whereabouts of surgeons, but it may be so in Norwich, where there was a Brotherhood of Barbers in 1389, but there seems to be no printed record of barber-surgeons before 1561. For these reasons there were probably more barber-surgeons in the country, and better provision for them than we know at present.

The fullest list of barber-surgeons' companies so far collected is that of Dr. George Parker, who found them in eighteen provincial towns.[4] In some of these the traces are only slight, for instance the appearance of barber-surgeons in a procession in Hereford in 1503, and there are a few to which the first reference is later than 1518. Such important towns as Canterbury, Cambridge, Northampton, Leicester, Nottingham, Derby, Shrewsbury, Coventry, and King's

---

[1] *Historical Manuscripts Commission, 10th Report, Appendix*, pt. iv, pp. 299–318. The date is not perfectly clear. The first nine companies each include three or four crafts and are perhaps medieval; the eleventh and twelfth name fourteen and thirteen respectively, more or less closely related.

[2] Toulmin Smith, p. 27.

[3] The earliest ordinances of the Hull guild, the last and thirty-fourth in the list, date from 1714: L. M. Stanewell, *City and County of Kingston-upon-Hull, Calendar of the Ancient Deeds* (1951), p. 372. In 1614 the Salisbury silk-weavers were granted a corpse for dissection.

[4] In a paper in the *XVIIth International Congress of Medicine, Sec. XXIII, Hist. of Medicine* (1927) and in his book *The Early History of Surgery in Great Britain* (1920). The paper includes some details not given in the book, but appears to be based on the materials mentioned in the useful bibliography of the latter. I have not repeated Parker's references for provincial guilds.

Lynn are not among them, but the evidence is enough to justify us in concluding that the barber-surgeons normally had their place in the medieval trade-organization.

Before we deal with the one outstanding body among them, the London Companies of Barber Surgeons, it will be convenient to touch briefly on the later decline of the craft associations. From the early sixteenth century this form of organization was gradually superseded for many purposes by others. The greatest reason for this was the rise of capitalism in industry and commerce, while the contemporaneous social and religious changes also furthered the process. In many industries the companies sank into obscurity, or ceased to fulfil their original purposes and continued, like the London City Companies in quite altered guise. Many perished altogether. It became unusual to set up a guild or such-like body to manage a newly-founded charity such as a hospital for the poor, an almshouse or a school. Instead of officers elected by a body of freemen, livery-men or the like, or responsible to them, the founders now appointed trustees or feoffees who generally co-opted their successors and were bound only by their trust-deeds. Another device, which like this had roots in earlier times, was the joint stock company, in the seventeenth century a familiar form for large enterprises and later for many others including some with religious and charitable objects. But when conditions still resembled those of earlier times, the older model was still sometimes followed. In the sixteenth and seventeenth centuries and even in the eighteenth bodies with nearly all the features of the old companies were created by charters or by municipal action. In London there were several of them, not only for new trades like the distillers (1638), but for old occupations like shipbuilding (1600) which grew in importance. On the Continent there are known examples of such late foundations of surgeons' guilds, and it would be the reverse of surprising if further research were to reveal that the barber-surgeons of Chester or St. Albans were first incorporated after 1518.[1] It will be useful to us later in another connexion to remember that this form of association still had life in it.

The civic authorities of London had recognized surgeons for generations past as having functions which concerned the good government of the city and as needing effective discipline in their

---

[1] That of Chester received a charter in 1540, that of St. Albans was in existence about 1563.

work.[1] It is said that as early as the fourteenth century they or some of them were formally appointed to keep the city gates, with the duty of preventing the entry of persons who might bring in contagious diseases. Surgeons first appear in the City records in 1354 when four of them were sworn before the mayor to report whether an injury which a complainant had received was curable when a person (as to whom it is not stated whether he was a surgeon) undertook to cure it. Fourteen years later masters of surgeons were sworn, and they received authority over all who practised surgery in London. Such appointments of masters or overseers continued into the fifteenth century, and the authority of these masters extended not only over matters of police, such as the duty of surgeons to report all cases of wounding and the like, but also to malpractices in the art, such as charging excessive fees or treating injuries and maladies unskilfully.[2] But, as the surgeons advanced in skill and influence, their association with the barbers became irksome. The barbers became a livery company in 1387, and thirty years after that there are signs that the general body of their commonalty wanted to keep the right to practise surgery, but a smaller element, presumably more highly skilled, wanted to reserve it for themselves.

This would have happened in any case, as it did in the continental countries, and the best English surgery was already something to be proud of. It had its own literature. John Arderne, who practised in fourteenth-century London after a successful provincial career, wrote books, which though not up to the contemporary French standard, were practical, readable and, what is more important, translated into English and used. So was the much greater work of the French surgeon Guy de Chauliac, and it is evident from their contents that they were translated not for interested members of the public but for practising surgeons. It has been shown from the careers of surgeons who served in the English armies against France under Edward III and Henry V that war-experience contributed, as it has so often done, to surgical progress, and that those who returned from it raised the status of their art. By the time of

---

[1] There are two valuable works, largely covering the same ground, in which the facts are given from record sources and leading documents are printed in full: J. F. South, *Memorials of the Craft of Surgery*, ed. (Sir) D'Arcy Power (1886) and S. Young, *Annals of the Barber-Surgeons of London* (1890). Both however, and particularly the former, are sometimes at fault in matters of interpretation.

[2] This was normal craft-organization. The statute 37 Edward III, c. 6 mentioned above, p. 9, orders that two each mystery are to be elected 'de surveer que nul usee altre meistere que cele il ad eslieu': they are called 'surveours'.

Henry V there was an established distinction within the Barber-Surgeons Company between the barbers and the barber-surgeons practising surgery (*barbitonsores cirurgie facultatem exercentes*). Each group had its own masters. In 1435 the surgeons proper formed their own association: the ordinances of the worshipful men and all the commonalty of the Craft or Fellowship of Surgeons were engrossed.[1] The number of members was seventeen. They were a specialized, superior group within the body of surgeons; the barbers had not given up their pretensions, and in 1451 their right to practise surgery was confirmed[2]; but for a considerable time the two companies existed side by side. They both held their heads high. In 1451 the two sets of masters within it successfully petitioned for a grant of arms to the Craft of Barbers[3]; in 1492 the Craft of Surgeons acquired a similar mark of status. By that time the Crown was growing in strength as the Wars of the Roses drew to an end, and it was beginning to control municipal affairs more tightly. In 1464–5 the parliament of King Edward IV gave statutory recognition to all Letters Patent granted to the warden or masters of any craft or crafts.[4] One of the grants was a charter of the same king, of 1462, setting up the Community or Fellowship of Barbers as a Company, with the power to govern surgeons by masters.[5]

For our present purpose we need not go into further detail about the relations of these two Companies, and we may leave the surgeons for the present with some general remarks. Socially they stood higher than the apothecaries. In the royal household there was a master surgeon who had a yeoman under him, besides two persons to wait on him and another servant and horses.[6] In London the Company and Fellowship of Barbers and barber-surgeons or, occasionally, surgeons-barbers, was no inconsiderable society. It had its own hall. Like the other companies it maintained its monopoly with the power of the City behind it. Most of its members plied an unimpressive trade, but they were numerous and so the Company was rich: in 1537 it had more members than any other City Company.[7] The specialized surgeons were not necessarily men of much general education, but their art was nearer than the

---

[1] Text in South, Appendix C.   [2] Ibid. Appendix D.
[3] Ibid. pp. 71–72.   [4] 4 Edward IV, repeated in 7 Edward IV.
[5] South, Appendix E.
[6] A. R. Myers, *The Household of Edward IV* (1959), pp. 124–5. Less satisfactory editions of this document have been available since 1790.
[7] Young, p. 94.

common handicrafts to the world of learning. It had, as we have seen, its literature. Licences to practise it were granted not only by the surgeons' own companies in London and the provinces, but also by the universities of Oxford and Cambridge.

Now at last we come to the people with whom we are chiefly concerned, the physicians. There is no need to draw up a careful definition of their functions; to make it too precise would probably be misleading. They did not keep shops like the apothecaries, and in their capacity as physicians they did not use surgical instruments. They regarded surgery, however, as a method of treatment. It was within their province to recommend it and supervise it; no doubt also on occasion actually to practise it. They examined patients and they also probably examined specimens of urine for a lower fee without seeing their patients. They prescribed diets and internal or external medicaments in writing; and their written *consilia*, even when they had not personally seen the patients, were valued in proportion to their professional repute. Sometimes they administered remedies in person; sometimes they watched while an apothecary did it. No doubt it was beneath the physician's dignity to sell his medicines, and where the apothecaries were organized it would have infringed their monopoly, but, as human nature was admittedly below the angels, the physician was exposed to the temptation of going shares in the apothecary's profits. He was, however, decidedly higher in standing than any of the other healers. What made him so was his superior education. We cannot say definitely that the name of physician was currently used only for those who had studied medicine in universities, but that was not very far from its accepted meaning. The physician was learned in the voluminous Latin literature of the medical tradition, which had been slowly gathered and synthesized for centuries from classical, Arabic and European sources, of late almost entirely in the universities. It was transmitted with their authority and by means of their pedagogic skill. After testing a candidate by a long-established system of examinations, they certified his proficiency by granting him a degree. His knowledge was supposed to make him understand all the healing arts in all their aspects.

The social figure of the physician, as we discern it in the fifteenth century, is remarkably clear, partly perhaps because it was carried on from one author to another, but at least partly because training and experience did produce a social type. Chaucer, who died in

1400, drew it with his master hand in the Prologue to the *Canterbury Tales* ; the tales were printed twice by Caxton, and they were part of the educated Englishman's panorama of society. From them and from scattered notices in letters and documents we may infer that the physicians were prosperous, worldly-wise and respected, and that in their dress and bearing they were much closer to the learned clerk than to the merchant or the man of action. In relations with the sick they may have stood somewhat aloof, as befitted the possessors of esoteric knowledge; we cannot tell whether they responded to what they had read in the *Aphorisms* of Hippocrates about co-operation with the patient. Our sources indeed are almost silent on many significant matters. We know little about the social *provenance* of individual physicians. Most likely they came, like the majority of university students, from the middling ranks of society: there are no physicians who were at work in the year 1500 of whom we know that their parents were rich and none of whom we know that their parents were poor. We cannot tell how many of them were the sons or nephews of medical men of any kind. We have to rely entirely on imagination for any idea of the motives which led them to 'enter on the physic line'.[1]

One reason why we are at a loss in these matters lies in a fact which deserves to be emphasized strongly: the physicians were very few. How many there were in London or in the country as a whole it would be very rash to say. Paris was a city of the same order of magnitude as London, and for Paris we have some estimates. For 1500 there is a quite unreliable conjecture that there were twenty-one *médecins*. In 1566, when the city had grown and the number of practitioners may have grown more than proportionately, the university faculty arrived officially at a figure which was probably sound: it was eighty-one.[2] The two cities were by no means alike in social structure, and a comparison between them cannot give more than a rough standard to judge by ; but these figures agree well enough with the result of enumerating known English physicians.

What was the place of this small group in the organization of medical services? At the first glance we might be disposed to say

[1] For the state of these matters in Italy see R. Ciasca, *L' arte dei medici e speziali* (1927), pp. 309–10.
[2] A. Franklin, *La Vie privée d'autrefois*, xi, *Les Médecins* (1892), p. 123. For some comparable figures for medieval Italian cities see Ciasca, pp. 277–8, 291. J. H. Baas, *Die geschichtliche Entwicklung des ärtzlichen Standes und der med. Wissenschaften* (1896), p. 184 gives eighteen for Vienna in 1511 and seventeen for Basel in 1557, and says that the first physician appeared in Bremen in 1519.

that they stood entirely outside it. There was no company of physicians as such. As we shall see in the next chapter, an attempt to collect them into a London association in 1423–4 had foundered without leaving wreckage behind it. We cannot indeed be certain that in London or in other towns there were not physicians who, precisely because of their fewness, joined some other craft or mystery; but even this is improbable.[1] One of the advantages of belonging to a company was that a member could enrol his agreements with his apprentices in the company's books, and through it with the municipal authorities. The apothecaries and the barber-surgeons regularly did this; but among the men of occupations which we now call professional we may already draw a distinction between those who served an apprenticeship and those who did not. The attorneys did, and the education of barristers was based on the same principle. The clergy had their own system; they proceeded through the minor orders to the priesthood, but they were not bound to an individual master. Many of them studied in universities which, as we have already seen, had no apprenticeship in the strict sense, and in their method of education the physicians were on this side, not on that of the urban craftsmen. At any rate there seems to be no clear case in Tudor England of a boy or a youth bound by indentures to a master to serve him and to learn the mystery of physic.[2]

This does not, however, mean that, although there was a craft-organization of the other medical services, the physicians had no recognized position. It was a characteristic of medieval society that no one could engage in a gainful occupation without leave from some appropriate authority, and those who had such leave enjoyed the protection of the authority which gave it. In London as early as 1382 one Roger Clerk of Wandsworth, was indicted for falsely pretending to be a physician, and the court held that no physician or surgeon should intermeddle with any medicine or cures (that is cases) within the City but those who were experienced in the said arts and approved. There seems to be no precise definition of the requisite experience or skill, but the City gave the physicians the

---

[1] This may, however, be the explanation of some cases where a physician is said also to have followed another calling: Thomas Nuthake, mercer and physician of Colchester referred to by D. Knowles, *The Religious Orders in England*, iii (1959), 377, may simply have been free of the Colchester Mercers' Company.

[2] For a boy bound for ten years in 1716 and released after three years by his master, a physician in Wells (Somerset) see *The Diary of a West Country Physician*, ed. by E. Hobhouse (1934). The editor speaks of him as the doctor's apprentice.

protection of its courts. The incident implies that in London, which was likely to be more advanced than any other English town, there already existed physicians who made their living from practice among a number of fee-paying patients.[1]

Not only were the physicians recognized in this way; there are also indications that their place was one of distinction or superiority. They were distinguished from the apothecaries by a fixed habit many centuries old.[2] From the surgeons they were kept apart by another old habit which has been the subject of much inconclusive controversy. Galen, whom all physicians revered and were supposed to study, had written that surgery was but a method of treatment, but it was a method which some physicians were not allowed to practise. Pope Gregory IX, who reigned from 1227–41, presiding over a General Council of the Church, had issued a canon to dissociate the clergy from the shedding of blood in judicial or military affairs, and also forbidding all sub-deacons, deacons, and priests to exercise that part of surgery which required cautery or incision.[3] Some of the English physicians were in orders and came under this prohibition. The separation of the two branches does not seem, however, to have been due to ecclesiastical rules. It existed in Galen's own time in pagan Rome[4]; it did not prevail in medieval Italy. Its most determined upholders were the medical faculty of the university of Paris, and, whatever its origin may have been, at this time it was one of the many monopolistic sub-divisions of employments by which one party limited its activities in order to prevent outsiders from encroaching on a profitable sphere of work.

There are two documents which throw light on the relations of the physicians in England with the apothecaries and the surgeons. The first is the ordinance by which King Edward IV regulated his household. Here the physician is the first to be mentioned, that is he ranks as the senior. He is simply called 'Doctour of Physique'. He advises the king on his diet and 'the nature and operation of all the meats', answering the king's own questions as well as regularly discussing these things with the steward, the

---

[1] H. T. Riley, *Memorials of London* (1868), p. 464.
[2] It comes in the Bible, Eccles. xxxviii. 13.
[3] Decretal. Greg. Ix, Lib. III, tit 1, cap. 50. *Corpus Juris Canonici*, ed. A. L. Richter (1839), i. 634–5: the reading *artem* for *partem* would extend the prohibition to all surgery, but does not seem so satisfactory from the point of view of language.
[4] *Opera*, ed. C. G. Kühn, i(1821): see also W. H. S. Jones, *The Doctor's Oath* (1924), p. 48 n., where it is suggested that the clause against operating was inserted in the Hippocratic Oath at this time. It is not in the Christian form of the Oath.

chamberlain, the asserver (who handled the dish at table) and the master cook. He prescribes medicines for the king, and he is responsible for keeping the court clear of infected persons. The spothecary is subject to his oversight. His retinue and general status do not differ much from those of master surgeon. During the reign of Edward IV there were usually more physicians than one in office, and perhaps they took it in turns to be in residence as the king journeyed about. It may be noted that the royal surgeon has nothing to do with barbery: anyone, gentleman, yeoman or groom may shave the sovereign and on Saturday night, if it please the king, may cleanse his head, legs or feet.[1] These arrangements were probably not much unlike those of the early years of Henry VIII. In the other document the physician appears as having authority over surgeons in their own art. It is a licence to practise surgery, unfortunately incomplete through damage, granted to Robert Anson in 1497, and stating that he was a member of the commonalty of the Company and Fellowship of Barber-Surgeons. He had been examined in their common hall in a great audience of many right well expert men in surgery and others by the instructor and examiner of the Fellowship. This instructor and examiner was John Smyth, doctor of physic.[2]

In the reign of Henry VII and the first years of Henry VIII, although there was no common organization of the healing services either for London or for the kingdom, and no organization of the physicians, these physicians were not a branch co-ordinate with the surgeons and apothecaries. They had a recognized seniority and on some occasions they exercised authority.

[1] Myers, pp. 123–6, 225, 245.
[2] Facsimile in Young's *Annals*. John Smyth does not appear in the books of reference as a graduate of Oxford or Cambridge, but in due course he was one of the physicians named in the charter of the London College.

II: FIRST STEPS TOWARDS PROFESSIONAL ORGANIZATION

THAT the number of physicians was so small is perhaps in itself a sufficient explanation of their having no organization as yet, but when the College came to be founded the reason was not, so far as we know, that the number had increased. It was that, under changing conditions, certain constructive ideas were coming into action. They not only brought the College into being; they also dictated its purpose and character.

All over western and Mediterranean Europe there was a wealth of well-developed vocational associations which acted under rules, disposed of funds and kept records of their work. Some of these already conformed to our modern concept of a professional organization. When we speak of a body of persons as a profession, we understand first of all that they render some service or some related kinds of services to their clients in return for payment. Their clients may be individuals or institutions or public authorities. The services that they render are not in the nature of buying or selling; we distinguish professions from trades.[1] They require skill, but so do many businesses or crafts, and if the special character of professional skill can be defined, the difference lies in its being connected with a comparatively high level of general education. One profession differs from another in its relation to society as a whole. Entry to it may be easy; it may be difficult in the existing social conditions, or it may be intentionally made difficult either by the members of the profession itself from a spirit of monopoly, or by people outside it from a spirit of jealousy or rivalry. Those who enter it may have a wider or a narrower choice of alternative occupations which are open to them. Education for it may be provided or controlled by the profession itself with no interference from authorities outside it, or with little interference, or with much. Once he is in it the professional man may be under the loose control of a 'free profession' or he may be subjected to close supervision by

---

[1] For a discusson of the meaning of the term see Sir Alexander M. Carr-Saunders and P. A. Wilson, *The Professions* (1933), pp. 284-7, where reasons are given for declining to give a precise definition.

authority. A point comes when the element of authority is so dominant that we cease to regard the collective body as a profession and prefer to think of it as a service, like a modern army or navy or civil service.

Membership of a profession implies not only skill but social responsibilities and consequently standards of conduct in relation to clients and to colleagues; it also confers a status. This status may or may not be legally recognized. It may or may not be symbolized by titles and forms of address or by a uniform costume peculiar to the members. It implies that the members are in some way organized together. A professional organization may be spontaneously formed by the members; public or other external authorities may give it their support, or they may even impose it on the profession; it may deal with some or with all professional concerns; it may or may not apply coercion to disobedient members; it may or may not provide benefits for its individual members, but in any case it will further their collective advantage, and it will at least claim that it also serves the public interest.

In all ages and in all places there is one fixed condition which limits the possible forms of organization for the healing arts. A physician may advise a government department, or he may work for a manufacturing firm in its capacity as a vendor of goods or an employer of labour, but even so he deals with the health of individual men, women and children. No professional structure, however elaborate and apparently impersonal, can eliminate the decision whether this or that treatment is or is not to be given to one single human being. Even the simplest forms of organization, such as partnerships and consultation among doctors, are influenced by this limiting condition, and it also gives a special character to the differences of rank and standing which develop among them. It is equally true, however, that the structure of the medical vocations always conforms in some ways to that of contemporary society. In the last resort social opinion governs the relations of practitioner and patient. The practitioner must find a livelihood where it is to be had, and it must be proportionate to his responsibilities and to the expense of his training. His social position must enable him on the one hand to live happily among the people he consorts with, and on the other to maintain authority in handling his cases. In a graded society this will often mean that there will be corresponding grades in the vocation. We have seen already that the king's physician was almost a courtier, and it is said that in Castile at this time he had to prove that he was of noble blood. Grade for grade, as we shall see, there were similar correspondences lower down the scale. But once a profession exists and is aware of itself, it ceases to be a mere product of social forces outside it. Its own ambitions and its own self-restraint, the discussions and the mutual criticisms of its members endow it with an independent social power. As an organized whole, by persuasion or merely by example, it works upon the other professions, or upon statesmen or upon the general public. So in the dynamic process of society professional organizations have become receivers and transmitters of power; but in the fifteenth century the only English profession which had reached this maturity was the law. Medicine was to be the next. We should not be justified in saying that the companies of barber-surgeons were fully-fledged professional bodies in the modern sense. The Craft of Surgeons came nearer to the modern notion, because its members stood higher than that general body of craftsmen among whom the barber-surgeons were ranged; but the mere surgeons were only a minority within their vocation, not a whole profession. In our sense the medical professions in England had not yet come into being. We have to trace the processes by which an articulate demand for this change in their status was made effective in the ever-changing social conditions.

Among these social conditions some of the most commonly misunderstood are those which relate to the Church. The Church was not one profession among others. The clergy were indeed by far the largest body of men who rendered special services requiring knowledge and training. Their organization and discipline set examples which were useful in one way and another to the professions as they arose. But in theory and in actual fact the church still included the whole population; the relation of the priest to the layman was quite unlike the modern relation of a professional man to his fee-paying client, and the complex international structure of the church embraced many functions which did not involve anything at all resembling that relation. There had been a time when priests and monks and nuns were virtually the only literates in Christendom. Then society looked to them for all the sciences and for all the services that needed book-learning; but that was in the distant past. There were now many literate laymen in the law and in the administrative offices of the kings, of the feudal lords and of the towns. There were well-educated men among the merchants and country landowners. As the vocations became differentiated a clergyman might have a dual character as a priest and chancery clerk or as bishop and lord chancellor. His secular work might easily absorb most of his time and attention. We have noticed clerical physicians in great households, and we shall notice others later; but there had also been lay physicians for centuries. Perhaps it is for this reason that 'Leech' had become a surname.[1] The clerical physicians were not a dominant element in the faculty, though they were still rather more than a remnant of what they had been. Some of the monks and friars still chose medicine for a private study and most of the monastic libraries contained medical books; but monks were forbidden to practise outside the cloisters, both because practice might be lucrative and because it might lead them to attend women. Even as students they could not equal those who enjoyed the wider opportunities of the universities. There were some, such as the Austin canons, who were allowed to treat one another even surgically; but the Benedictine abbeys employed physicians much as the large lay households did.[2]

Without generalizing rashly about its many organs and institutions we may say that the Church wished the physicians well. There is a chapter in the Bible which begins 'Honour the physician' and adds substantial reasons for the command.[3] The evangelist St. Luke was 'the beloved physician'. The brothers St. Cosmas and St. Damien, both physicians who charged no fees, were revered for their martyrdom and for a surgical miracle. One physician had risen to the supreme office in the Church as Pope John XXI (1276–7). Medical faculties in some of the universities were under ecclesiastical supervision. Many modern writers do indeed suppose that there was a fundamental discordance of aim between the physician as such and the priest. It is said that *ubi tres medici duo athei* had long been proverbial. This can only be true if it means proverbial among people who understood Latin, and that is a serious reservation,

---

[1] If all the physicians had been celibate priests it could still have arisen from a nickname. Another English surname, 'Arts', suggests the Dutch and German names for a medical man. 'Pothecary' and 'Potticarry' are well known. 'Barber' is common, and 'Chirurgeon' occurs as a surname.

[2] See D. Knowles, *The Religious Orders in England*, ii, *The End of the Middle Ages* (1955), p. 235 and P. Flemming in *Sidelights on Medical History*, ed. by Sir Zachary Cope (1957).

[3] Eccles. xxxviii. 1. I refrain from mentioning certain less complimentary passages of Scripture.

because the educated men of the Middle Age had their own special kind of tolerance, which indeed is implied by their being able, as a joke, to accuse the *medici* of the heinous crime of atheism. Their tolerance enabled them to hold in high regard medical authors who were not Christians, such as Galen, who lived in the second century A.D. and could have been a Christian if he would.[1] This tolerance, however, implied a degree of sceptical detachment which went only with a high level of education, while popular religious belief included much that was incompatible with any scientific view of health and disease. The *Golden Legend*, for instance, a widely-read compendium of sacred history and of the lives of the saints, written by an Italian bishop, was not merely a survival from the thirteenth century: Caxton printed it, and so helped to perpetuate scores of stories of improbably miraculous cures. Holy wells with healing virtues, some of great antiquity but some of recently acquired reputation, were not far apart in any region of the country. Churchmen sponsored pilgrimages to them and to shrines where miracles were expected and reported. They believed not only that prayers could alter the course of disease but, more generally, that the course of nature was interrupted by supernatural interventions of many kinds. They took part in the detection and punishment of sorcerers, not because sorcerers professed to bring about miracles by invoking occult powers, but because they summoned the powers of evil. In the universities, as it happened, the authorities were on the watch at this time for heresies, so that in many different ways the Church may seem to have barred the way to the advance of medical knowledge.

Some obvious considerations suggest that there are flaws in this reasoning. It appears, first, that dissentient opinions on matters of anatomy or therapeutics, even on their primary principles, would not have been regarded as heretical; and secondly that no one seems to have been censured in the universities for propounding such opinions. That might indeed only be a symptom of the mental torpor induced by a system of repression; but it was not a sign that the Church wished to perpetuate credulity. On the contrary the Church was deeply committed by the habituation of centuries to upholding rationality. Just as its inquisitors exerted their powers

---

[1] Galen's exact position in this matter is explained in a work of finished scholarship, R. Walzer, *Galen on Jews and Christians* (1949), which uses some previously inaccessible materials; the main fact was known all along, though some denied it.

against magic or sorcery or witchcraft in the sphere of action, in the sphere of belief its theologians investigated, defined and condemned superstition. That this ranged them in a wholesome alliance with the physicians ought not to be disputed even by those who hold that the belief in a supernatural world was groundless and that the clergy traded on it for their own advantage. The Church, as the oldest, most powerful and most elaborately articulated organization in Europe, was committed to the side of regularity not only by its higher aspirations but also by its material interest. When a supposed miracle kindled excitement and a spontaneous cult arose, there was a danger not only that uncontrolled emotion might get out of hand, but also that the faithful might neglect the established objects of their devotion and their offerings. That these evils still called for repression in the sixteenth century is shown by the Decree of the Council of Trent that new miracles were not to be admitted without the approval of the bishop.[1] The constituted authorities of the Church did not always find it easy to decide whether to recognize or to discountenance a particular manifestation, and no doubt they recognized some which could not be reconciled with the principles of medical science as it was then understood; but in England in the century before the foundation of the College of Physicians there does not seem to be any record of conflict or even of theoretical disagreement between theologians and physicians over any question of miracles or healing. When the king performed his miracles of touching for the king's evil and blessing cramp-rings, his physicians participated in the ceremonies along with the clerics.[2]

Throughout the history of the world those who seek wealth or power or reputation or other desirable ends by the means which are generally regarded as proper and permissible have had to contend against competitors who take short cuts and disregard the accepted rules. Impostors infest every royal court, every political assembly, every enviable social circle, and every financial centre; they even penetrate into churches, armies, courts of justice, universities and learned societies. Nowhere have they persisted more incorrigibly than in the healing arts. The history of the warfare of the physicians against the quacks is not a story with a plot, a story of strategy, defeats and victories, leading on to a peace-settlement;

---

[1] Sess. xxv, *De Invocatione, Veneratione et Reliquiis Sanctorum et Sacris Imaginibus.*
[2] For the origin of these see M. Bloch, *Les rois thaumaturges* (1924), for English practice Sir Raymond Crawfurd, *The King's Evil* (1911) and 'Cramp Rings' in *Studies in the History and Method of Science*, ed. C. Singer, vol. i (1917).

it is an interminable succession of incidents in which one half of human nature collides with another. One series of such incidents occurred in England in the first half of the fifteenth century, and, although our knowledge is tantalizingly incomplete, we are compelled to regard this as part of the prehistory of the College. In the year 1421 the parliament of King Henry V took up the question of irregular practitioners of medicine. We do not know why this happened at that particular date and not earlier or later. It may have been because quacks were unusually prominent then; at any rate one chronicler does mention a character who called himself 'the Baron of Blackamoore' and wanted to be the 'principal Phisition in this kingdome'.[1] For whatever reason, the house of commons sent forward to the king a petition against unqualified practitioners of physic.[2] This is sometimes referred to as the Physicians' Petition, but there is nothing to show who promoted it, and it may perfectly well have emanated from aggrieved members of the commons.[3] It premised that all except university graduates should be excluded from the practice of physic, and asked that a warrant should be sent to all sheriffs and to every practiser in physic, ordering that all those who intended to practise from that time were to present themselves within one of the English universities by a stated date to be examined and to receive a degree. Those who did not pass the examination were to be forbidden under penalty to continue in practice or to intermeddle with it until they were qualified.[4] This proposal implies that the physicians were few in number and easily identifiable: even if the warrants were to be passed on to them through the sheriffs, it is unlikely that each sheriff was expected to deliver them to more than a manageable number. We do not know whether the universities had any knowledge of the petition, but even if it was drawn up without their advice, the promoters most likely knew that their capacity for examining and teaching was limited. Although it was so vague and badly drafted the petition met with a favourable answer. The lords of the council were to see

---

[1] This was in 1419: J. Stow, *Survey of London*, ed. C. L. Kingsford (1908), i. 58.
[2] The text is in *Rotuli Parliamentorum* (1783), iv. 130 and is reprinted in South, pp. 50–51.
[3] The alternative notion of a petition from the universities to the commons does not fit in with what is known about the ways in which they were accustomed to do their business.
[4] The word used twice in the original is 'able' which means in this context 'fit or qualified' for practice, presumably by taking a degree. The sentence has been misunderstood as referring to their being able to present themselves for examination or to pass. An erroneous interpretation of the clause has followed from this.

that its recommendations were carried out.[1] Whether they took any action is unknown; but perhaps the absence of any further record in the matter and of any warrant addressed to a sheriff or a physician proves that they did nothing.

Our sources are silent again as to the connexion, if there was any, between this event of 1421 and a more mature and complex, though in one way more circumscribed, attempt which followed it two years later. The parliamentary petition related to the whole kindgom, but only to physicians. We now have to deal with a petition addressed to the mayor and aldermen of London and limited to the City and its Liberties, but ambitious enough to include both physicians and surgeons in its scope.[2] At this time, it will be remembered the surgeons had not yet obtained their own charter, but they had established their separateness within the Barber-Surgeons' Company, and it seems highly probably that this separating and the new petition were both manifestations of the improved skill and standing of the army surgeons of Henry V. It is evident from the wording of the petition that London physicians at this time had three officers recognized by the civic authorities, a rector of medicines in the City of London, and two surveyors of the faculty of physic in the said City. It seems safe to conclude that the Rector had some disciplinary powers over the apothecaries, and that all three were elected by their fellow-physicians; but we do not know whether the physicians were organized for any other purpose beyond these elections or whether the officers we hear of in the petition were the first of their kind or came in succession to others before them.

The five named petitioners are all well known to history. The rector of medicines, Gilbert Kymer, a priest, was a doctor of Oxford University, of which he was about ten years later to become 'chancellor'. Soon after this time he was closely connected with Humphrey, duke of Gloucester; he became rich and influential, and he wrote a book on diet. The first of the surveyors was a layman Master John Somerset, still only a bachelor of medicine (probably of Cambridge) who also became a member of Duke

---

[1] The procedure normal in such matters was thus followed: there was not, as has been supposed, any question of a Bill or Act.
[2] The text is given accurately enough for all ordinary purposes in South, Appendix B; see also Young, *Annals*, pp. 42–43. The civic proceedings are recorded under their dates in *Calendar of Letter Books of the City of London*, *Letter Book K*, ed. R. R. Sharpe (1920).

Humphrey's circle and wrote medical treatises, rising to be physician to King Henry VI and, among other dignities, chancellor of the exchequer. The other, was an Oxford bachelor of medicine named Thomas Southwell who came to a bad end, for he was involved in the duchess of Gloucester's treasonable dealings with magic, and he died in the Tower of London on the night before he was to be executed.[1] With these three physicians were the two masters of the Craft of Surgery, Thomas Morstede and John Harowe, with whom were associated as petitioners all other surgeons of the City.

Their petition was for authority to found a college for the better education and control of physicians and surgeons practising in the City of London and its Liberties. The mayor and alderman granted this authority and sanctioned articles for giving it effect. Before considering the outcome we may pause for a moment over the word 'college'. It has a certain significance here, if only because there was no other body in England called a college which was at all closely similar to this new association. Even at that time the name was applied to several different kinds of societies, not necessarily alike in anything except that each performed common functions and possessed special rights and privileges. The most numerous class consisted of the residential colleges of canons attached to some of the cathedrals and other churches. There were also the residential colleges of Oxford and Cambridge, the older of which had existed for generations before they were known by this name. In ordinary speech it could be used for any company or assemblage of persons. That the physicians and surgeons chose it now does however make some slight distinction between their conjoint body and the City companies. Perhaps it provides a thin thread of connexion with the Continent, for the Parisian surgeons had their College of St. Cosmas and the word appears in similar contexts in Italy.[2]

The College duly came into existence. Kymer, Somerset, and Southwell were annually presented by the physicians and sworn in to their offices, just as the surveyors of surgery, varying in number between two and four, were presented by the surgeons. In 1423 Gilbert Kymer's name appears as rector of the faculty

---

[1] The most complete summaries of the careers of these three are in A. B. Emden, *Biographical Register of the University of Oxford*, ii (1958), iii (1959).
[2] See below p. 66.

in a list of masters of mysteries so that from the municipal point of view the College counted as a craft company.[1] There is only one glimpse of their work. A man named Forest was wounded in the hand. John Harowe, the free surgeon,[2] and two members of the Barbers' Company admitted as surgeons only, treated him by cautery, but in the end he was left with a mutilated hand. He sued the surgeons, and seven arbitrators were appointed to decide the case. The first two were the surveyors of the faculty of physic, Somerset and Southwell; with them were John Corby, *practicus* in physic,[3] Thomas Morstede and William Bradwardyne, the surveyors of surgery for the year, and also two other free surgeons. They reported in June 1424, with equal learning and discretion, that the surgeons were not to blame: the mishap was due either to the phase of the moon, or to a defect in the patient or to the original nature of the wound.[4]

Just before Michaelmas 1425 the three officers of the physicians were sworn in for another year, but that is the last we hear of their offices. The College was a failure. Its demise must almost certainly be connected with a disagreement among the surgeons which had come to a head in the previous year. The rector and surveyors of the physicians and the masters of surgeons—that is the officers of the College—in virtue of its Ordinance had set up a claim (*calumpnia*) to control the members of the Barbers' Company, but the Company protested, and a new Ordinance issued forth from the mayor, aldermen and sheriffs. The masters of the faculty of surgery in the Mystery of Barbers in the City were to exercise the said faculty as fully as they did in the days of Thomas Fauconer, late mayor. As Thomas Fauconer was mayor in 1415[5] this did away with any encroachment of 1423, and, although we do not know the nature of the encroachment, it seems clear that the surgeons in the Barbers' Company acted in the manner normal to a medieval craft organization in resisting any limitation of their rights. We do not know

[1] 'Lechis' are mentioned after grocers and barbers in an unofficial list of 111 London crafts (*artium*) in 1422 in the records of the Brewers' Company, of which there is a facsimile at p. 167 and printed text pp. 370-1 in G. Unwin, *Gilds and Companies of London* (1908) but they were probably the surgeons.

[2] This should mean not a surgeon independent of any organization but a freeman of some body of surgeons, probably the College or its surgical component.

[3] Perhaps identical with John Corkeby, formerly of St. John's Hospital, Oxford.

[4] *Calendar of Plea and Memoranda Rolls of the City of London, 1413-1437*, ed. A. H. Thomas (1943), pp. 174-5.

[5] This was the date of the first recorded appointment of overseers of the Barber-Surgeons, and therefore presumably of some Ordinance for the Company.

whether anything ever came of the purpose of the College to improve the training of surgeons, nor whether it attempted to raise the standard of the examination for mastership. If it tried to do this and the physicians asserted their superior authority, then the combination of the physicians with the surgeons may have contributed to the failure of the College. The bare records which now survive were available at Guildhall from that time forward, and very likely there were others there and at the Barbers' Hall; whether anyone looked at them, or any oral tradition explained them, we cannot tell. It may well be that this example was remembered as an encouragement and a warning when a new beginning was made in the organization of the professions in the reign of Henry VIII, three generations or so later. Among so many points which are doubtful one at least is clear: throughout the formation and life of the College the physicians took precedence as the senior branch.

During the interval after the disappearance of the proto-College the English physicians, so far as we know, had no authority above them, but they were not without discipline. Their art gave them a sense of community and prevented them from acting irresponsibly. We have seen that, although it was embodied in a voluminous literature on the study of which much learning was brought to bear, it did not provoke any conflict with the Church. It was not regarded as a science in the modern senses of the term, still less as positive science in opposition to abstract thought. It necessarily dealt with physical facts, and there were men among the physicians who reached high standards of observation and accuracy, not to mention common sense, but no research was carried on and there does not appear to have been any consciousness that the art needed, as we know now that it did, improvement by research. The prevailing attitude to authority was one reason for this. The classics of the tradition were treated with great respect, although they were known to disagree with one another. Only study of the commentaries on these classics and of their use in university teaching could show exactly to what extent the respect for authority retarded the growth of knowledge. Perhaps another element of the tradition had a similar effect. It included much philosophy,[1] and one of its principles was that the good physician must also be a philosopher. The more it presented itself as a rounded whole of all that the

[1] This is true both in the modern, restricted, senses of the word 'philosophy' and in the older senses which included what we now call 'science'.

physicians needed to know, the less likely was it to take notice of what was thought or discovered by laymen.

For these reasons there is little to say about the relations of medicine in this period to two sciences which were neighbours to it, astrology and alchemy. Both of them were amplified and specialized developments of matters touched upon by medical learning. Astrology, which had its origins in remote antiquity, studied mathematically the supposed influence of the stars. Alchemy, more recent but still with a long history behind it, did practical work on substances. Both, like medicine, connected their proceedings with metaphysical ideas; both were poised precariously on the edge of magic. Both offered help to the physician: we have seen a reference to the moon in the award of a medical board. In status, however, they were very different. Astrology was a high specialism. It predicted events and it judged when the cosmic conditions were favourable for the various acts of treatment, down to routine bleeding. The astrologers had a position comparable to that of the physicians. In the time of Henry VII the most successful astrologer in England was a native of Piacenza whom the English knew as William Parron. He published almanacks in Latin and English, and the king accepted a treatise on astrology from him as a New Year's gift for 1500. He used without acknowledgement the contention of the Arab Albumasar that physicians do more harm by their mistakes than astrologers by wrong prognostications; but at court prophesying was a dangerous trade, and William Parron soon had to disappear.[1] The physicians knew their ground better, and do not seem to have regarded the astrologers as competitors.

Still less did they need to pay attention to the alchemists, who wrote and experimented in obscurity, for the most part unknown to the academic world, and who had no wide influence or reputation in England before the book-printing trade was well established. There are practically no alchemical *incunabula*.[2] It was a felony to use the craft of multiplying gold and silver[3]; but this was only a means of protecting the royal mint and its coinage. Licences were granted for operations of this kind. A litigant maintained in court that he was competent in them,[4] and 'alchemy gold' was the

---

[1] See the agreeable essay on him by C. A. J. Armstrong in *Italian Renaissance Studies*, ed. E. F. Jacob (1960), pp. 433 ff.
[2] L. Thorndike, *History of Magic and Experimental Science*, iv (1934), 332.
[3] 5 Henry V, c. 4.
[4] *Select Cases in Chancery* (Selden Soc., 1896), pp. 127–8.

current name for a kind of yellow metal. On the medical side alchemy was of less account. One of the licences was to produce an
elixir of life,[1] and the *Book of Quinte Essence*, a translation of Hermes
Trismegistus which circulated in manuscript about 1460–70,
really did show with much mystification how to distil alcohol.[2] A few
names of English alchemists are preserved, but nothing is known
of the men except for George Ripley, a canon of Bridlington, a
popularizer and versifier who dedicated his books to King Edward
IV and Archbishop Neville, and has found a place in the *Dictionary
of National Biography*.[3]

The traditional art of medicine contained the medical ethics of
the time. There was nothing like a code, and no authority that could
have enforced a code. Those authorities which could enforce their
will in ethical matters were not concerned with medicine as such
but only with its simplest social aspects. As we have seen, the
municipalities might on occasion encourage and regulate it as a
public craft. The law of the land knew it as a means by which one
citizen might do a service or an injury to another. In 1470–1 a
judge, Sir Richard Choke, said that if a man undertook to cure
another of a certain disease, and sent a messenger with medicine
which made him worse, no action lay against the servant but against
the master.[4] But he said this while trying a case about an alleged
fraud in a delivery of cloth; it was merely an illustration of the
principles governing civil liability in tort. There was, however, a
principle of criminal law which specially concerned medical practice. According to the books if a surgeon or a physician treated a
patient who died under or soon after the treatment, this was no
felony; and the practitioner could not have acted feloniously because
the death was gainst his will.[5] This seems to imply that a professional
qualification is a guarantee of good intentions, and it does nothing
to define the qualifications that make a man a physician or a surgeon.
The unqualified person whose patient died from malpractice committed a felony. Most of the writers agreed that it would be man-
slaughter, though later one thought it would be murder.[6] This,
however, seems to have been a purely academic question. There
seems indeed to be mention of one man indicted for such a felony
in the reign of Edward III but it was for a jury to decide whether

[1] T. Rymer, *Foedera*, xi (1710), 879.   [2] Ed. F. J. Furnivall (E.E.T.S., 1866).
[3] Thorndike, iv. 351–3.   [4] *Year Book*, 11 Edward IV, Trin. pl. 10.
[5] Sir William Stamford *Les plees del coron* (1560), p. 17 in edition of 1617.
[6] W. Lambarde, *Eirenarcha* (1591), p. 242.

he was guilty, and the law altogether was too vague and primitive to provide any real protection either for the public or for the medical men.

The Church in the same way did not lay down rules for the conduct of medical practice as its casuists did in later times, although it already did something of the kind for legal practice. In the *Summa Theologica* St. Thomas Aquinas six or seven times mentions courses of action which are recognized as proper for *medici*; but he uses them only as illustrations or parallels for his general ethical precepts. Only in one passage does he decide a specifically medical problem. This one passage relates to the social aspect of practice, and comes as a pendant to a discussion about the duties of lawyers. An advocate is not under an obligation to plead gratuitously for every poor man who cannot afford to pay him. He need only do so for people who are in some way personally connected with him; otherwise he would have to give up all other business and do nothing else. The same is to be said of the *medicus* in relation to the treatment of the poor.[1] There was indeed an ancient canon still in force which defined the places of the priest and the physician at the bedside: the physician was not to urge anything on his patients for the health of their bodies which might imperil their souls. Before beginning treatment he was to persuade them to send for a priest, the physician of souls, whose medicine was penance.[2] Within these limits he was left to his own responsibility.

The physicians themselves had no code in the sense of a systematic collection of rules, but they had precepts and principles generally accepted and considered to be morally binding. Most of them, including the principle that the poor were to be treated as a matter of charity, were set out, sometimes with reasons and sometimes only casually, in the medical classics. The most authoritative were best known in the Hippocratic Oath. This wonderful document has been historically 'the nucleus of all medical ethics'.[3] No explanation either of its original purpose or of the meaning of some of its clauses has won the approval of all scholars; but there can be no doubt of its influence. At this time many versions of it were in

---

[1] *Summa* 22e q. 71. 3. 1m.

[2] Lateran Council, 1215, in W. Lyndwood, *Provinciale* (ed. of 1679), p. 330. In various countries the canon was subsequently elaborated, for instance by the rule that the physician must not visit the patient more than a specific number of times before he had made his confession.

[3] L. Edelstein, *The Hippocratic Oath* (1943).

circulation, belonging to two main types, one pagan and the other, which may be older than Galen, Christian.[1] In forms modified to suit the circumstances this oath was taken during the ceremony of the medical doctor's graduation in some, at least, of the universities.[2] Traces of it, or more than traces, appear in the oaths taken by members of the related calling of surgery. In those days it was customary for everyone entering on a function of social significance to swear to some oath or assent to some charge, and for such use as this the Oath was treated not as a sacred text but as a working model. The man who took it did not bind himself to a legal interpretation of each word and each sentence, but he submitted to it as a guide for his conduct.

The Oath begins with the very general promises that in treating the sick the physician will prescribe diet and remedies, to the best of his ability, in accordance with the rules of the art and for the health and comfort of the patient. That may seem so much a matter of course that it scarcely need be mentioned; but such a judgement would be doubly mistaken. First, it was not then and it never has been a mere matter of course for the physician to make the patient's good his over-riding aim. By doing so he subordinates his knowledge to an ethical control, and it is by accepting this control that the medical profession has won its place among the beneficent and civilizing forces. But, secondly, the physician does not merely promise to work for the good of the patient; he promises to work according to the rules of the art. He agrees, if only in an indefinite way, to submit his own momentary and personal impulses to the system of principles in which he has been trained. Other promises follow which are relatively precise. He will not administer, or cause or permit any apothecary to administer any poison. This again is not a matter to be taken for granted. We shall see before long that in the sixteenth century doctors came under pressure from more sides than one to take a more indulgent view of poisoning.[3] Then among further promises there is one against procuring abortion. Another group of promises cover some of the main problems of what is now called professional etiquette. There are

[1] W. H. S. Jones, *The Doctor's Oath* (1924), p. 55.
[2] The form used at Louvain (with no date but apparently considerably later than the foundation of the university in 1426) is printed in *L'université de Louvain à travers cinq siècles*, ed. L. van der Essen (1927), p. 309. All the four Scottish universities are said to have administered the oath to their graduates from their inception.
[3] See below p. 128.

secrets to be kept, secrets of the art itself and also other people's secrets, both medical and non-medical, which are learnt in the course of practice. There are also limits beyond which the doctor ought not to pursue his own personal interests. His fees must be reasonable; he must not take undue advantage of his power over his patient; he must not compete unbecomingly with his fellow-practitioners. He is one of a body of men committed to all these renunciations. Up to a point, no doubt they are generally the same as the rules of the fraternities or companies of craftsmen and traders; but, if we consider how much of human good and ill hinged upon them, we see that they stood on an altogether different, a much higher, plane.

Only by allowing full weight to the binding authority of their art is it possible to explain the position which English physicians enjoyed; but they would have been under better discipline and they would have acquired greater influence if there had been authorities to interpret and if necessary enforce these principles of ethics and etiquette. Those of them who travelled abroad must have observed that the more populous of the continental countries possessed such authorities. It does indeed seem to be the case that England was backward in most departments of medical progress. Not only did Englishmen study medicine abroad and foreign doctors practise in England. In France and Germany two specialized branches of practice were known which were yet to come in England. There were doctors at the watering places to which people resorted for curative baths, and there were *médecins fonctionnaires* whose duties were miscellaneous but not unlike those of our medical officers of health. Bordeaux had two *médécins ordinaires* in 1414, who were to be resident and to deal with the plague and sanitation; Lille had a similar officer by 1501, and they soon became common in northern and north-eastern France.[1] In Italy there were activities far in advance of what was possible in England: the Florentine medical guild published a book of medical recipes in 1498.[2]

That England was medically backward is suggested by facts like these, but this comparison would only go part of the way to explaining her backwardness in professional organization. In France the medical faculties of the universities, not without some opposition from local organizations, exercised authority over practitioners in

---

[1] P. Delaunay, *La vie médicale du 16ᵉ au 17ᵉ siècle* (1935), p. 253. For Germany see Baas, pp. 186–7.   [2] See below p. 159.

the university towns and also over apothecaries and surgeons. From the thirteenth century onwards they had many contests with the *cabusatores*, untrained or unlicensed practitioners. This was the earliest social duty other than study and teaching ever fulfilled by universities, and it brought them into contact and collaboration with public authorities. The English system of university degrees was in substance copied from the French: the bachelor of medicine had the right to practise, and the doctor to teach in the universities; but the small English faculties do not seem to have issued public pronouncements on medical matters as those of Paris and Montpellier did. Their degrees gave the right to practise throughout the kingdom but any other rights they may have exercised in the two small market towns of Oxford and Cambridge were of no national importance.[1] A strong monarchy might, however, set up a system of medical regulation independent of the universities. In the twelfth and thirteenth centuries the kings of Sicily had issued comprehensive decrees for the training, licensing and discipline of physicians, surgeons and apothecaries.[2] In Castile there was a state and municipal institution called the *protomedicat* with disciplinary powers over the physicians and surgeons and with a tribunal of judges (*alcaldes*) and examiners to test the competence of aspirants. It was founded in 1422, the year after the parliamentary petition in England, and it was regulated anew in 1477 and 1491 by Ferdinand and Isabella. It was imitated in Aragon.[3]

Before the end of the fifteenth century, England also had a strong monarchy. Its servants took a grip on many of the lieges who had been left to their own devices, and the chances for a regulation of medical affairs from above were greater than ever before. There is one small piece of evidence that King Henry VII himself, who knew parts of France and the Low Countries at first hand, looked to the continent for examples of medical provision. When the time came for him to make his will a long and suitably impressive document was drafted for him with detailed provisions for the foundation of three large hospitals, one at the Savoy in London and the others in York and Coventry. The bequests were introduced by a discourse

---

[1] See below p. 113.
[2] They were circulated widely throughout Europe when they were printed as Tit. xxxiv of the Constitutiones Regni Sicilae in F. Lindenbrog, *Codex Legum Antiquarum* (1613).
[3] L. Comenge, *La medicina en Cataluña* (1908), pp. 76–77, 89 ; J. M. S. de Guilleuma, 'Jaime de Bofill' reprint from *Medicamenta*, xi (1959), p. 4.

to the effect that the 'nearest' way to execute the six corporal acts of mercy was to maintain common hospitals where poor people might be kept. The king is represented as 'understanding also that there be fewer or noon such commune Hospitallis within this our Reame', and that for lack of them infinite number of poor people daily die.[1] This may surprise a reader. St. Bartholomew's and St. Thomas's Hospitals and St. Mary of Bethlehem should have been known to the king, and besides 200 lazar-houses there were some 500 other hospitals in his kingdom.[2] Hospitals, however, included houses for travellers, for the aged and for the homeless and, if visiting the sick was one of the acts of mercy performed in most of them, in many it was only incidental. But for the moment what interests us about the king's wish to do something new is that he provided himself with a set of the statutes of the famous Hospital of Santa Maria Nuova in Florence.[3] The time was ripe for advance in English medical services and there were some who were looking to the Continent for plans. Before long one of them was to put such a plan into action. This was Thomas Linacre, whose life touches our subject on so many sides that we must review it as a whole.

[1] W. J. Loftie, *Memorials of the Hospital of the Savoy* (1878), pp. 87–92. For the steps taken during Henry's lifetime towards building the Savoy hospital see R. Somerville, *The Savoy : Manor : Hospital : Chapel* (1960), p. 9.

[2] Rotha M. Clay, *Mediaeval Hospitals of the British Isles* (1909) p. xvii and App. B.

[3] The Bodleian MS. Bodley 488 is no doubt the original presentation copy. It is described in the Bodleian *Summary Catalogue*, no. 2068 and the handsomely illuminated fo. 3 is reproduced in F. Saxl and R. Wittkower, *British Art and the Mediterranean* (1948), pl. 36, no. 4. Brit. Mus. Add.MS. 40077 is a plainer copy with the same textual content. The preliminary letter to the king speaks of him as planning a hospital for the sick: 'Amplissimum paras aegrotantium domicilium et subsidium condere.'

III : THOMAS LINACRE

THOMAS LINACRE,[1] when he died on 20 October 1524, was in his sixty-fourth year, and must therefore have been born in 1460 or 1461. The place of his birth is uncertain. Dr. Caius, whose information is likely to have been good, described him as *Cantuariensis*,[2] but no reference to his surname has been found in Canterbury archives before his time.[3] The name itself tells us nothing about the local origin of its bearers. It is a straightforward English word meaning 'flax-field', and it occurs in widely separated parts of the country. There was once a landed family of Linacres of Linacre Hall near Chesterfield in Derbyshire, to which Thomas Linacre's nineteenth-century biographer assigned his hero without citing any evidence.[4] There is a township of Linacre in the parish of Walton on the Hill in Lancashire[5] and there was once another place so called in Cambridgeshire.[6] The surname may have been derived from one of these, but there are also two places in Kent, the manor of Linacre Court in Whitfield near Dover, and the hamlet of Linacre-street in Eastwell near Ashford.[7] Dr. Caius can scarcely have intended *Cantuariensis* to mean a Kentish man, which should be *Cantianus*, but the word he used would apply correctly enought to an inhabitant of the diocese of Canterbury, so that perhaps Linacre's ancestors came from one or other of these two places. We shall see that he had to do with other places in Kent in more than one connexion, but that in itself does little or nothing to strengthen the possibility.

[1] The main facts of his biography are given, with most of the authorities in full, in J. N. Johnson, *Life of Linacre* (1835). J. F. Payne made important corrections and additions in his introduction to the facsimile reprint of Linacre's edition of Galen *De Temperamentis* &c. (1881), and wrote a shorter account of the life in the *Dictionary of National Biography*, vol. xxxiii (1893).
[2] *Historiae Cantabrigiensis Academiae Libri Duo* (1574), p. 126.
[3] Information kindly supplied by Mr. W. Urry.
[4] J. Weever, *Ancient Funeral Monuments* (1631), p. 370 says that Linacre was 'borne in the town of Derby', but gives no evidence.
[5] C. W. Bardsley, *Dictionary of English and Welsh Surnames* (1901).
[6] E. Ekwall, *Oxford Dictionary of English Place Names* (1936).
[7] P. H. Reaney, *Dictionary of British Surnames* (1958) mentions one of these and Mr. Reaney was kind enough to inform me of the other; for both see E. Hasted, *History of the County of Kent*, iii (1790), 202 n., iv (1799), 14–15.

Even so we know nothing of his parentage. The first well-attested fact of his life is that in 1484 he was admitted a fellow of All Souls College, Oxford.[1] The whole of his childhood and education fell well within the period which we call medieval. He was born when Henry VI was king and the Wars of the Roses were in their fierce early stage. He gained his fellowship under Richard III, in the year before the battle of Bosworth. During this time, however, two movements were spreading into England from the Continent which were to bring intellectual revolutions. The first was the printing of books. When Linacre was born there was no printing outside Germany; he was still a boy when Caxton set up his press at Westminster Abbey, and he must have gone up to Oxford within a year or two before or after the first printers began to work there, in 1478. The other great movement was the intensified study of the Latin classics and of Greek. For generations this had been gathering force in Italy, where it was only one of many vital influences in literature and the arts. Oxford had felt its inspiration now and again since the first half of the fifteenth century.[2] It was not only a revival of linguistic scholarship; it was, among other things, an advance in intellectual courage and confidence. With better critical methods of establishing exactly what the ancient writers had written and exactly what their writings meant, the humanists found that they could understand the subject matter of those writings more clearly. This meant that in every subject, including science and medicine, there were men who believed that they were uncovering forgotten truths and principles.

The two great movements formed an alliance. In 1465 came the first printing in Italy,[3] and there in the same year for the first time words were printed in the Greek language (not yet any whole book in Greek). In 1475 there was an edition of some books of the Roman writer on rhetoric, Quintilian. The first printed text of a classical

---

[1] A. B. Emden, *Biographical Register of the University of Oxford to A.D. 1500* (1958). In the remainder of this chapter where footnote references are not given for biographical statements about Oxford men they may be traced from this admirable work. It contains valuable information supplied by Mr. Neil Ker on the contents of Oxford libraries. When the present work went to press, Dr. Emden's corresponding Register for Cambridge was awaiting publication. Linacre was still a fellow of All Souls in 1493: there is nothing to show why or exactly when his fellowship was vacated.

[2] For details see R. Weiss, *Humanism in England during the Fifteenth Century* (2nd edn. 1957).

[3] The significance of this is shown in the brilliant lecture of V. Scholderer, 'Printers and Readers in Italy in the Fifteenth Century' in *Proceedings of the British Academy*, xxxv (1949), 25 ff.

medical book, the one great medical text in Latin of the best period, the newly discovered Celsus *De Re Medica*, came in 1478. But when Linacre became a fellow of All Souls not a single Greek letter had been printed in England; and no Englishman had made a solid contribution to the new knowledge of the Greek or Latin classics.

We do not know how or when he first embarked on classical or on medical studies[1]; but, even if he was drawn to them by contact with people outside Oxford, there was enough within the walls of his own college to arouse either of these interests. It was then the youngest but one of the Oxford colleges. Though well established it was not rich, and its short history had not been untroubled. Forty celibate fellows lived in one small quadrangle, but they could sometimes obtain leave not to reside. Unless they became doctors of law they were required to take Holy Orders. Their emoluments were small; they had duties in chapel but no undergraduates in the college to teach, and the warden examined them three times a year in the progress of their studies.[2] Among the former fellows there were some notable men, and several of them had travelled to Italy. One of them was James Goldswell, bishop of Norwich since 1472, who gave both manuscripts and printed books to the college library, including two copies of Lorenzo Valla's book *De Elegantia Latinae Linguae*, the book which was to be 'a beacon-light of culture for Erasmus in his youth'.[3] The first copy was a manuscript bought in Rome in 1467; the second the edition printed there four years later.

The fellowships at All Souls were for students of law and arts, but out of not more than 185 fellows who had been elected before Linacre,[4] there were three who were certainly medical men, besides four others[5] who owned medical or anatomical books or gave or bequeathed them to the college library. The three doctors were considerable figures. William Goldwin, admitted in 1455, took his medical degree at Cambridge, and practised as a physician in London. One of his prescriptions still survives. When he died in

---

[1] Professor R. Weiss refers in his 'Notes on Thomas Linacre' in *Miscellanea Giovanni Mercati*, iv (1946), 374 to his own earlier article in *Journal of the Warburg Institute*, ii (1938–9) where he shows that Cornelio Vitelli only went to Oxford in 1490, from which it follows that he did not teach Linacre Greek there.

[2] Sir Charles Grant Robertson, *All Souls College* (1899).

[3] J. Huizinga, *Erasmus of Rotterdam* (1952), pp. 13, 27.

[4] See *All Souls College List of Fellows 1438–1937* (privately printed, Oxford, *s.a.* ?1938).

[5] These four others were John Norfolk, John Asheby, William Denys and John Betts. It is not known whether any of them practised medicine, and there is no reason to suppose that they did. Every important medieval library contained medical books.

1482 he bequeathed all his manuscript books of physic to All Souls 'to be chained in the common library for ever' and ten of them are still there. One of these contains medieval Latin translations of eight works of Galen and other related matter.[1] John Racour, who was admitted to All Souls in 1467, became a doctor of medicine. He gave the college three medical books, one of them printed, and he seems to have been a medical author. Nicholas Halswell, who was a fellow of sixteen years standing when Linacre was admitted, survived to be a foundation fellow of the College of Physicians. We are not concerned with the later history of medical studies in All Souls, but it is not irrelevant to the life of Linacre to add that the first fellow of the College of Physicians elected in the ordinary course after its foundation was Richard Bartlatt, who was admitted to All Souls in 1495.

In 1487 William Selling, prior of the Cathedral priory in Canterbury and perhaps the foremost classical scholar in England, set out with two bishops on an embassy from King Henry VII to the pope. Linacre probably went with him. At any rate he went to Italy about that time, and possibly he did not come back to England until 1499.[2] Thus for ten or twelve years he knew the revival of classical learning at its source. More than that, he learnt from the greatest living masters. He studied Greek in Florence under Politian and Chalcondylas. Politian was on terms of friendship with the Medici duke of Florence, Lorenzo the Magnificent, and Linacre was well received in Lorenzo's celebrated court. Long afterwards, in 1521, he dedicated a book[3] to a fellow-student, the duke's younger son, who by then had become pope as Leo X.[4] In 1489 he was admitted to the confraternity which was attached to the English hospice in Rome. He was accepted as a responsible enough person to be elected in 1491, presumably for one year, as warden of the hospice itself. In Rome he knew Hermolaus Barbarus, a scholar whose interests lay

---

[1] This is MS. lxviii. The list of its contents in the *Catalogue* of H. O. Coxe (1852) is far from complete.
[2] The facts of Linacre's stay in Italy are accurately and cautiously set out by G. B. Parks, *The English Traveller to Italy*, vol. i, *The Middle Ages* (1954). Some subsequent writers have unfortunately repeated errors corrected in this book. See, however, p. 42 n. 3. below for a possible indication of his presence in England in 1497/8. P. S. Allen in *English Historical Review*, xviii (1903), 514-17 explained the origin of the mistaken belief that Linacre returned to England in 1491. Miss R. J. Mitchell, ibid. 1 (1935), 696-8 gave particulars of his graduation in Padua.
[3] The Cambridge edition of Galen, *De Temperamentis et de Inequali Intemperie.*
[4] For Linacre's stay in Florence see R. Weiss in *Il Poliziano e il suo tempo : Atti del IV convegno internazionale di studi sul Rinascimento* (1957), pp. 231-6.

close to those which we know were Linacre's not long afterwards. Hermolaus Barbarus, a patrician from Venice, was one of those who took up a kind of work which was new at that time, the close textual study of ancient classical works on science. He even exposed some of the errors in Pliny's *Natural History*. He was not a physician, but physicians regarded two of the Greek authors on whom he worked, Aristotle and the botanist Dioscorides, as high authorities. He had been a professor at Padua, that illustrious home of Aristotelian and also of medical studies. To Padua Linacre proceeded, and there in 1496 he took his degree as doctor of medicine. At some point in his Italian travels he probably met an older scholar whose chosen path lay very close to his own, Nicholas Leonicenus of Ferrara, the first of the humanists to publish (in 1500) genuine Greek texts of Galen. Linacre, towards the end of his life, published one of Leonicenus's translations in London along with two of his own.[1]

Padua was in the territory of the Venetian republic, and Venice was a short day's journey from it. It so chanced that Linacre was at Padua exactly at the time when Venice became the most productive centre of printing in Italy, and the most active centre of Greek and Latin printing in the world. The most famous name in Italian printing is that of Aldus Manutius; and it is still the most famous name among publishers of the classics. Aldus settled in Venice in 1494. Five years later he published the first of Linacre's translations from the Greek. Their association seems to have been very close. Aldus refers to 'Thomas Anglicus' as one of his witnesses to the pains taken over his printing from Greek manuscripts.[2] The publisher of the first complete Galen, Aldus's son-in-law Andreas Asulanus, wrote afterwards that Linacre lived for several years in Aldus's house.[3]

By the time when this first work of his appeared Linacre was back in England, the first Englishman to publish a work of the new classical scholarship. Every important library in Europe acquired it. He was also the first who had put in a long spell working as an

---

[1] *De Naturalibus Facultatibus* and *De Pulsuum Usu* (?1523): the translation by Leonicenus is *De Motu Musculorum*.

[2] In the preface to the second volume of the first printed edition of the whole works of Aristotle (1497), in *Prefaces to the First Editions of the Greek and Roman Classics and of the Sacred Scriptures*, ed. B. Botfield (1861), p. 201.

[3] In the preface to the fifth volume of the Galen of 1525 (ibid., p. 362) 'Thomas Linacrus Aldi nostri contubernio ad aliquot annos usus'. The two Latin poems on Linacre's departure from Italy printed without reference by Johnson, pp. 147-8 are from Paulus Jovius, *Elogia Doctorum Virorum* (1571), under Linacre's name.

equal with the Italian leaders of the movement. We may indeed say that he was the first Englishman who gained a European reputation as a humanist. From the time of his return he was one of the small and intimate band of scholars who began the continuous history of Greek scholarship and of classical teaching here.[1] Only one of them was older than himself, William Grocyn, who had been with him for part of the time in Italy. Among the others were the great John Colet, who was to be the founder of St. Paul's School, and William Lily its first high master. The youngest was Thomas More, who learnt Greek from Linacre. When Erasmus paid his memorable visits to England he lived familiarly with all these men and from his letters we can know their circle almost as if we had lived in it. Yet for ten years after Linacre's return we do not hear the news of him that might have been expected. He dedicated his first book to Prince Arthur, the elder son of King Henry VII, but that did not lead on to a career at court. Erasmus had a story that this dedication aroused the jealousy of Bernard Andreas, a Frenchman who was tutor to the prince, and who set the old king against the translator as a possible competitor for favour.[2] This may well be true; but, even if Linacre was disappointed of the special kind of success that would have been most desirable, that does not explain the extreme scarcity of information about how he lived for the next ten years. He published nothing. There is no record of his sources of income.[3] There is not even anything to show definitely whether he spent these years mainly in London.

The explanation may perhaps be the obvious one, that he spent them in an occupation which would leave no trace in our records, namely in medical practice. We can say with reasonable assurance that Linacre incorporated as a doctor of physic in Oxford, and that he read a 'shagling lecture' there—which means that he had no regular teaching appointment—earning the gratitude of the Oxonians by giving his lecture gratis.[4] In later years, as a court physician with distinguished patients, he rose to great heights and published

[1] The best estimate of their place in the history of learning is still that of W. F. Schirmer, *Der Englische Frühhumanismus* (1931).

[2] *Opus Epistolarum Desiderii Erasmi*, ed. P. S. Allen, ix (1938), 108. Subsequent references to *Opus Epp.* in the footnotes are to this edition.

[3] According to Hasted, ii (1782), 556–8, it was in 1497–8 that Linacre bought the two estates in Kent which ultimately formed the endowment of his Oxford and Cambridge lectureships. This implies that he was, whether by inheritance or from his earnings, a man of means. It also seems to suggest that he was not in Italy at the time.

[4] A. Wood, *Athenae Oxonienses*, i (1691), 18.

further books, but it may be inferred from his characteristics as an author that he snatched what opportunities he could in a busy life to make public parts of the store of learning that he had accumulated. In his first ten years of practice he may well have found no such opportunities.

He was slow to publish. In a prefatory letter to his first work Aldus mentions other translations that he had made, in particular of the commentaries of Simplicius and Alexander of Aphrodisias on Aristotle's *Physics* and *Meteorologica*; but these two were never printed. Erasmus reproached him for this failing.[1] Linacre was a severe judge in matters of scholarship[2] and no doubt he judged his own work severely. Certainly he corrected more than one of his works after its first appearance. Like many other learned writers he contemplated various extensive works that he never completed, and we have evidence from his friends that some of these were not only well begun but far advanced. Sometimes he finished something off because some personal reason made him wish to offer a book: he says so himself in his dedications to Prince Arthur and the Princess Mary. Like other authors who have occasion to do that, he drew on his stock, and it looks as if he had a mass of material brought back from Italy. There is no trace of any Greek manuscripts in England which he could have used; but in Venice they were available for almost all the books.[3] This suggests that Linacre may have procured transcripts when he was there; but we also know that in 1512 or 1513 manuscripts were being transcribed in Florence to his order.[4]

It seems likely, then, that most of his published works were completed during an active professional life. They do not reflect any significant process of development in his methods or opinions, and it will be convenient to pass them all rapidly in review at this point. He wrote two books on Latin grammar. The first was a short

---

[1] *Opus Epp.* iv (1922), 571. This was in 1521.

[2] Erasmus in 1516, ibid. ii (1910), 252.

[3] See the enumeration of manuscripts under the separate titles in *Claudii Galeni Opera Omnia*, ed. C. G. Kühn, i (1821), pp. lxvii ff., still the most convenient work of reference for the literary history of Galen's works. Kühn does not mention any Greek manuscript of *De Pulsuum Usu*.

[4] See his letter written from London on 13 December 1512 or 1513 to Giampiero Macchiavelli, doctor of arts and medicine, printed by R. Weiss in *Miscellanea Giovanni Mercati*, iv (1946), 379. Linacre sends greetings to an unnamed youthful pupil of this unidentified Macchiavelli. Antonio Francino says in the preface that Giambattista Macchiavelli has persuaded him to dedicate his edition (1520) of Julius Pollux *Vocabularium* to Linacre.

book in English, originally intended for St. Paul's school but rejected by Colet as too advanced for the schoolboys. It seems that Linacre did not take this too hard.[1] This book or something like it was printed in or about 1517, and reprinted with a dedication to Princess Mary six or seven years later.[2] After Linacre's death a Latin translation of it went into at least ten editions in France. The other grammatical work, the *De Emendata Structura Latini Sermonis Libri Sex* of 1524 was much more important. It is a systematic syntax with many examples of the constructions and figures of speech from the best authors, especially Cicero. Linacre modelled his own much-admired Latin style on Quintilian, which was not the fashion and, naturally enough, later scholars have corrected him on sundry points; but there seems to be no doubt that his book marked an advance on his predecessors, such as Lorenzo Valla. It was accepted as a high authority and it was reprinted many times in continental cities. It was mentioned in the Oxford statutes of 1564/5 and again in those of 1636 as one of the the textbooks which might be used by the readers in grammar for their ordinary lectures.[3]

The rest of Linacre's literary works were translations of Greek scientific and medical books. The humanists of his time did not regard themselves as literary men in any sort of contrast with what we should call scientists. Some of them, for instance Grocyn, preferred positive information about nature to philosophical speculation.[4] Erasmus himself watched over the recovery of Greek science as eagerly as he did over that of the rest of the Greek inheritance.[5] Like their medieval predecessors they did not grade the branches of study as more or less humane according to their contents. When Utopia was discovered, the European visitors brought a few Greek books with them. Besides a grammar and a lexicon they brought Homer, two of the dramatists in Aldine editions, historians, Plato and Aristotle; but they also brought Dioscorides and 'some small treatises of Hippocrates, and the *Mirotechne* of Galen, to which works they attribute great value. For though there is scarcely any nation that needs medicine less, yet nowhere is it held in greater

---

[1] Erasmus to Colet, 13 September 1511, Allen i (1906), 467.
[2] A. W. Reed in *Transactions of the Bibliographical Society* xv (1920), 173-4.
[3] *Statuta Antiqua Universitatis Oxoniensis*, ed. S. Gibson (1931), pp. 378, 389; *Statutes of the University codified in 1636*, ed. J. Griffiths (1888), p. 34.
[4] Sir John Cheke, in *De Pronuntiatione Graecae Linguae* (1555), p. 176.
[5] See his list of those 'qui medicinam vindicant' written in 1517 (*Opus Epp.* ii. 489). The names he mentions are Leonicenus, Ambrosius Leo Nolanus, Cop, Ruell, and Linacre.

honour; for they regard it as one of the finest and most useful parts of philosophy.'[1] In his scientific and medical translations then, Linacre worked in full sympathy with his humanistic friends.

The first of them, the first of all his publications, was the translation of Proclus *De Sphaera* which he dedicated and presented in manuscript to Prince Arthur. Proclus was the last of the greater Greek philosophers, but this was a minor work, suitable for a young prince to read. It is a short account of the terrestrial globe, mathematical, not descriptive, and Linacre's translation only occupies eight pages in the folio volume of ancient texts which is usually called *Astronomici Veteres*. At the time when it was published Linacre, as we saw, had been working on Aristotle. Sixteen years later More still hoped that he would publish the *Meteorologica* with the commentary of Alexander Aphrodisiensis on which he had lectured with More as one of his audience.[2] This is the only book of Aristotle which we know to have been amongst those which Linacre intended to translate. The whole of it is concerned with science. Here and there in all parts of it there are allusions to physiology, and the last part is purely physiological, but it was supposed to be relevant as a whole to medicine since meteors and the weather, the phenomena of the sublunary sphere, its main subjects, influenced the human body. It was one of the texts used in the medical teaching in the university of Caen in the early sixteenth century.[3] Linacre put it aside because his attention was claimed by Galen, the 'dux et imperator medicae rei'.

The Greek text of the works of Aristotle was published by Aldus in five folio volumes, amounting altogether to 1847 pages, in 1495–8. More than a third of this great body of writing had to do not with philosophy but with science, and thus for the first time it was possible for those who knew Greek to use the advantages of print in surveying and comparing an encyclopaedic collection of Greek scientific writings. It included much about physiology and anatomy, but no medical or surgical treatises in a narrow sense. It was generally believed that no Greek writings were more useful than the writings of the *medici*, and Andreas Asulanus, who was in a position

[1] More, *Utopia* (1516), Bk. 2, c. vi.
[2] More to Martin Dorp, 21 October 1515, in *Correspondence of Sir Thomas More*, ed. Elizabeth F. Rogers (1947), p. 65. See also Erasmus in 1518 (Allen, iii. 403).
[3] H. Prentout, 'La vie de l'étudiant a Caen au xvie siècle' in *Mémoires de l'Académie Nationale des Sciences de Caen* (1905); the text implies that it was compulsory at least until 1521, and remained in the list after that date.

to know, wrote that no Greek texts were more frequently asked for or more ardently desired by the learned than these, especially the works of Galen and Hippocrates.[1] He met this demand by publishing Galen in five volumes, nearly as long as the Aristotle, and Hippocrates in a single folio, both in 1525.

The Galen was much more important at that time than the Hippocrates. The Hippocratic writings, some of them 600 years older than Galen, were a heterogeneous collection in which even the most serviceable presented, as they still do, discouraging difficulties. Galen was comprehensive and systematic. Some of his books were easy to understand and easy to use. For these and other reasons, even in bad Latin translations of Arabic versions, he had supplied the medieval medical schools with some of their textbooks for two centuries. The humanists had high hopes of the Greek text. They thought well of it, to begin with, from the point of view of language.[2] It seemed to offer a key to medical science. Galen, as he said himself, was a Hippocratic eclectic; he offered in the first place a key to Hippocrates. As Linacre wrote, his 'fusa, iucundaque claritas' preserved Hippocrates.[3] Once Greek medical science was restored in authentic and unencumbered texts, once the knowledge of it was spread, medical practice could revive as the arts and letters were reviving. These hopes were not to be fulfilled. Those who entertained them did not in fact know more than a little about their great masters; but this in itself excuses them for expecting far too much. During Linacre's lifetime no one directly impugned Galen's authority, and indeed the restoration of his authentic text was the essential first step to subverting it.

Although Linacre and his friends thought so highly of the Greek medical texts they never proposed that Greek should be made a requirement for medical education. On the contrary, they set to work to enable medical men in general to profit from the new knowledge without undergoing the labour of learning the Greek language. Before Galen's works were printed as a whole in Greek there was a period of nearly thirty years during which they were explored by scholars who knew Greek and published Latin trans-

---

[1] Botfield, pp. 352–3.

[2] Erasmus, in acknowledging the gift of the five volumes from Asulanus, no doubt did not rein in his pen, but he called Galen 'autor per se gratiosus . . . mihi vero peculiari quodam vel sensu vel iudicio adamatus': *Opus Epp.* vi (1926), 405. For his opinion of the edition contrast his letters, ibid. pp. 336, 346, vii. 497.

[3] Preface to *De Sanitate Tuenda.*

lations from it.[1] Linacre's main literary work lay here, and the two questions deserve to be answered, what was the value of this labour and what did Linacre's share in it amount to. The first is easy to answer; except for the purposes of Greek scholars, who were still very few even in Italy, a good Latin text was the best means of making the true Galen known. Erasmus himself translated the first three treatises from the Aldine Galen for Froben's complete Latin edition.[2] A century later, when Harvey made notes on Goulston's edition of Galen's *Opuscula*, he invariably annotated the Latin and left the Greek columns without marks throughout.[3] All the professional men in Europe knew Latin. Special medical terminology in classical Latin was available in Celsus. A good translation explained as it went along and so accomplished in the minimum of space much of the essential work of a commentary. In the vernacular languages the terminology was not ready to hand. Even in 1821 Kühn's twenty-volume edition of Galen, which is still the standard edition, had a running Latin translation at the bottom of each page.

The second question is a little more difficult. In quantity Linacre's six translations amounted to about a tenth of Galen's works. There were two long treatises. The first *De Sanitate Tuenda* was published in folio in Paris in 1517 and, by a command conveyed by Cardinal Wolsey, was dedicated to Henry VIII. The title-page has an engraving with Galen and Linacre, both bearded, facing one another. The other, the *Methodus Medendi* was published also in folio in Paris in 1519 and also dedicated to Henry. The Greek text had been printed in Venice and published in 1500: this is the only one of Linacre's translations for which he had the original before him in print. He afterwards made no less than 2,250 emendations to it, which were appended to two later editions and incorporated in that published by Lucas Panetius in Venice in 1527 with the title *Terrapeutica*. The frontispiece of the Paris edition of 1530 is a picture of a dissection, an early example of the 'anatomy lesson' subject which Rembrandt made famous. Both these two translations were accepted as authoritative and, besides separate editions, they appeared in collections of Galen's complete works.

[1] For the bibliography of all these see R. J. Durling, 'A Chronological Census of Renaissance Editions and Translations of Galen' in *Journal of the Warburg and Courtauld Institutes*, xxiv (1961), an admirable study with full catalogue.
[2] *Galeni Exhortatio ad Bonas Artes* (1526).
[3] N. Moore, *History of the Study of Medicine in the British Isles* (1908), p. 184.

Two shorter works were published together at Cambridge in quarto in 1521, being among the first nine books printed there and among the first books in which Greek words were printed in England. They were dedicated to Pope Leo X, with a reference to his munificence to Linacre and to their old acquaintance. They were the treatise *De Temperamentis* and that *De Inaequali Temperie*, which had already been translated both by Giorgio Valla and by Leonicenus. Next, in all probability, came *De Naturalibus Facultatibus* published in quarto by Pynson in London in or about 1522 with a dedication to Archbishop Warham. There was another edition in Paris in 1528, with a prefatory letter which seems to imply that the translation was little known abroad. The writer, John Gunter von Andernach, says that he has corrected some errors and that the book was brought by Petrus Bellus, physician to the duke of Vendôme whom he had accompanied on an embassy to England. Pynson's edition appeared together with *De Pulsuum Usu*, a mere complimentary trifle—six pages of 'elenchus', twenty-four of text and three of errata—dedicated to Wolsey 'literatorum unice Maecenas'. This latter piece was reprinted in Paris in 1528 with the *De Naturalibus Facultatibus*, but in general it seems that these shorter pieces were of little importance on the continent. The last of them were published together by Pynson, in 1524 but after Linacre's death: *De Symptomatum Differentiis* and *De Symptomatum Causis*. One of these two had been translated earlier by Leonicenus.

Some excellent work has been done on Galen in recent years, but so far as the present writer can learn no modern scholar has made any close comparison between the different Renaissance translators of Galen, nor even established the total effect of their labours on the interpretation of his works. Linacre's successors, like his contemporaries, have had nothing but praise for his knowledge of Greek and his use of Latin. A modern opinion worth citing is that of Dr. A. J. Brock, who translated *Galen on the Natural Faculties* into English and wrote of Linacre's translations as 'all marked by minute accuracy and elegant Latinity'.[1]

After the ten blank years Linacre's biography emerges again in 1509. That was the year in which Henry VIII came to the throne, a young king not unacquainted with good letters, and a patron for the humanistic circle. Linacre received the first of his many ecclesiastical preferments. There is no need to enumerate them, since

[1] Introduction (1916), p. xxii.

there is no reason to suppose that he discharged any of their duties otherwise than by deputy. He held some of them for long periods, but others briefly, only long enough, we may infer, to arrange with a successor to pay him a pension from the emoluments. He received them, according to the custom of the time, as rewards for services outside the strictly ecclesiastical field and perhaps for general distinction. Early in the new reign[1] he was established at court and he remained so for the rest of his life. In 1514 the king's sister, the Lady Mary, set out for Calais to marry Charles, prince of Castile, and afterwards emperor. Linacre was in attendance with two servants (her chamberlain and treasurer each took three).[2] The party was halted at Dover by the news that the match was broken off. Next year the lady was married by proxy to the king of France, and Linacre was in her suite when she travelled to Paris. He met the great French scholar Budaeus more than once. Budaeus liked him, noted that he had nothing haughty about him, and after his departure sent him a copy of his own newly published book on Roman coinage.[3] Two years later Linacre sent his French friend a handsome present of a different kind, cramp-rings hallowed by King Henry, eighteen of silver and one of gold. What the physician thought of their virtue we cannot tell. Erasmus once wrote that medical attendance on the great is a branch of flattery; and when Budaeus distributed the rings to his friends, he told them that these were amulets against slander and calumny.[4]

Linacre's principal function at Court was evidently medical, and he was a familiar figure there in his scarlet or purple gown.[5] The dates of his appointments have not been published. From 1516 to 1520 he was paid quarterly at the rate of £50 a year, while the queen's physician, her fellow-countryman Don Fernando de Victoria, received £66 13s. 4d. in two half-yearly instalments.[6] In 1521 Erasmus, changing his style of address wrote to Linacre no longer as 'Medicus Regius' but as 'Serenissimi Anglorum Regis

---

[1] George Lily, in Paolo Giovio, *Descriptio Britanniae* (1548), fo. 49, says that the appointment was made by Henry VIII 'renovato patris exemplo' but there is no confirmation of this and the example may only be the appointment as tutor to Prince Arthur.

[2] *Letters and Papers*, i, pt. ii (1920), no. 2656 (6).

[3] Budaeus to Erasmus, 7 July 1516 in *Opus Epp.* ii. 273.

[4] *Epistolae Gulielmi Budaei* (1520) *passim*.

[5] George Lily, loc. cit. 'talari toga purpurea amictus' is too classical to make it clear exactly what the garment was.

[6] *Letters and Papers*, i, pt. ii, p. 1472, iii, nos. 491, 1114. 1535.

Medicus Primarius', from which we may infer that he had become the senior of the medical household.[1]

There is reason to believe that he deserved his promotion. We have not only the general expressions of friends who praised his professional skill, but definite facts about some of his cases. He strongly advised against an injudicious operation, for a boil or a carbuncle on the hip, which proved fatal to his schoolmaster-friend John Lily.[2] He gave Erasmus a prescription, and as the patient lost it and wrote to ask for another copy, we know that it gave satisfaction.[3] Erasmus also tells the story of Linacre's treating him for calculus. He did not like asking favours (although he often did it) and Linacre required stimulation before he attended to anything, so on the advice of a friend, Erasmus made a moving appeal. Linacre came at once. An apothecary was summoned. A *pharmacum* used in the baths of Germany was prepared in the bedroom and applied in the presence of the physician himself. Two applications achieved the desired result.[4] All of Linacre's other patients whose names have been preserved, with the exception of one elderly knight of the garter, survived him.[5]

Outside his medical practice we have such other notices of Linacre as might be expected of a successful and reliable man. There is no reason to doubt that he introduced the damask rose to gardeners and to apothecaries.[6] He acted as executor for his friend Grocyn, whose library he catalogued with his own hand.[7] Long before, he had been one of the recipients of bequests of books from an older Oxford man, John Mower.[8] He wrote to John Claymond, president of Magdalen (1504–17) passing on a pupil and recommending Claymond to persevere with learning Greek.[9] In 1520, when he was about sixty, there comes a surprise: he was ordained

---

[1] Letters of 5 June 1516 and 24 August 1521 in *Opus Epp.* ii. 247 and iv. 570.
[2] George Lily, loc. cit. fo. 48.   [3] Letter of 5 June 1516 in *Opus Epp.* ii. 247.
[4] To Willibald Pirckheimer, 14 March, 1525, ibid. vi. 47.
[5] Linacre witnessed the will of Sir Reginald Bray, who died in 1503. Other patients were Wolsey, Warham, Richard Foxe, Colet and More.
[6] R. Hakluyt, 'Memoranda' in *Voyages*, II, i (1582), 165: the first mention of the damask rose in England goes back to about 1540.
[7] The catalogue is printed with Grocyn's will in *Oxford Historical Society, Collectanea*, vol. ii (1890).
[8] See H. R. Plomer in *Trans. Bibliog. Soc.* vii (1904), 118–19. Mower's will, dated 12 April 1489, refers to 'eidem domino Thome studenti Florencij'.
[9] Claymond, a friend of Erasmus, afterwards became the first president of Corpus when it was founded by Foxe. The letter was found by his successor, P. S. Allen, and printed in *The Pelican Record* (1925), reprinted by R. Weiss in *Miscellanea Giovanni Mercati*, iv (1946), 378.

priest.[1] As he had held church benefices for so long, this step cannot have been taken in the interests of his career. We do not know when he took the prior step of ordination as a deacon, nor whether he was in minor orders in his early days at All Souls. It seems from some expressions in his dedication of a book to Archbishop Warham that the purpose was to gain greater leisure for literary work, perhaps by discharging some of his duties in person and living in the house belonging to one of his rectories.[2] Soon after this he caused a petition to be presented to Pope Leo X, the same Giovanni de' Medici whom he had known as a boy and fellow-pupil in Florence. The pope promised to accord it.[3] Perhaps this was in furtherance of the plan for relief from practice. There is one story which turns on a change in Linacre's way of life. This is the story that after he became a priest he read the New Testament for the first time, and that when he had read the fifth, sixth, and seventh chapters of Matthew, in other words the Sermon on the Mount, he flung away the book, exclaiming 'Either this is not the Gospel or we are not Christians'.[4] This has been interpreted as meaning that Linacre, like Erasmus, turned away from some of the current religious practices towards a simpler evangelical piety. It would be unjustifiable to suppose that it connects him in any way with the dawn of the Protestant Reformation. The story comes at second hand and late in time; and the teller is a questionable witness. In any case, if Linacre gained leisure he did not enjoy it long. In 1521 his health gave trouble.[5] He received his last court appointment as Latin tutor, along with Luis Vives, to the Princess Mary, afterwards Queen Mary I; but all he was able to do in this capacity was to dedicate his shorter grammar to his pupil. After much suffering he died, it was said of calculus, in 1524.[6]

It remains to speak of him as a founder and benefactor. The most memorable achievement of his whole life was the founding of the College of Physicians. In the eyes of the law, to be sure, it was a royal foundation: the king brought the College into existence by his

[1] He was ordained on 22 December, his title being the rectory of Wigan to which he was instituted on 10 December 1519 (*Victoria County History, Lancashire*, iv. 62).

[2] See above p. 48.

[3] Silvestro de' Gigli, bishop of Worcester, to Pace 29 March 1521, calendered in *Letters and Papers*, iii. no. 1204; Pace to the Pope, ibid. no. 1275.

[4] Sir John Cheke in *De Pronuntiatione Graecae Linguae* (1555), p. 281.

[5] Erasmus to him, 24 August 1521 in *Opus Epp.* iv. 570.

[6] Erasmus to Vives, Cop and Francis, ibid. v. 577, vi. 380, 424; but George Lily, op. cit. fo. 49v, writes of him as 'diu ante valetudinarius ad extremum disruptae herniae doloribus confectus'.

charter and conferred its privileges and powers. But he did not claim to have initiated it; the charter granted what had been asked for in a petition which bore Linacre's name. That name did not indeed appear alone; it was the second among seven names, but Linacre was in a different position from the others. He became the first president of the College and remained so until his death. More than that he was its first benefactor. The work it was intended to do required no great endowments: its members were all engaged in a calling which provided their livelihood, some of its activities would be supported by fees and the members paid subscriptions to support the others. The chief material need was a place of meeting. During Linacre's lifetime it met in his house, the Stone House in Knightrider Street, between St. Paul's Cathedral and the river. He conveyed the forepart of this house to the College with the lower room as a meeting-place and the upper for the library.

We must discuss the origin and purposes of the College at length in our next chapter, but something may be said here about its place in Linacre's plans. There was no university in London, but the charter does not contemplate a teaching college. We know that Linacre was zealous for education: he endowed three lecture-ships with estates in Kent worth £30 a year, but they were to be settled in Oxford and Cambridge, where they have had a chequered history with a conspicuously happy ending. It was not long before the London college undertook teaching and other functions which are not mentioned in its charter, but this was a departure from the original intentions, arising from experience and from changing conditions. So far as we have evidence of its founders' purposes it was a vocational body, charged with the repression of unqualified practitioners, with examining and licensing those who wished to practise, and with some kind of supervision over medicines. It set high ethical and intellectual standards for its members. From its foundation it 'established a permanent relation' between the medical profession and the world of learning; and it confirmed the tradition by which 'a physician in England was rightly thought a member of the learned world'.[1]

How are we to regard Linacre's great public service in this foundation? Did he bring back from Italy the spirit of the Renais-sance, or the spirit of scientific progress (which was by no means

---

[1] Sir Norman Moore, *History of the Study of Medicine in the British Isles* (1908), pp. 55–56.

identical with it), or an enquiring, secular spirit, calling for a new freedom from ecclesiastical dominance and intellectual conservatism? Was he, in short, a reformer? The writers who have praised him thus were misled into subtle anachronisms by the enthusiasms of their own times. The foundation of his College did not imply any innovation of principle: 'the lawyer and the constitutional historian will regard the later Middle Ages as the time that witnessed the greatest extension of corporate and collegiate life known in this country'.[1] It is tempting to think of the Italy in which Linacre travelled as the Italy of Leonardo da Vinci, but Leonardo's anatomical studies were secret. We do not know whether Linacre had any inkling that a new and penetrating curiosity was already at work in anatomy. The Italy in which he moved was the Italy of Lorenzo the Magnificent, of Aldus and of Pope Leo X. The English circle which revolved round Erasmus was also the circle of Sir Thomas More. Unknown to itself it was preparing the way for revolutions. So were the kings like Henry VIII and Louis XII of France, who were soon to nominate their own professors of medicine, and so were the citizens of London who were to save St. Bartholomew's and St. Thomas's Hospitals from abolition. But so far as Linacre's own mind and action are known to us we must conclude that he used his judgement and his wealth in the ways which the ruling ideals of his early manhood would have dictated. He was one of the few founders who have themselves practised the arts and sciences to which they have dedicated their foundations, one of the very few who, having established a new institution, have themselves guided it safely through its early dangers. His College, growing through the centuries, has encountered experiences which he could not have imagined. It has helped to emancipate science and medical practice from religious and social intolerance; it has helped the profession to forget Galen and to disembarrass itself of Greek scholarship and even of Latin. Its constitution has been imitated far and wide. Like all great corporate institutions it has lived its own life, and its founder's greatness is measured by its achievement.

[1] E. F. Jacob, *The Fifteenth Century* (1961), p. 289.

IV : THE FOUNDATION OF THE COLLEGE OF PHYSICIANS OF LONDON

THE parliament of the third year of King Henry VIII, which sat from 4 February 1511 to 23 January 1512, passed an Act which was closely related to the foundation of the College of Physicians six years later.[1] Both the royal charter and the first known statutes of the College refer to this Act. It was the first parliamentary enactment about medical affairs, and it was not repealed until 1948. Its preamble is a petition presented to the king in parliament, but unfortunately this does not tell us who the petitioners were. This preamble is a challenge:

Forasmuch as the Science and Cunning[2] of Physick and Surgery (to the perfect knowledge whereof be requisite both great Learning and ripe Experience) is daily within this realm exercised by a great multitude of ignorant persons, of whom the greater part have no manner of Insight in the same, nor in any other kind of Learning; some also can no Letters on the Book, so far forth, that common Artificers, as Smiths,[3] Weavers, and Women, boldly and accustomably[4] take upon them great Cures,[5] and things of great Difficulty, in the which they partly use Sorcery and Witchcraft, partly apply such Medicines unto the Disease as be very noious, and nothing meet therefore, to the high Displeasure of God, great infamy to the Faculty,[6] and the grievous Hurt, Damage, and Destruction of many of the King's liege People, most especially of them that cannot discern the cunning from the uncunning.

It was therefore enacted that no person within the City of London nor within seven miles of it[7] should take upon him to 'exercise and

---

[1] 3 Henry VIII, c. 11.   [2] 'Cunning' is here equivalent to 'art'.
[3] Farriers were the veterinary practitioners of the day. It is not until 1611 that we find a horse-doctor (*hippiater*) mentioned in the College Annals.
[4] Customarily, usually.
[5] That is cases or treatment; it seems doubtful whether 'cure' ever implied successful treatment before the late sixteenth century or even later. It may have this sense in the passage quoted from Thomas Gale in J. F. South, *Memorials of the Craft of Surgery*, ed. D'A. Power (1886), p. 125.   [6] The art.
[7] The City companies enjoyed monopolies varying in radius from three to eight miles; seven miles was the limit within which the City had the sole right to hold markets: S. and B. Webb, *The Manor and the Borough* (1908), ii, 572. From what point the distance was reckoned seems to be obscure and quite unimportant.

occupy' as a physician or surgeon except he were first examined, appointed and admitted by the bishop of London or by the dean of St. Paul's 'calling to him or them[1] four doctors of physic and for surgery other expert persons in that faculty'.[2] For the first examination they were to call such doctors of physic and surgeons as they thought convenient: and after that, four of those already approved. Anyone who practised without being so examined and admitted was to forfeit £5 for every month, of which half was to go to the king and half to any informer. Since there was no adequate police force in those days it was normally left to common informers to bring criminals to justice. Outside the City and the precinct of seven miles no one was to practise as a physician or surgeon without being similarly examined and approved by the bishop of the diocese, or in his absence by his vicar general,[3] who were to call to themselves such expert persons in the said faculties (that is, the said arts) as their discretion should think convenient. They were to give letters testimonial under their seals to the persons approved, and the penalty for practising without approval was to be the same as in London. Nothing in the Act was to be prejudicial to the privileges of the universities of Oxford and Cambridge. At the end comes a two-line Memorandum that surgeons are to be comprised in this Act like as physicians, for like mischief of ignorant persons presuming to practise surgery. This reads oddly since surgeons were comprised in each part of the Act, and it suggests that the Act was intended in the first place for physicians, or at least that someone thought so.

Here, then, was a mature and practical plan with sanctions and administrative machinery for carrying out the same ultimate intentions as those of the futile petitions of 1421. The universities were to retain their right of granting licences to practise throughout the realm, but it was not to be an exclusive right.[4] There were to be examinations in London and in each of the sixteen other English dioceses. It will be noticed that the arrangements for the provinces differed from those for London[5]: in London four doctors were to examine, as well as surgeons, but for the provinces no number was

---

[1] That is the bishop and dean.   [2] The art of surgery.

[3] An official whom a bishop deputes to represent him in the exercise of his jurisdiction. Bishops were often absent from their dioceses and their functions under this Act seem normally to have devolved on the vicars general.

[4] For further details of this matter see below p. 209.

[5] It should, however, be remembered that the diocese of London then included Hertfordshire and Essex.

specified, presumably because in some dioceses it would be difficult
to bring as many as four together. That the whole system was under
ecclesiastical control is in no way surprising. In London the bishop
and the dean had granted licences to surgeons ever since their
guild was founded in the fourteenth century, though not to physicians. Only the church had a developed administration covering
the whole country and capable of carrying out this function. A
good many of the boroughs could have done it for their own immediate districts, as they already did for the craft of surgery, but
their officers did not patrol the countryside, and in all ages there
have been quacks who have relied on mobility as one of their
tactical advantages. The sheriffs, the village constables and the
intermediate authorities were not well fitted to conduct examinations, or closely enough organized to watch a wide area. The
clerical hierarchy on the other hand from the archdeacons, through
the rural deans to the parish priests, covered the whole country and
knew the affairs of every hamlet.

That the church should have undertaken this responsibility is
indeed significant of its position in England and at this time. So
far as has been ascertained at present no English bishop had ever
had to do with such business before.[1] Nor does there seem to be
any instance on the Continent of the licensing or regulating of
physicians or surgeons by bishops in their spiritual capacity. The
bishops who took charge of such matters seem to have been some of
those who were also secular rulers, and who are usually called
prince-bishops.[2] In England the monarchy was gaining in strength,
improving its control over the country, and desirous of clearing up
a variety of abuses, but it had no administrative organs suitable for
this purpose. It was on good terms with the church, which still
supplied the state with officials of every grade, and had officials of
its own who were competent to supply this new need.[3]

We do not know for 1511 any more than we do for 1421 exactly
what led to the action of parliament; but we do know something
significant about the men who were concerned. The bishop of
London and the dean of St. Paul's must have been consenting
parties. The bishop, Richard Fitz-James, was of a decidedly con-

---

[1] G. Parker, *Early History of Surgery in Great Britain* (1920), p. 83.
[2] Such as the count-bishop of Verdun, whose vicar general drew up synodal regulations in 1507 for medical practice in the diocese: Delaunay, p. 292.
[3] For the cognate subject of the licensing of midwives see note at the end of this
chapter.

servative disposition, but he was at least aware that there was such a thing as the art of medicine, for among the nineteen manuscripts which he gave to his Oxford college, Merton, two were medical.[1] But the dean was Linacre's friend the great John Colet. Most probably the City of London was consulted, and at that time Thomas More was its under sheriff. We do not know how close Linacre's association with Archbishop Warham had become at this date, but they were both frequently at court, and the archbishop must have agreed to a proposal which affected all his bishops. Altogether we may be sure that Linacre was at least aware of the parliamentary proceedings and the discussions that lay behind them.

Little can be said with certainty about the effects of the enactment in its first few years. In London the earliest record, which appears to relate to the first actual admissions, comes from 1514, when seventy-two surgeons were examined and admitted. This figure is interesting. It may well be that all or most of the practising surgeons in the two companies, or at any rate in the Barbers and Surgeons' Company, submitted themselves to the prescribed procedure, and if this is so we thus know approximately how many surgeons there were in and about the City.[2] After that there is a gap in our information until 1529. By that time or soon afterwards the system was not working so well: many of those who should have done so no longer took out licences.[3] Even for the earlier date we have no list of physicians, and the only thing we learn about physicians is that one of them conducted the examination along with four barber surgeons. This was Dr. John Smythe, whom we have met already as instructor and examiner to the Barber Surgeons' Company in 1497.[4] It seems that in London the new Act made no difference to the conduct of the surgeons' examinations, and only led to the issue of bishops' certificates testifying to the results. For the other dioceses there seems to be no published information.

This is the more regrettable because even some small scrap of evidence might have helped us to understand why the Act of 1511

[1] Emden, *s.n.*: one contained ten tractates of Galen, the other Avenzoar, *Practica Medica*.
[2] R. R. James, 'The Earliest List of Surgeons to be Licensed by the Bishop of London under the Act of 3 Henry VIII, c. 11' in *Janus*, xli (1936), 255 ff. prints the names, with annotations to some of them largely from Young.
[3] See below, p. 84.
[4] See above p. 18. The four physicians stipulated for in the Act may have been a panel of whom any one could examine alone.

was found insufficient after only seven years, and superseded, so far as London was concerned, by the College charter. We can indeed point to one fact which is probably relevant. It was in 1518 that an English government for the first time issued orders for the prevention of the plague. These orders to some extent followed French and Italian models. There was some attempt to enforce them in the provinces: Sir Thomas More reported to Wolsey on measures that he had taken to deal with the plague in Oxford.[1] We do not know in what capacity he took this action but we know the reason: the king was at Woodstock only seven miles from there.[2] There was evidently a sense of emergency. This may explain why a new organization of physicians was set up in London, and set up not by the City but by royal authority. At that moment, however, it happened that there were men about the king who were alive to the importance of medical matters, emergency or no emergency, and even if the new departure was due to a change in circumstances, it was shaped by their thought and will. On 23 September 1518 the king granted his letters patent under the Great Seal incorporating the President and College or Commonalty of the Faculty of Medicine of London.[3]

Except in two points this Charter, finely written out on vellum, follows the standard forms and wording of the period. Like other Tudor charters it is in Latin. Several parts of it—the forms of incorporation, the authentication and the clause saving the rights of the City of London—follow established usage word for word. The first deviation from the normal is small and has no bearing on the substance. The penman has traced the outline for an illuminated initial at the beginning and for a line of decoration at the top; but no limner has ever done his work on them. There are other charters which have the same defect, but we cannot explain it beyond saying that they must have been handed over in their present state to recipients who neglected to have the finishing touches applied.[4] The other irregularity is that at the bottom a note has been added

[1] Proclamation in *Letters and Papers, Henry VIII*, ii (1864), 16, Doc. 875; F. P. Wilson, *The Plague in Shakespeare's London* (1927), especially p. 57, n. 1.

[2] I have to thank Dr. Robb-Smith for drawing my attention to this fact about the king.

[3] The text has often been printed; the most accessible places to find it are in Munk (see p. 59 n. 2 below) and, with translation, in the *Charter and Bye-Laws* periodically re-issued by the College.

[4] For this point and for the forms of charters generally see *Catalogue of an Exhibition of Borough Charters*, with Preface by Sir Hilary Jenkinson (British Records Association, 1959). See also p. 104 below.

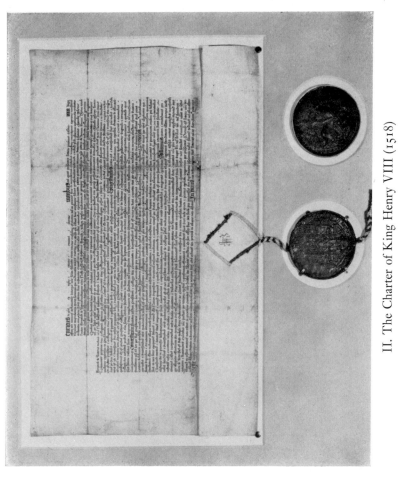

II. The Charter of King Henry VIII (1518)

that the ratification of the Charter in parliament was to take effect from the date of granting.[1]

The king's motives for the grant are given as three. The first is general: it is part of his office to resist the endeavours of wicked men and especially to repress the boldness of those who profess medicine rather because of their own avarice than in any assurance of a good conscience, whence arise very many ills for the rude and credulous populace. Next is a more specific reason, a frank admission that this matter was managed better abroad: the king is acting partly in imitation of well regulated cities in Italy and in many other nations. We shall consider later what Italian and other cities provided the examples, but here it should be noticed that the imitation of foreign models is ascribed to the king, and not to the petitioners named in the following clause. We must therefore regard it as possible that some of the king's servants or even the king himself considered the foreign models of their own motion and independently of the petition, which is cited as the king's third reason. It had been presented, the Charter tells us, by seven weighty men. Six were physicians.[2] Three royal physicians come first, John Chambre, Thomas Linacre, and Ferdinand de Victoria, and after them Nicholas Halswell, John Francis[3] and Robert Yaxley.[4] The seventh name is the weightiest of all, Thomas cardinal archbishop of York and lord chancellor. Wolsey was at the height of his power; his sponsorship must have settled the outcome, and he may have done more than merely lend his support. Linacre was his personal physician.

The petitioners had asked for the creation of a perpetual College of learned and weighty men who should practise medicine in the City of London and for seven miles about it, the same geographical limit that we have seen already in the Act of 1511. This was granted and the members of the College were charged to deter the ignorance and presumption of the aforesaid malicious persons by their own example and also to punish them by using the recently promulgated

[1] See below p. 76.
[2] There are biographical notices of all known fellows and licentiates of the College down to 1700 in W. Munk, *Roll of the Royal College of Physicians*, vol. i (1861, 2nd edn. 1878). In the present work it will be assumed that the reader has access to this, but some supplementary facts will be given in the footnotes.
[3] John Francis succeeded Linacre as physician to Wolsey: Erasmus to him, 27 December 1524, *Opus Epp.* v (1924), 613.
[4] Robert Yaxley, born in London, M.A., Cambridge 1482, M.B. 1486-7, M.D. 1496-7, fellow of Clare 1489; J. Venn, *Alumni Cantabrigienses*, pt. i, vol. iv (1927).

laws (again the Act) and by statutes (*constitutiones*) to be enacted by the College itself. The six medical petitioners and all men of the same faculty of and in the City were to be a perpetual body and commonalty (*communitas*) or perpetual College. They were empowered to elect annually one of their number as president for one year to supervise, inspect, and govern the College and all men of the faculty and their affairs. The president and College were to have perpetual succession, a common seal, and the right to own lands, tenements, rents, and other possessions. The limit of the lands and tenements they might hold was fixed at the annual value of £12, a very small amount in comparison with those allowed to Oxford and Cambridge colleges, which might run to hundreds. They might sue and be sued; they might hold meetings (*congregationes*) and make statutes and ordinances for the wholesome government, supervision and 'correction' of the College and of all the men of the faculty in London and within the seven miles. Furthermore no one was to practise this faculty within these limits unless admitted by the President and College by letters sealed with their common seal, on pain of paying £5 for every month of unlicensed practice, half to go to the king and half to the president and College. Every year they were to elect four of their number who were to exercise their powers over the physicians of London and over all those from outside who in any way practised medicine within it, to punish their delinquencies in practising it ill, and to supervise and examine the physicians' prescriptions for internal and external medicines. The punishments were to be by fines, amercement, imprisonments or other reasonable and fitting ways. The physicians were exempted from service on all juries, inquisitions and the like in London or elsewhere.

The College thus received a power of licensing almost exactly like that of the bishop. It was to be enforced by four annually elected officers, the same number who were to be called by the bishop. We hear of no dispute like those which arose in later generations between the bishop's vicars general and the surgeons, and so it seems likely that the bishops of London from the beginning regarded their licensing power in the City as abrogated by the Charter.[1] After they were licensed, the four officers had disciplinary

[1] At any rate after it was confirmed by Act of Parliament. For the legal position see the view of Sir John Popham, below p. 156. In 1599 the bishop agreed that he would license as surgeons only those approved by the Company (South, p. 154) but there were disputes about the application of this agreement until the eighteenth century.

powers over physicians, and the College as a whole had the right
to prosecute unlicensed practitioners and take half the fines (on the
same scale as in 1511), besides further rights to inflict fines and
imprisonment itself. Instead of the common informer the pretended
physician now had to fear a constituted body of skilled prosecutors.
There was no clause saving the rights of the universities: perhaps
therefore their graduates could not practice in the London area
without the approval of the College.

From the wording of the charter it is not perfectly clear who were
to be members of the College. It seems to include all the licensed
physicians of the City (the six petitioners and all the rest are to be a
College) but in the clauses regarding the president and the four
officers, the College and all the men of the faculty are mentioned
separately. This may not imply that there were to be any practitioners
outside the College; it may only be that the five officers were to act
both in the corporate affairs of the College and in the affairs of its
members as individuals practising their art. The numbers concerned were still very small, and at this stage the College was almost
certainly an organization of the profession in London, not an
organization within the profession: this was the view of the best
legal authorities in later times when the question became important.[1]

In this and in several other provisions of the Charter it resembled
the City companies, but it was never reckoned as one of them, and
some of the words which occur in the Charter were not used in
connexion with City companies. It was unlike them in several ways.
As we have seen it had nothing to do with apprenticeship. It was
not, like the Barber Surgeons' Company, bound by the Acts of
Parliament which made the ordinances of the London crafts,
guilds, mysteries, and fraternities subject to the approval of the
lord chancellor, the lord treasurer, and the two lords chief justices
or any two of them.[2] It was subject only to the vague visitatorial
power of the king as founder and the still imperfectly defined
supervisory power of the court of chancery.[3] We have already noticed
the name 'College'. Those who introduced it in 1518 may have
known that it was used for the unsuccessful venture of a century
before. The title of the president is also interesting. The word has

---

[1] For this question see further below, vol. ii, c. xxvii. The legal authorities are mentioned by J. W. Willcock, *The Laws relating to the Medical Profession* (1830), pp. 44 ff.
xxxix.
[2] The most recent was 19 Henry VII, c. 7, which followed 15 Henry VI, c. 6.
[3] See Sir William Holdsworth, *History of English Law*, ix (1926), 57–62.

a long history, but in England it seems never to have been used officially before this date except in ecclesiastical and academic bodies. For these it was coming into fashion but it was still uncommon. In Cambridge one of the colleges (Queen's) had a 'president' as its head and in Oxford two. One of these two was Corpus Christi which was founded in the previous year, and the other was Magdalen, where John Claymond, the first president of Corpus, had held the same office and where Cardinal Wolsey in his younger days had been fellow and bursar.

But the physicians' new body was not a craft-guild with an academic veneer. It belonged to a new type of association which was emerging as the professions separated out from the crafts, and there were already two dissimilar specimens of the type in the narrow streets close to old St. Paul's, where Linacre had his abode.[1] The older of the two was the College of Arms or Heralds' College in which were associated all the officers of arms, thirteen in number. Their charter of incorporation, granted by King Richard III confirmed their established rights as the sole authorized practitioners in certain matters concerning state ceremonies and heraldry. They had powers of inspection and discipline throughout the kingdom over all who contravened the laws of arms. They were indeed officers in a service rather than members of a profession, and instead of prosecuting offenders in the king's courts or those of the City, they did so in the court of the marshal, their own head. The marshal also appointed them to their offices; but their college was a private body in the same sense as the ecclesiastical colleges or the colleges in the universities. It owned property. Its members rendered services to clients, who paid them fees.[2]

The second body, in Paternoster Row, was less like the College of Physicians in some respects but on the whole more like it. This was the Association of Doctors of Law and of the Advocates of Christ Church at Canterbury, usually known as Doctors' Commons, founded in 1511. It did not obtain a charter of incorporation until 1768; it never exercised authority over any members of the legal profession outside its own numbers, nor did it grant licences. Its control over admission to its fellowships was not absolute; the candidates had to be previously admitted by the ecclesiastical

---

[1] I have not found any document in which the three institutions are grouped together before the year 1679: see below p. 346.

[2] See Sir Anthony Wagner, *Heralds and Heraldry in the Middle Ages* (1939).

authorities. But it comprised all those who were licensed to practise a particular higher branch of the law. It 'considered it to be its duty to see to the interests of the profession'. It was not a teaching body: instruction in its sphere of canon and civil law was left to the two universities, and a degree at either was a condition precedent to admission.[1] Its existence was certainly known to Linacre: some of the advocates resided in the building; Erasmus's friend Andreas Ammonius stayed there and complained of the food.[2] We cannot point to any evidence that it influenced the arrangements of the College of Physicians, but it provided in a rather similar way for rather similar purposes.

Like Doctors' Commons the new College seems at first not to have undertaken any teaching functions: Linacre's benefactions to Oxford and Cambridge sufficiently show that his hopes for medical education were fixed on them. Nor did it acquire any endowment in its early days except that portion of his house, the Stone House in Knightrider Street, which Linacre assigned to it. This may have been fortunate, for a time was coming when endowments attracted the eyes of confiscators, but even a safe endowment might have been superfluous. The work the College was intended to do required no great resources of money. Its members were all engaged in a calling which provided their livelihood. It was to receive a share of fines, and presumably fees for examinations and licensing. Five years after the foundation, as we shall see, the members agreed to pay a subscription to meet the cost of prosecuting offenders.[3] The income from fines may have fallen short of their expectations, but even so there can never have been any prospect that the College would put much money into their pockets. We are often told that Tudor England was materialistic: but only a cynic could deny that in the foundation of the College there was an element of disinterested public spirit. The officers and the fellows were to render services in raising the standard of practice by making it harder to engage in it without some proof of capacity. To be sure this meant eliminating rivals: but it would have paid the six founder physicians far better to spend their time and energy on enlarging their own

---

[1] Sir William Holdsworth, *History of English Law*, iv (1924), 235–7; W. Senior, *Doctors' Commons and the Old Court of Admiralty* (1922), especially pp. 72–75.

[2] See his letter to Erasmus, 18 November 1511, *Opus Epp.* i (1906), 488. For some details about the building and its use see P. W. Chandler in *London Topographical Record*, xv (1931), pp. 4–50 where there are street plans.

[3] See below, p. 74.

practices. The three royal physicians had nothing to fear from the quacks. We cannot speak with the same certainty about all the other three, but Halswell was rich and so, in all probability, were the other two. They served not their own personal ends, and not only those of their profession was a whole, but as their charter said, the happiness of the men of the king's dominion.

It remains to answer a question which might not have occurred to us if it had not been raised by the charter itself: what did the foundation owe to Italian and other foreign examples? The act of 1511 did nothing to create any organization of the physicians. The physician might display a parchment with the seal of a university or a bishop and this would protect his right to practise, but he remained in isolation, without the discipline, or the support or the social amenities of any fellowship. This position was unusual: most of the arts and crafts could only be exercised in each town by the members of privileged bodies. On the Continent there were few if any countries where the physicians were so completely outside the system of association as they were in England. Of France it has been written, in words which would be substantially applicable to Germany, the Netherlands, Italy, and Spain:

Sous l'ancien Régime, le diplôme doctoral ne confère pas de droit personnel à l'exercice de la médecine, pas plus que la lettre de maîtrise a celui de la chirurgie. Le practicien n'existe qu'en tant que membre de sa corporation. Docteur ou maître il ne vit que d'une vie empruntée, et en tant qu'il fait partie de sa Faculté, de son Collège ou de sa communauté.[1]

The last sentence mentions two or three types of society. First were the university faculties, which had extensive rights of licensing and supervision over physicians, surgeons and apothecaries in their own towns and the surrounding districts. Second were the bodies then or later called colleges. These were found in towns where there were no universities. That of Nîmes dated from 1397; that of Bordeaux, founded in 1411, continued after the establishment of a university there. The college at Troyes admitted only doctors or *licenciés* of Paris and Montpellier; that at Rouen only those of Paris, Montpellier and the neighbouring Norman university of Caen. Somewhere about seventeen of them were founded in France in the seventeenth and eighteenth centuries,[2] so that, as with the

---

[1] Delaunay, pp. 289–90.
[2] Ibid. pp. 292–3; C. A. E. Wickersheimer, *La médecine et les médecins en France à l'époque de la renaissance* (1905).

surgeons' companies, it is a mistake to think of them as characteristic only of the Middle Ages and the sixteenth century; but they were already well known by this time. It has been suggested that the idea of founding such colleges was in the air. The picturesque soldier-physician Symphorien Champier is even said to have had 'la première pensée de ces Sociétiés de médecine qui depuis ont fait faire tant de progrès à la science'[1]; but there were medical colleges before his time; that in his own city of Lyon (which had a university) was not founded until long after it, and his thoughts seem to run chiefly in the direction of endowing the *médecins* with material privileges.[2]

It is sufficiently clear that London was exceptional (it might be rash to say unique) among the greater European cities in having no medical organization, and that in some of the places known to English men of affairs there was a kind of organization suited to cities which were like London in having no university. Perhaps nothing more is needed to explain the appeal to foreign precedents in the charter: but it is tempting to go further into detail. The king's ministers in general had access to any information they needed about France, Spain, Italy, and the Netherlands. Wolsey in his ecclesiastical capacity had standing correspondents in Rome. Nothing seems to be known of the education of Ferdinand de Victoria or of his career before he came to England with Katherine of Aragon; but in later years he corresponded with Spain, and he must have known something about its medical institutions. We saw in connexion with Linacre's treatment of Erasmus[3] that there was knowledge in England of medical practice in Germany, so that any one of the major continental countries may have made a contribution.

There are difficulties in the way of narrowing the question down. We know nothing for certain about the constitution of the College in its first four or five years except what we find in the charter. Features of which we hear for the first time in 1522 or 1555 may date back to the beginning, but they may have been introduced later, and so it is best not to anticipate the chronological sequence.

---

[1] P. Allut, *Étude biographique sur Symphorien Champier* (1859), p. 69.
[2] Ibid. p. 67 n. See also p. 104 below. In the seventeenth century the Lyon college tried to impose a higher standard of qualification for practise than that of the Lyon doctoral degree: G. Patin, *Lettres choisis* (Cologne, 1691), ii. 5–6, 9–10. Baas (p. 188) says that in the sixteenth century there were many *collegia medica* in Germany, but names only that of Augsburg, founded in 1582.   [3] See above, p. 50.

The few points that the charter mentions have parallels not in one city or country but in several: they belong to the general morphology of the institutions of the time. The use of the word 'college', for instance, may be explained without citing foreign examples at all, but it may owe something to them. It was the name of the association of physicians in Florence,[1] though they also were members of a composite *arte* or guild. In Siena there are documents from 1405 which speak of the medical *collegio*.[2] The name was also used in Venice. There too *arte* was the ordinary word for a guild: but in 1565 the ordinances of the *collegio* of apothecaries regulate their relations with the most excellent *collegio* of the *signori* physicians.[3] As with this word, so it is with the substance of the charter. It has been suggested that the number of the four officers who were to exercise the jurisdiction of the College bore some relation to the four consuls of the Florentine *arte*.[4] This cannot be disproved, but it is not necessary to look so far afield for a precedent. In fifteenth-century London, as we saw, there had sometimes been four surveyors of surgery.[5] There are indeed so many parallels for the number four that it might have come from anywhere. So might the right to punish it by fines or imprisonment.[6] The question of foreign indebtedness cannot be answered precisely.

Note on The Licensing of Midwives

In his *Breuyary of Health*, published in 1547, Andrew Boorde wrote that it would be a laudable thing if no woman were allowed to practise as a midwife in England unless she were presented to the bishop by honest women of great gravity. The bishop, with the counsel of a doctor of physic, ought to examine her, instruct her and admit her. Boorde's words are obscure but seem to say that something of the sort had been known in his time in England as well as in other regions and in remote antiquity. There are medieval records of the licensing of midwives by

[1] For a late sixteenth-century reference to the costume worn by members of the College see V. Borghini, 'Dell'arme delle famiglie Fiorentine' in *Discorsi*, ii (1585), 14. In 1498 the title-page of the Florentine *receptario* stated that it was composed by the college of doctors but it was dedicated to the consuls of the *arte* of *medici* and *speziali*.

[2] A. Garosi, *Siena nella storia della medicina, 1240–1555* (1958), p. 284.

[3] *Ordini et capitoli del collegio de gli spetiali della inclita citta di Venetia . . . MDLXV* (1891). The statutes of the *fratalia* of apothecaries in Padua, dating from 1260 to the early sixteenth century are published in M. Roberti, *Le corporazioni padovani* (*Memorie del R. Istituto, Veneto di Scienze e Lettere*, xvi, no. 8, 1902), pp. 223 ff. Padua, also had a *fratalia medicorum*, ranking from 1287 below the barber-surgeons and above the apothecaries (ibid. pp. 122, 136, 277).

[4] A. P. Caravadias in *Sidelights on Medical History*, ed. Sir Zachary Cope (1957), pp. 77–80.   [5] See above, p. 27.

[5] The London Grocers' Company had this right by charter.

bishops in France. English bishops certainly did license them in later and probably in earlier times. An oath to be taken by the midwife on admission by the bishop has been reprinted from a seventeenth-century compilation that contains no oaths for apothecaries, physicians or surgeons though it does give the oaths of the scavenger of the City of London and the scavengers of its wards.[1]

Two theories have been suggested to explain the origin of the custom. The first is that the church was concerned because midwives often had to baptize infants in emergencies. Against this it may be urged that only one of the fifteen clauses of the oath refers to baptism, and this is the last, which, in language, looks like a later addition to the others. It dates from after the Reformation and deals not with anything peculiar to baptism by midwives but with the risk of baptism otherwise than according to the use of the Church of England. The other theory is that the licensing of midwives was a corollary to the licensing of surgeons.[2] The ecclesiastical authorities may have made out that, because surgeons must be licensed, midwives must be so too, on the ground that midwifery was a branch of surgery. It was held in the seventeenth century that the ecclesiastical courts could not have cognisance of cases of exercising the trade of a midwife without a licence because it was not a spiritual function.[3] It may indeed be asked whether there are any records of legal proceedings against unlicensed midwives. Even if there are it may be doubted whether there was any effective restraint on unlicensed practice in the sixteenth or seventeenth century. The bishop's licence may have conferred no exclusive legal right and yet may have been sought by some women as a recommendation or a guarantee of competence and reliability, like the royal warrants granted now to shopkeepers who supply the court.

In the diocese of Norwich the oath actually taken by midwives seems to have had only one clause, of which two variant forms are printed in E. H. Carter, *The Norwich Subscription Books, 1637–1800* (1934). It binds them to use their skill and knowledge indifferently between the poor and the rich.

[1] *The Book of Oaths and the severall forms thereof both Antient and Modern* (1649, another edition 1689), p. 284, reprinted in Sir Robert Phillimore, *Ecclesiastical Law of the Church of England* (1873), pp. 2061–2, not in later editions. This was presumably printed from a City Book of Oaths such as that referred to by F. P. Wilson, *The Plague in Shakespeare's London* (1927), p. 26, n. 4.
[2] Alice Clark, *The Working Life of Women in the Seventeenth Century* (1919), pp. 275–9.
[3] H. Rolle, *Abridgement* (1668), ii. 286.

V : THE FIRST PHASE 1518–55

VERY soon after the foundation of the College a revolutionary era began and the fortunes of men and institutions rose and fell with the vicissitudes of power. Among the great men who had been close to Linacre, Sir Thomas More acquired influence and office while Wolsey tottered and fell, but More in his turn was sacrificed when the king overthrew the old balance between church and state. Deep social changes, accompanied by rebellions, wars and alternating innovation and reaction lasted for a generation. Even a small, almost entirely private body like the College could not escape from some degree of interference. Until 1555, the year of Queen Mary's accession, our information about its affairs is scrappy and discontinuous and we cannot be sure that they were not radically affected in ways of which we have no record; but in some directions we can estimate the social effects of these disturbances both on the medical professions as a whole and on the College.[1]

First we have to notice the results of the dissolution of the monasteries, hospitals, and chantries, which was spread over a period of twelve years or so, from 1536 to 1547 in the reigns of Henry VIII and Edward VI. Some have thought that this liberated or threw on the world a large number of monks and priests, medically qualified, who had practised in religious houses; but we have already seen that the numbers of medical men who lived in these houses were not great.[2] Those who resided in them or were retained to attend their members now had to practise elsewhere; but there was no mass exodus of physicians who were monks. In the days when medical education was almost entirely a matter of book-learning it was not difficult for educated men, such as were many of the monks and priests, to make the transition. There are earlier instances. Andrew Boorde, an ill-adjusted Carthusian monk took to physic before the troubles began. We shall come across a former

---

[1] Almost our sole source of information is the Latin *Annales* of the College, begun in 1555, of which the first volume, going down to 1572, is printed in *The Works of John Caius*, ed. E. S. Roberts (1912). In the present chapter no references are given to this book: its chronological arrangement is so clear that any statement derived from it can readily be checked. References are given to the authorities from which it has been supplemented.   [2] Above, p. 22.

Franciscan friar who lived to become a fellow of the College.[1] There seem to have been other cases of the kind.[2] The dissolution of the monasteries seems not to have caused much direct change of orientation among physicians. It may well have indirectly set back the movement towards better standards. It did away with many historic communities where the arts and thought and learning were at home, and, however much this may have been compensated by the mental energy of the age, it entailed a loss. English intellectual life lost something of its variety and therefore something of its freedom because it now had fewer geographical centres, and because there were few societies left outside the universities where speculation and tolerance could develop.[3]

There were individuals among the fellows of the College who suffered for their religious convictions. John Clement, who was tutor to the children of Sir Thomas More and was admitted to the College in 1527-8, was president five years after More's execution. Under Edward VI he retired to Louvain. Returning after the accession of Queen Mary he practised in Essex, but in Queen Elizabeth's time he went into exile again and died in Malines. John Fryer, who was president in 1549-50, was twice imprisoned, first in his early days as a Lutheran and then, having returned to his earlier beliefs, under Queen Elizabeth as a Romanist. There were some, such as Sir William Butts, who made their fortunes as adherents of a religious party. Besides those who suffered and those who took advantage of risky opportunities, there were others who must have watched and calculated, hopefully or uneasily, and one of these was the great Dr. Caius. But the College as a body seems not to have been involved. Although all Tudor governments were jealous of societies where their subjects assembled in private, the College, by prudence or good fortune or both, seems not to have come under suspicion. Not until the Elizabethan settlement was

---

[1] Simon Ludford, see below, p. 112.

[2] T. Powell *The Art of Thriving* (1635), reprinted in *Somers Tracts*, ed. Sir Walter Scott, vii (1812), 187 ff., which is sometimes mentioned in this connection, has nothing to do with it: the story on p. 200 relates to a deprived nonconformist in the reign of Queen Elizabeth I and in any case need not be taken seriously. In 1546 the visitors to the university of Oxford prescribed that none should practice medicine until they had been examined by the regius professor, because many scholars had taken to practice 'upon a foresight of the ruin of the clergy'.

[3] For this difficult subject interesting indications will be found in Sir Thomas Kendrick *Antiquity of Britain* (1950), pp. 105-8, which gives a glimpse of intellectual liveliness in a monastic circle, and in A. G. Dickens, *Lollards and Protestants in the Diocese of York* (1959), pp. 139 ff.

well established do we find any communications from above on matters of religion or state. Those which we do find show that even when the government was apprehensive about the loyalty of fellows, it was constant in maintaining the College as part of the new order.

The foundation of the College was in line with a general disposition of statesmen in earlier Tudor days to encourage and regulate the physicians, but they could no longer hold to this course when the turbulent period set in. There were signs that, like their European neighbours, they still wished for constructive action. In France the kings assumed a direct part in the provision of medical teachers: Louis XII made the faculty of Montpellier a royal institution and took over the nomination of its professors; in 1530 his successor Francis I founded the Collège Royal, where medicine was one of the subjects taught. Henry VIII of England established the regius chairs of medicine at Oxford and Cambridge at the end of his life. But little or nothing more was achieved. More than twenty years earlier Henry contemplated setting up a model hospital, perhaps in execution of his father's bequest for the Savoy. But the model hospital was never built. Many hospitals of all kinds all over the country were destroyed by the confiscation of their endowments on the ground that they were religious foundations. The two greatest in the country were only salvaged by the public spirit of the citizens of London, St. Bartholomew's in 1544 and St. Thomas's in 1552. In the reign of Edward VI, under Protector Somerset, the plans for reform in Oxford and Cambridge included provisions for medical education, but they were abortive.

The College of Physicians in its earliest days may have had some religious affiliations. It may, for instance, like the guilds and companies, have gone in procession to St. Paul's or some City church for a special annual service, perhaps on St. Luke's day.[1] But if there were such associations they have left no traces, and in any case there were no endowments that could be confiscated. The College owned no property except the fore-part of the Stone House and its contents. It did not attract the attention of predatory reformers.

It was a very small body. Six members[2] were named in the Charter and six more were admitted in 1519–22. We have the names of

---

[1] See Appendix I below.

[2] They were not called fellows in English in any document earlier than 1540, and we have no evidence to show what they called one another before 1555 when they were *collegae*: see below, p. 71 n. 5. For convenience in the earlier part of this chapter they are called members or full members.

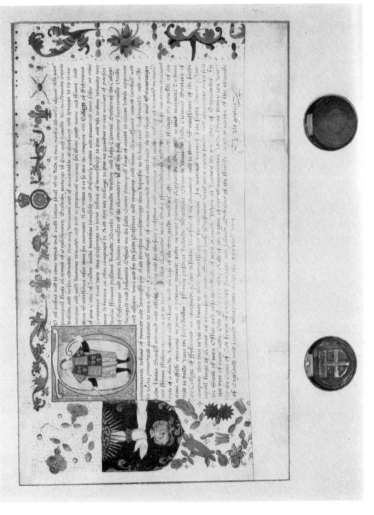

III. The Grant of Arms (1546)

thirty-one new members down to 1553. In that year four were admitted; in no previous year are there more than three noted. The roll may well be incomplete: for the ten years 1531–40 there are only three new dated admissions. At least seventeen and almost certainly more than twenty died before 1555. It is not recorded that any resigned. From these figures it appears that the number rose after 1522 but probably did not exceed twenty, and there is one piece of outside evidence to confirm this impression. At the Guildhall there is a list of members of the College who agreed on 8 October 1538 'to doo theyre duetyes' according to a certain Act of Common Council.[1] They were

Mr. Yaxley	Mr. Freeman	Mr. Burges
Mr. Bartlet	Mr. Gwyn	Mr. Pyerson
Mr. Bentley	Mr. Nycholas[2]	Mr. Owen
Mr. Clement	Mr. Cromar	Mr. Augustin[3]
Mr. Wotton	Mr. Fryar	

Now these fourteen names include those of all the members except four who are known to have been alive at the date of the agreement. Of these four one was Sir William Butts, who was a court physician and presumably did not practise in the City. The others were Dr. John Chambre, warden of Merton College, Oxford, and two of his fellows, Dr. John Blysse and Dr. Robert Huicke. Their absence from the list may be similarly explained. We are justified in concluding that at that date the College had eighteen members.

One of the eighteen was in a different position from the others, although apparently a full member. This was John Person. He had no doctor's degree, and in recording his appointment as one of the subsidiary censors in 1542[4], Dr. Caius described him as a licentiate who had been 'inter Collegas' from Linacre's time, a licentiate being one who had no doctor's degree but was a bachelor or held a university licence to practise. It seems likely that in the first years there were other licentiates whose names are not preserved and that they were regarded as members of the College in some sense, perhaps even in the fullest sense.[5] Dr. Caius could not

---

[1] Guildhall, Repertory 10, fo. 50ᵛ.
[2] Nicholas Encolius.   [3] Agostino de Angostini.
[4] This is the only known reference to the office of assistant censor.
[5] The later position was stated by Lord Mansfield in Rex v. Askew et Al' Censors of the College of Physicians (1770): 'I consider the words *socii, communitas, collegium, societas, collega*, and fellows as synonymous terms, and every *socius* or *collega* as a member of the society or corporation or college' (Willcock, p. xlviii).

very well omit all mention of a licentiate who held a College office, but, as will appear later, he may have preferred to say nothing else about these, to his mind, inferior physicians.[1]

The few London practitioners who are known to us for other reasons may or may not, therefore, have been licentiates. Richard Smyth, doctor of physic and surgeon, committed some misdemeanour and was banished from the City in 1536. He produced a letter on his behalf from the formidable lord privy seal, Thomas Cromwell, but finally he seems to have complied.[2]

A few of the members are mere names to us, but enough is known of the others to give a fairly clear idea of their standing and manner of life. Sir William Butts was the first of the long line of English medical knights. He was one of the physicians to Henry VIII; he seems to have been friendly with some of the religious innovators and he received a grant of monastic lands. His knighthood was a sign that laymen were now in the high places of the profession, and this was not peculiar to England. The two other sovereigns who engaged in a rivalry of grandeur with King Henry had each anticipated him in conferring knighthood on practitioners of the healing arts. Francis I of France knighted Symphorien Champier after the victory of Marignano in 1515. He was a combatant, but a year later the Emperor Charles V knighted his surgeon Jaime de Bofill after his coronation.[3] King Henry much later knighted the surgeon John Ayleff. Besides Sir William Butts twelve others of the early fellows held royal appointments, Drs. Linacre, Victoria, Chambre, Cromer, Huicke, Angostini, Bille, Owen, Caius, Huys, Wendy and Caesar. Edward Wotton, of whom the same has sometimes been written did not in fact hold such an office, but he was physician to Margaret Pole, countess of Salisbury, and her son the cardinal, two kinsfolk of the royal family. Thus more than a quarter of the number practised in the highest sphere, and this was useful to the College.[4] Three of them were foreigners, and there were two other foreigners on the roll. Of one, Petrus Hispanus, who was admitted in or before 1522 nothing seems to be known: it is curious that he bore the same name as that of the physician John XXI before he became pope. Angostini was a Venetian; Caesar a Dalmariis, the father of a more famous son,

---

[1] See below, p. 103.   [2] Repertory 9, fos. 177, 189, 234, 236.
[3] J. M. Simon de Guilleuma in *Medicamenta*, xi (1959), 6.
[4] Owen, Wendy and Huys, according to the Annals, were active in connection with the Act 1 Mary Sess. 2. c. 9, for which see below, p. 88.

Sir Julius Caesar, was a graduate of Padua and the son of a doctor of laws in Trevigni. The last of the foreigners, Hector Nones, or Nuñez, was of another stamp. He was the head of the London community of marranos or converted Jews; he engaged in foreign trade on a large scale, enjoyed the confidence of ministers and lived to give Mr. Secretary Walsingham the first news of the defeat of the Spanish Armada.[1]

Except for the licentiate John Person and four others, the mysterious Petrus Hispanus, the equally mysterious John Bartholomew, John Blysse and Hector Nuñez (who may have been at Padua) all are known to have held the degree of doctor.[2] There were six doctors of Padua, one of Bologna and one of Pavia. The Englishmen who took foreign degrees were in the habit of incorporating in their own universities with the same degrees on their return, though there were some exceptions: six or seven of these travellers did so. The total number of Oxford doctors was at least thirteen, of Cambridge at least seven or eight. Of the Oxford and Cambridge men sixteen or seventeen were or had been fellows of colleges, that is nearly a third of the entire roll. Although there is only one whose father's occupation can be stated (Edward Wotton, son of one of the bedels of Oxford University), there are other facts which confirm the impression that the College was, on the whole, a compact society of men with various mutual ties. Dr. Huys married Dr. Cromer's widow.[3] John Clement and Wotton and Caius, all of whom served then or later as presidents, were the most notable for their learning, but the general level of scholarship and accomplishment was high.

A small body like this, composed of men of whom all were probably busy and several of whom had interests outside their profession, must have depended for carrying on its business on finding a few able and energetic leaders.[4] How it fared in this matter seems uncertain. When Dr. Caius came to write the Annals he seems

[1] C. Roth, *History of the Jews in England* (1941), pp. 140, 279.
[2] For the purposes of this paragraph the facts given by Munk are supplemented for Yaxley (see above, p. 59).
[3] R. R. James on Huys in *Janus*, xl. (1936) and on Cromer in *The Practitioner*, xxxiii (1934), 200.
[4] I do not know from what period it becomes reasonable to presume that an eminent physician was heavily occupied. As late as 1627 Edward Hyde, afterwards earl of Clarendon, wrote, it is true jokingly, that he was waiting for a week's physic from Dr. Moore (for whom see below, p. 192) but that the illness of the lord treasurer 'confined him to an attendance solely there, and he would not undertake two persons of such quality together': B. Whitelocke, *Memorials* (1853), i. 76.

to have used no materials except what he found in the College, where papers were evidently not kept in very good order, and he seems to have underrated the activity of these years. Comitia seem to have been held quarterly and perhaps at other times in April or October. In 1523 it was resolved that attendance should be compulsory, which perhaps implies that there had been absentees before that. Some statutes were passed,[1] though not a complete code. There are a few entries relating to the conduct of business. In 1531 the comitia met on 25 October but immediately dispersed without doing any business in order that the members might attend the many sufferers from the plague. In 1552 the president was authorized to have the College's part of the Stone House divided from the rest of the house by a party wall, and to have the front door moved; but nothing came of this.

Of the finances we know little. In 1523 it was resolved that once a quarter each *collega* should pay 20*d*. towards the expenses of prosecuting offenders against the Acts of Parliament about practitioners, this to be repayable if funds, presumably from the College's share of fines, sufficed. In and about 1529 there was a payment on admission of 6*s*. 8*d*. Drs. Huicke and Ashton were each fined 3*s*. 4*d*. in 1544. In 1546–7 the College had 6*s*. 8*d*. in hand, but in 1551 it had £2 0*s*. 4*d*., of which half was lost by the depreciation of the coinage.

The significance of a royal charter in the sixteenth century was in most ways greater, though in some ways less, than it is now. At present it may confer valuable powers or it may only add a new lustre to a body already fully equipped with them, but in either case the body which receives it will operate in a field where a mass of legislation and an immense official administrative machinery guide, control and supervise its work. In the sixteenth century there was no administration worth mentioning except for the armed forces and for the raising of revenue. All the other social functions which are now carried out by the civil service were entrusted to county dignitaries or to urban bodies, and, while it may be appropriate to describe rural society as still feudal, that of the towns was under a regime of chartered liberties. Once they were set up, these bodies carried out their vaguely defined functions under no day-to-day accountability. Urban society was an aggregate of these independent organisms. The common law included some

---

[1] For these see below, pp. 90.

principles under which the acts of corporations and unincorporated societies could be nullified or upheld, and a few parliamentary statutes were in force by which the Crown was given control over their affairs, but the only public authorities which could give them orders or settle disputes about the validity of their proceedings were the courts of law.

A newly chartered corporation found itself surrounded by chartered bodies already existing, all jealous of their privileges and ready to pounce if they were infringed. If any of them resisted the newcomer, there might well be litigation, which would probably be expensive and might end unhappily. The College in particular might find itself involved in difficulties with the two companies of surgeons, with the Grocers, or with a much more formidable body, the City of London. The clause in the Charter reserving the rights of the City was no empty form. Behind the annoyances which rival corporations might inflict by resorting to the courts of law there lurked an even graver danger. A charter was granted by the king, and what the Crown had granted it might revoke. As the College was to discover in due course[1] a procedure existed by which charters might be forfeited, and once the attorney general set this procedure in motion there was little or no chance of resistance: it was then for a court of law to decide whether the charter was valid. It was invalid if it conflicted with the common law, and in the same way, acts done under its authority, or purporting to come under its authority, must be proved to conform to that intricate body of rules and precedents the knowledge of which was virtually confined to the legal profession and inaccessible to the ordinary members of the chartered corporations.

There was, however, one way in which a corporation might strengthen itself for any such eventuality. If a charter was confirmed by Act of Parliament, it was not exposed to some of the objections which might otherwise be raised in a court of law, and, more than that, it was secure against forfeiture by this single-handed action of the Crown. Only an Act of Parliament could annul what had been enacted by parliament. The note at the foot of the charter of the College implies a promise that the machinery for obtaining an Act would be set in motion.

A body corporate had to watch not only its legal limitations, but also the realities of social life. The law itself was not interpreted or

[1] See below, pp. 270, 353 ff.

enforced impartially and accurately as it is in well-governed countries today. The lawyers, including those who had risen to be judges, were not mere mouthpieces of written reason but human beings whose ambitions and interests rendered them liable to be intimidated or corrupted or at any rate prejudiced by respect for persons. In England, though perhaps not in other countries,[1] the principle of equality before the law existed in theory, but even in theory it was qualified by many exemptions which put the great and their dependents outside the normal operation of justice. The immediate servants of the king and queen and princes could not be prosecuted in the ordinary way for ordinary offences without leave from their masters, still less brought to book by the College for offences against its statutes. There were numerous holders of high offices who had similar privileges. These legal buttresses of greatness were essential to the hierarchical system on which society was built, but it was not only through them that the system did its work of keeping those of low degree in subjection to those of high degree. When a king granted a charter he did not mean to empower a corporation to act against his will, nor did the officers through whom he exercised that will. They in turn had power, authority and influence of their own, not all of it derived from their master, and sometimes they acted independently of his will or even against it. Down from them there branched a perpetually shifting network of clientage, patronage, protection and mutual support. The College had to thread its way through this tangle. Every physician who had a friend at court might be needed at times, but from the granting of the charter onwards, the main footing of the College in the world of power was that of the royal physicians with their daily access to ministers, favourites and the sovereign.

No parliament was sitting when the College obtained its Charter in 1518, and none met until 1523, but then the College took the opportunity of petitioning for incorporation by statute. They petitioned as the six charter members by name and 'all other men of the same faculty within the City of London and seven miles about' and an Act was passed[2] which recited the Charter and gave

---

[1] For a short statement of the legal position in France see E. F. Heckscher, *Mercantilism* (1935), i. 168–9, who concludes that 'at a time when every calling was an "office", the authorities yielded to quackery much more easily than to-day, although in theory to-day the exercise of a profession is considered a transaction between buyer and seller and even exceptions to this are based upon the principle of equality before the law'.   [2] 14 and 15 Henry VIII, c. 5.

it the further authority of the king in parliament. It also added some new provisions. The six persons named in the Charter were to choose two more of the commonalty and these eight were to be called elects. The elects were yearly to choose one of their number as president. Vacancies among the elects caused by death or otherwise were to be filled by co-option, on condition that the persons so chosen should be first strictly examined by the surviving elects, after a form devised by them, and approved. This creation of an inner body to choose the president, though it deprived the commonalty of any voice in elections, was not in any way exceptional. A lady who disapproved of oligarchies, summed up the late medieval municipal practice in England thus: 'People talked . . . of election by the whole community, and this was the theory of ordinance and charter, but the universal fashion of the day in all ranks and classes was to adopt some more or less complicated system of indirect election which, whether intentionally or not, was admirably suited to the use and convenience of the minority.'[1] For the first few years the elects were actually a majority of the full members but no doubt they were an inner ring. Why the number was set at eight it would be idle to guess. The name 'elects' deserves notice. The *Oxford English Dictionary* knows no other instance of its use in this special sense, and 'elector', which was used as the Latin translation of 'elect', might have been more appropriate in English too. Just possibly the use of 'elects' may be due to Italian influence. *Eletto* does not appear to be a name used in similar cases in Italy, though it was used by sixteenth-century military mutineers for their leaders; but in documents regarding guilds there are references to persons chosen for offices as *gli eletti*, the adjective being used as a noun.

The Act had one more clause, which greatly extended the powers of the College. This stated that in the dioceses of England outside London it was not always easy to find men able sufficiently to examine such as should, according to the earlier statute, be admitted to exercise physic. It therefore enacted that no one should be suffered to practise physic throughout England until such time as he should be examined at London by the president and three elects of the College, and receive letters testimonial of their approving and examinations, unless he were a graduate of Oxford or Cambridge who had fulfilled all the requirements for his degree without being excused from any of them. This measure of centralization

---

[1] Alice Stopford Green, *Town Life in the Fifteenth Century* (1894), ii. 253.

cannot at first have affected many people. The burden of a journey to London must have been considerable for some of them. As to its working in the early days nothing can be said, for the first record of the admission of an extra-licentiate, as they came to be called, is in 1559. They were not to become in any sense members of the College. It is curious that, in spite of the wording of this clause, the powers conferred on the bishops by the Act of 1511 were neither confirmed nor explicitly revoked. These powers were, as we shall see, ignored by the College on other occasions in this century.[1] In later periods they were often exercised in the licensing of physicians in the provinces, but for this early period there is no evidence one way or the other. If the bishops, with their administrative machinery, had tried and failed to use their powers, it is surprising that the College should have taken the responsibility at this early stage of doing the same work with scanty means or none at its disposal. Altogether the clause is slipshod. That the different method of examination implies a lower standard for the provinces is not surprising; but there was no provision for 'governing' the provincial physicians, no tribunal to judge them, and no rule that they must belong to any society.

It will be convenient to mention here, out of chronological order, another Act of Parliament which affected licensing. This was 25 Henry VIII, c. 21, passed in 1533–4, a statute of many clauses doing away with the powers of the pope in England. Among other things it enacted that the archbishop of Canterbury might grant licences for any such cause or matter whereof such licences had been accustomed to be had at the court of Rome.[2] Thenceforward the archbishop had two separate licensing powers, one for his own diocese under the Act of 1511 and the other for the whole of England under the Act of 1533–4. It is under the latter Act that Lambeth degrees in medicine and other faculties are granted; and from time to time archbishops granted licences to practise. Thus there were two authorities, besides the universities and the College, who could issue licences in the provinces, and one in London. This was an accidental result of the religious changes.

---

[1] See below, p. 117.

[2] The archbishop's powers under the 1533–4 Act were exercised by an officer called the master of the faculties, and all such licences should be recorded in the Faculty Office. The only important gap in this series of records is for the period when Henry Paman, a nonjuror, served as clerk: he probably took his register away with him when he was ejected. Ironically he was a physician and a fellow of the College.

Turning back to the affairs of the College we find that in 1523,[1] the year of their Act of Parliament, they elected two sets of officers, two *consiliarii* (Dr. Yaxley and Dr. Francis) and three censors,[2] Dr. Chambre, Dr. Ferdinand de Victoria, and Dr. Bentley. What their duties were had better be noted when, in 1555, a statement is available on the matter. On 12 March 1524 Dr. Bartlot and Dr. Bentley were co-opted as the two additional elects under the Act. The College was ready to carry out its duties.

The delay of four years before parliament gave its authority to the Charter probably explains the absence of any recorded discharge of its functions during that period. It does not seem to have made its terms with the City until it had strengthened its position with the Act. No doubt it took the initiative which led to an Act of Common Council of 28 April 1525. This settled its position in London handsomely, though with some reasonable conditions. It ran as follows:

Journal 12, fo. 281ᵛ.   28 April 16 Hen. VIII 1525 Phisicons.

Item   At this commen counsell it ys agreed & decreed that suche as occupie physike within the liberties of this Citie not beyng examinede & approvyd by the collegge accordyng to the statute in that behalf ordered & provided may be at the requeste of the college commandyd & compelled upon the payne of imprisonament of xx days totiens quotiens that they shall no more occupie phisike till they be examyned & approvyd.[3]

Item   Whereas all the college & those whom they admytte be sworne that they shall sell no medicynes theym self yf they may have the same of the apothecaries[4] so that it be provydyd that thapothecaries may be sworne and uppon a payne commandid that they shall not serve any byll of any physicions not examyned & approved.

Item   That thapothecaries shall kepe the billis that they serve uppon a fyle to thentent that if the pacyent myscary it may be by the College considerid whether the bill weere medecynall or hurtfull to the sickness.

<hr />

[1] The College year ran from Michaelmas to Michaelmas, but unless there is a note to the contrary dates are given in the present work by calendar years. See Note on Dates, above p. xxiii.

[2] In calling them *consiliarii* and *censores* the Annals may be anticipating the usage of 1555.

[3] It will be noted that here imprisonment is a punishment in itself. Its use as such was authorized by the charter of the College, and the College, as we shall see, used this power. This seems to disprove the view that 'The common gaol of the sixteenth, seventeenth or eighteenth century . . . was . . . theoretically a place of detention only, not of punishment': S. B. Webb, *English Prisons under Local Government* (1922), p. 4.

[4] See below, p. 96.

Item That when any persone ys admytted by the seyd college to occupie phisike that then they shall from tyme to tyme certifie the same to my lord mayor for the tyme beyng to thentent that it may here remayne of recorde.

On 21 September Dr. Bentley and Dr. Yaxley, 'doctors of physike, examyners admytted to hable or disable such as practise phisik and surgery in London' certified by way of complaint to the court—the mayor, recorder, six aldermen, and a sheriff—that three persons daily practised physic having 'no manner speculacion and cunnyng that to doo'. They were Roger Smyth, apothecary, Roys, surgeon at the Grey Friars, and one Wescott of St. Swithin's Lane. They were summoned for the following Tuesday, on which day the doctors promised to be there. The proceedings ended for the time being with an injunction against Roys that he should 'no more occupy physic upon pain limited in the said Act of Common Council'.[1]

After an inexplicable interval the case of Roger Smyth, the apothecary, was taken up again: the College resolved on 15 April 1527 that measures should be taken against him on the following day. What followed we do not know; but it is permissible to infer that three typical figures, an apothecary, a surgeon who had ventured out of bounds, and a mere pretender, had been selected for a test prosecution but two of them had baffled their accusers by the simple expedient of keeping out of the way.

Either because of this disappointment or for some other reason the College debated on 23 December 1530 whether to seek a confirmation of its privileges in the next session of parliament. Nothing came of this but in the same year a curious little one-clause Act of Parliament was passed which, though it did not concern the physicians directly, clarified the position of four occupations in London, among them surgery.[2] It states that foreigners resident in the realm who followed certain callings had been vexed with informations under the statutes which forbade foreigners to exercise handicrafts, and for their relief it declared that these callings were not to be accounted handicrafts. They were those of brewers, bakers, scriveners and surgeons. The first two were presumably treated in this way because they could be carried on in relatively

---

[1] Guildhall, Journal 12, fo. 281ᵛ. In their edition of Thomas Vicary's *Anatomie* (E.E.T.S., 1888), p. 156. F. J. and P. Furnivall print, accurately enough, the corresponding entries from the Repertories fos. 201-2.   [2] 22 Henry VII, c. 13.

large establishments, the other two because they did not involve buying and selling goods. They were approaching the status of professions, but, although they were not handicrafts, the statute refrained from saying what they were.

In one particular the privileges conceded by the charter of the College were less ample than might have been expected. Its members were exempted from serving in London or elsewhere on any municipal assizes, juries, inquests and the like, but at the time when the charter was granted surgeons enjoyed a greater freedom from civic duties than this. In 1513 there was a petition to parliament from the warden and fellowship of the craft and mystery of surgeons enfranchised in London, that is to say not from the Barber-Surgeons Company but from the newer, small and more distinguished un-incorporated body which existed alongside of it. They said that both because of their continual daily and nightly service to the king's lieges, and also because in war they had not been combatants but had gone unarmed like the heralds, for time out of mind they had never been summoned to any armed duties. In consideration of these facts, and also of their small number, not passing twelve, the Act exempted them not only from all inquests and juries but also constableships and watches, and it extended the same privileges to the surgeons who were members of the Barber-Surgeons' Company.

Not until 1538 did the City offer a like privilege to the physicians and then only at a price. On 28 March in that year the lord mayor moved that if a physician were elected constable he should pay 30s. to the use of the parish (apparently to be excused from acting), that each time his turn came for the watch he should pay 3d., and that he should pay his contributions to the parish clerk's wages and all other dues of the parish. After some modifications of the details, and a reduction of the first payment to 20s., the College agreed in October, and this was the occasion of the list of fourteen members which we have quoted.[1] The City intended apparently that there should only be twelve physicians so favoured: there is a resolution that 'the names of twelve such physicians as shall fortune to be of the College of Physicians shall from time to time be enrolled in the chamber of Guildhall at their own suit and costs'; if any of them be chosen constable he is to pay 20s. to the churchwardens for their discharge, and so forth.[2]

[1] Guildhall, Repertory 10, fos. 27ᵛ, 35, 50.
[2] Journal 14, fos. 100ᵛ–101. The records of the chamber do not survive.

The City was no doubt more familiar with surgeons than with physicians; they were certainly more numerous and more in evidence in the streets, but there is no reason to suppose that they were more highly esteemed. The negotiation over this matter only shows that the mayor and common council took the civic obligations seriously. In the case of the three unqualified practitioners the College examiners are stated in the City record to be empowered to enable or disable practitioners of both physic and surgery[1]; we know that physicians examined at Barber Surgeons' Hall, and there is no reason to suppose that there was any disharmony between the two branches. The king's physicians and his surgeons had both professional and personal relations at court. All through the first phase of the history of the College there are signs that both sets of officers were at least influential in the most important decisions about their 'faculties'. They had much to do with two Acts of Parliament of 1540, the one concerning physicians[2] and the other, surgeons.[3] The two Acts do not run on continuously in the Statute Roll; they are separated by an Act which decides which innholders may bake horse-bread within their houses; but in spite of this comic interruption they form in effect a single legislative work, introducing new reforms in each branch and defining the organization which each was to have. As the apothecaries are also mentioned we may say that these two Acts cover the whole range of the professional and semi-professional services of health.

The physicians' Act, like that of 1523, begins by reciting a petition of the College, which seeks parliamentary authority for the relief from watch and ward and the office of constable and other offices both in London and other towns and villages. The ground alleged is that divers of them who attended lords of the council, the nobility and other lieges had many times been compelled to serve these offices 'to their great fatigation and unquiet and to the great peril of their patients'. The first clause duly frees them[4] from the burden in London and the suburbs, and by implication ends the liability to make the former payments to the parishes; but it says nothing about any other part of the country. The second clause

---

[1] See above, p. 80.   [2] 32 Henry VIII, c. 40.   [3] 32 Henry VIII, c. 42.
[4] Except in this place the Act always mentions commons and fellows together, without distinction; but here the exemption is stated to be for the president commonalty and fellowship for the time being, and the commons and fellows of the same, and every fellow that now be, or that any time hereafter shall be their successors, and so forth. If this is meant to include existing commons and exclude their successors, we may take it that the commons were licentiates.

enacts a much stricter subordination of the apothecaries than the City had ordered. The President, commons and fellows were annually to elect four of their number, of the best, wisest and most discreet, with experience in physic. These four were to take an oath and were to have full authority and power, whenever they should think meet and convenient, to enter the house of any apothecary in the City of London and to view his apothecary wares, drugs or stuffs. If they then found any of these defective, corrupted and not meet to be administered in medicine, the four were to summon the wardens of the mystery of apothecaries[1] or one of them and cause the same to be burnt or otherwise to be destroyed. Any apothecary who obstinately denied entry to the four was to forfeit £5 for every such offence, half to go to the king and half to the informer (who would presumably come from the College.) If any of the four persons so elected refused to be sworn or obstinately refused to carry out his duties, he was to forfeit 40s. for every such default.

It is not laid down that these four viewers of the apothecaries' wares were to be the same persons as the four elected annually under the charter to exercise disciplinary powers, but in practice, so far as we know, the four censors always acted in both capacities. In viewing drugs and medicines they were doing what the officers of crafts and mysteries had done in their own spheres from time immemorial. This function had sometimes been committed to outside authorities, not only to municipal authorities, the natural supervisors of the companies, but, for instance, to the universities, which had their own clerks of the market. But it is notable that the College of Physicians received this power not only in virtue of its interest in maintaining the quality of the wares, but in virtue of its higher skill and knowledge. A profession was empowered to control the trade, a difficult relationship. We chance to know that from an early date the College was dissatisfied with its practical working: Walter Cromer, no doubt using his influence as a royal physician, tried unsuccessfully to promote legislation for strengthening the College in its dealings with the apothecaries.[2]

A short third clause completed the Act. 'Forasmuch as the science of physick doth comprehend, include and contain the knowledge of surgery', it was enacted that any of the said company or fellowship of physicians being able, chosen, and admitted by the president and fellowship might exercise the science of physic 'in

---

[1] In the Grocers' Company.   [2] See below, p. 120.

all and every his members and parts', as well in the City of London as elsewhere in the realm. This does not seem to mean that there was to be a separate admission to practise surgery, but that admission to the College carried this right with it.

The Act for barbers and surgeons does not begin with the recital of a petition, but it too is concerned with the institutional structure of the craft in London. Its preamble mentions the existing Acts for the exercise and maintenance of physic and surgery, and then says that in London there are men of greater experience in the theory ('speculation') and practice of surgery than in any other parts of the realm, so that surgeons are trained there who will practise in other parts. The enacting clauses merge the Barber Surgeons' Company with the unincorporated surgeons' company in a single body corporate under the name of the Masters or Governors of the Mystery and Commonalty of Barbers and Surgeons of London. There were to be four masters or governors, two expert in barbery and two in surgery. In order to prevent the spreading of contagious diseases no one practising barbery or shaving in London or within one mile of it was to practise surgery, blood-letting or any other thing belonging to surgery, drawing of teeth alone accepted. Nor was any surgeon to practise barbery. No reason is given for the merger. It is merely pronounced to be necessary, but it is easy to see that each company must have been embarrassed by the separate existence of the other.

There are other provisions, of which two are interesting. Every surgeon in London must show an open sign on the street-side where he lives, so that all who pass by may know whither to resort for their remedies in time of necessity. Only freemen of the Company might keep barber's shops in London; but any of the king's subjects might keep a barber or a surgeon as his servant, to exercise his art or faculty in his master's house or elsewhere by his master's licence or commandment. A third provision is more important. Every year the surgeons might take the bodies of four executed criminals and dissect them for their further and better knowledge, instruction, insight, learning, and experience. This means of providing subjects for anatomical teaching was legalized in one country after another in the course of the sixteenth century. As early as 1505 King James IV of Scotland granted one criminal's body a year to the Edinburgh barber-surgeons.[1] Philip II of Spain made a

---

[1] C. H. Cresswell, *The Royal College of Surgeons* of Edinburgh (1926).

similar grant to the Amsterdam surgeons' guild in a long reasoned document which said that anatomy was being daily brought into light and explained[1]; but the years between 1540 and 1555 in which latter year this document was written, had seen stirring events in the anatomy theatres, and this was not the reason for the London grant. Its significance is that the surgeons organized in their company took a collective responsibility for educating themselves and their apprentices, thus distinguishing themselves from the handicraftsmen and adopting one of the characteristics of the universities and the Inns of Court. We could wish that more were known about Dr. Nicholas Encolius, who was a fellow of the College of Physicians from 1523 or earlier and died an elect in 1552. Late in the last year of his life he received a grant of £10 a year from the Crown for his services in instructing young surgeons near the Savoy, and also of all the bodies of men and women hanged in Middlesex, Sussex, and Essex.[2]

The new Barber Surgeons' Company thus obtained full parliamentary authority. A ceremony, imaginary not historically real, was depicted by Holbein. The king, seated, hands the Act sealed like a charter to Thomas Vicary, the sergeant surgeon, who kneels to his left in front of fourteen other barbers and surgeons; but on his right kneel the two royal physicians, Dr. John Chambre, and Sir William Butts, with the king's apothecary.[3] To the physicians, especially to these two, much of the credit must be due for the two statesmanlike Acts of 1540, and possibly most of all to Dr. Chambre. He has not been allowed a place of much honour in the history of the College. Dr. Munk wrote that he did not appear to have been warmly interested in the management and success of the infant institution, and this on the ground that, though surviving its foundation for more than thirty years, he was met with only once as elected to any office namely to that of censor in 1523. But this is doubly unfair. In five years the Annals name him as an elect. For 1525 and for the whole period 1532-40 no names of College officers except consiliarii are preserved, and we cannot declare it impossible that Chambre was ever president.

Down to this point the successive Acts of Parliament tell a coherent story: the College applied for improvements in its powers

---

[1] J. G. van Dillen (1929), no. 415.
[2] *Calendar of Patent Rolls, 1550-1553* (1926) 261, no. 18.
[3] For the history of the picture and the original cartoon see the *Preliminary Report* prepared by Mr. R. C. Strong for the special exhibition at the National Portrait Gallery, 1963, which supersedes previous accounts.

and these were granted by public authorities who watched over medical services of all kinds and were in general agreement with its aims.[1] But in 1542–3 an Act was passed which rudely disturbed the pleasing outlook.[2] Historians do not take preambles at their face value, and, ever since the reviewers applied themselves to the work of James Anthony Froude, Tudor preambles have been specially suspect, but there is nothing to account for the origin of this new Act except the allegations of its preamble. This skips over the Barber-Surgeons' Act of three years before and refers only to the Act of 1511 about licensing by the bishops, since which, it says, the Company and Fellowship of Surgeons of London (which is not the correct name for the company existing then) minding only their own lucres have sued, troubled and vexed divers honest men and women who without taking anything for their pains and skill had ministered to poor people for neighbourhood, for God's sake and for charity. God (by what process or instrumentality we are not told) had endued these persons with knowledge of certain herbs, roots, and water and with their use for customable diseases such as sore breasts, pin and web in the eye, oncomes of hands, burns, scaldings, sore mouths, the stone, strangury, saucefleme and morphew, and such like diseases. It was well known, the preamble continued, that the admitted surgeons would undertake no case unless they knew they would be rewarded with a greater sum or reward (in kind) than the case 'extended to'. The greater part of the licensed surgeons were much more to blame than the persons they troubled. The Act therefore provided that any subject of the king who had knowledge and experience of herbs, roots and waters by speculation or practice in any part of the king's dominions might treat any outward sore, oncome, wound, apostemations, outward swelling or disease by means of any herbs, ointments, baths, poultices, and plasters.

This Act has been deservedly known as the Quacks' Charter.[3]

---

[1] It does not seem justifiable to regard the Statute of Sewers, 23 Henry VIII, c. 5, as another instance of this general agreement. It is sometimes spoken of as a sanitary measure, but there is nothing about public health in its preamble or indeed in the enacting clauses. Its main concern was with land-drainage and waterways. S. and Beatrice Webb, *Statutory Authorities for Special Purposes* (1922), pp. 13–106 seem to mention no sanitary functions of any seventeenth-century court of sewers except that of Westminster.　　　　　　　　　　[2] 34 and 35 Henry VIII, c. 8.

[3] W. Lambarde, *Eirenarcha* (1591), p. 242 writes that the Act leaves so great a liberty of practice to unskilful persons 'that it will be hard now to make any felonie in such a case'.

It said nothing about physicians, but it hit them as well as the surgeons. Whereas the physicians and surgeons had to pass examinations by responsible bodies, the herbalists' cunning and experience were to be virtually taken for granted. The preamble talked only about the persons who took no fees, but the benefits of the Act extended to all comers, whether charitable or extortionate. To a modern ear it may sound as if herbs, roots and waters might well be less deleterious than the more loathsome medicines of the current pharmacy, but there was no guarantee that noxious herbs, roots and waters would not be used. The only legal restriction remaining was that unlicensed practitioners might not operate by cautery or incision or prescribe internal medicines, the special provinces of the surgeons and physicians. The lists of diseases, in any case absurdly inexact, seem to open the door wide to dangerous practices. On the Continent as well as in England two operations frequently undertaken by unqualified persons were couching for cataract and cutting for the stone. The willingness of surgeons to allow this to go on is hard to understand. This Act does not authorize it, but it would seem to make it easier for such practitioners to make contact with patients.

Before the first phase of the history of the College ended there were two more incidents in which the City took a line of its own. In 1541 the admirers of John Lytster, a practitioner who was not licensed by the bishop, desired the aid of the court on his behalf against 'the physicians of London'. This was not forthcoming, but he was given a sealed testimonial, whether for use in applying for a licence does not appear.[1] We learn from the Annals that Lytster (Lister or Lyster) was a Frenchman and that proceedings were begun against him and John Wisdom at Guildhall besides civil proceedings in which Lister was ordered to pay £30 11s. and Wisdom £10, half to the king and half to the College. Ottywell Wylde, surgeon, appeared on behalf of the College. Lister in the end paid £15 and Wisdom £5 on condition that the suit should be dropped. In 15 January the defective *pharmaca* of the two were burnt in the street of the apothecaries, Bucklersbury, in the presence of the censors and the second warden of the apothecaries. It may well be that Lister had not only sold injurious drugs but also prescribed to patients. About the same time an apothecary named

[1] Repertory 10, fos. 237, 238ᵛ.

Hammon settled an action by paying £1 6s. 8d., and promising not to exercise medicine in the future.

In 1552 the College took proceedings against John Vandernote. The Court of Common Council resolved that the lord mayor and three named alderman should talk with the physicians for staying the proceedings and that the physicians should be content to work therein with the assent of the lord mayor and the court.[1]

One more Tudor parliament passed an Act for the College.[2] In 1553, the first year of Queen Mary, its existing powers were strengthened in three respects. First, the Act of 1523 was confirmed 'any Act, Law, Custom, or any other Thing made, had or used to the contrary in any wise notwithstanding'. As the future was to show, this frustrated some attacks on the College's authority, at least in London. Secondly when the College or its officers committed an offender to any prison in the City and precinct (the Tower of London alone excepted), the warden, gaoler or keeper of the prison was to receive the prisoner and keep him (at the prisoner's expense) until the College ordered his release, on pain of forfeiting double the fine or amercement, not exceeding £20,[3] which the prisoner was to pay. This is the end of some story of evasion about which we know nothing. In those days the prisons were nominally the king's or belonged to some 'franchise', but actually they were run for the profit of the keepers, and we can well imagine that it could be made more profitable for a keeper to shut his door against a malefactor than to let him in.[4] Another tale of evasion evidently led to the next provision of the Act. If the wardens of the Grocers refused or delayed to accompany the president or 'four of his College elect' according to the former Act for the viewing of apothecaries' wares, then the physicians might proceed without them. The penalty for resisting the search was raised to £10. After that, in spite of unceasing efforts, it was not until the eighteenth century that the College succeeded in obtaining any parliamentary extension of its powers.

[1] Repertory 12, No. 2, fo. 555.

[2] 1 Mary, Sess. 2, cap. 9. No particulars seem to be available of the Bill 'for the better exercise of surgery' which had its first and only reading on 7 March 1552/3: *Commons' Journals*, vol. i (1742).

[3] As fines were not effective beyond the amount which could be enforced by imprisonment this became the maximum for the fines imposed by the College and remained so throughout the Tudor period.

[4] The prisons most frequently mentioned in the Annals are the Counter in Wood Street, Newgate and the Fleet. A counter was a prison attached to a city court: that in Wood Street was close to the Guildhall. Newgate was the prison of the criminal court of the London sessions. The Fleet was principally for debtors.

VI: THE EARLIEST STATUTES

THE earliest surviving statutes of the College are now in the Bodleian Library.[1] They are in a fair copy, but not that referred to in the Annals for 1563, where we are told that the statutes were completed and elegantly transcribed. The neat little Bodleian volume was not the principal copy.[2] The descriptive title contains two dates both of which need to be explained away. It says that the statutes were begun by the illustrious Thomas Linacre and the College under royal authority (namely that of the charter, we may add) and *edita* in 1520, but reduced to order, augmented and completed by John Caius in 1555. The date 1520 is not a slip; Dr. Caius gives it in one of his published books as the date of the foundation of the College[3]; but his own Annals mention the passing of statutes in 1523 and 1524, the last two years of Linacre's presidency, and again in 1541, and 1543, but none in 1520. Perhaps he mentioned 1520 because he thought it was Linacre's first year, and 1555 because it was his own first year as president. In any case 1555 cannot be the date of the manuscript, because it contains several statutes which are known from the Annals to have been passed in later years down to 1563 and these are indexed with the others at the beginning. These facts seem to lead to two conclusions: the manuscript belongs to 1563 and chronology was not one of Dr. Caius's strong points.

The connecting passages and many of the separate statutes bear very distinctly the stamp of Dr. Caius's personality. The Latin style, with its repetitions and its tiresome variations of words, is his, and the didactic tone; so are the energy and conviction that run through every page. The statutes show not only what the constitution of the College was, but what aims Dr. Caius set before it. They certainly embody some portions of the statutes passed before his time, but these may or may not have been amended in language or in substance when they were codified, and so it will be best to survey the body of statutes as Dr. Caius left it, merely

---

[1] MS. Ashmole, 1826. For the text see below, Appendix I. The identification of these as the earliest statutes is due to Mr. L. M. Payne.
[2] See below, p. 94.   [3] *De Libris Propriis* (1570), in *Works*, p. 77.

8

noting which subjects had been dealt with earlier, and not attempting to determine exactly what he found on paper when he began his work.[1]

There is another respect in which the origin of the statutes can be traced only partially. Although they read more like a literary work than a legal document, they embody clauses closely similar to some which are found in the statutes or ordinances of older English or foreign colleges and companies. Only a small proportion of the vast body of such enactments is available in print, and so it by no means follows that a similar clause in an earlier document known to us is the model after which a clause in the College statutes was drafted. Here too, when precedents are mentioned, they will serve not to show exactly where the provisions came from, but to place them roughly in their historical context.

In the use of the Latin language the statutes resemble those of ecclesiastical and academic corporations, but in some other respects they are more like those of guilds, fraternities and City companies. The first operative clause deals with the eight elects, whose function was to start the process which brought the other officers into being. The elects must be doctors and they must be Englishmen. The exclusion of foreigners may seem illiberal in a society to which they had contributed so much; it may, however, have been due to a cautious desire to avoid entanglement in political difficulties, or it may only have been that foreigners might not easily understand some of the personal questions which the elects had to consider. At first sight the number eight, prescribed by the Act of Parliament of 1523, seems ill-chosen. An odd number would have made decisions easier, and there were precedents for similar bodies of seven.[2] But the subsequent clause about the election of the president

---

[1] The entries in the Annals state the subjects, but not the purport of the statutes. They cover the following points:
 1523 Compulsory attendance at comitia.
 1524 Passing and revision of statutes.
  Obedience to president.
  Payment of fines.
  Against making or selling medicaments.
 1541 On the fourfold examination.
 1543 Ethical (formerly penal) statutes.
  (Pro-president: implied by entry of 1553).
 1555 Pro-president. Consiliarii. Censors. Accounts. Perjurors.
  Examination of new arrivals and four-year period of practice.
  Precedence of consiliarii. (Ornaments: implied.)
 [2] As in the Ordinances of the Cambridge Guild of the Holy Trinity, Toulmin Smith, p. 266, not to mention the seven electors of the Holy Roman Empire.

explains that, if there is a tie, that side is to prevail in which are more of the more senior doctors, and if these too are equally divided, then that side is to prevail with which the president (or in his absence the senior fellow, who is *presidens natus* or 'natural president') votes. We may suspect that the number eight was positively attractive, because an artful president could produce two successive ties and so take the choice into his own hands. The president was to be chosen from among the elects themselves, and no other fellows were to be present at the election. The inner ring was supreme. There follows a rule which, according to the Annals was passed in 1562. Anyone who resisted or questioned these statutes about elections by his own action or through another was *ipso facto* and for ever to be expelled from the College. This ferocious sentence, however, has the weakness that it does not say who is to decide whether the offence has been committed.

The president's powers and duties were tightly defined. He was to preside in the comitia, and like the heads of Oxford and Cambridge colleges in those days, he was himself to keep and read out what we now call the 'minutes'. He was to write them up in the Annals in the form initiated by Dr. Caius. In elections to the College he was to vote and to take the votes of the fellows: there is no provision for a second or casting vote. He was to inflict the penalties for the more serious offences, but only with the common advice and vote, privately given, of the two consiliarii. If the two consiliarii disagreed the president was to follow the decision of the majority of a body of four, the consiliarii and two of the elects, specially sworn in for the purpose. Under other minutely prescribed arrangements he was to settle disputes among the fellows. He was responsible for the safe custody of the common seal in the College chest and for applying it to all duly agreed decisions of the College. He was to receive gifts of books on behalf of the College and to hand them over, with a list of the titles, to his successor. He was similarly accountable for all moneys; he and the consiliarii were to have the three keys of the chest. He might appoint a pro-president to take his place, but only during his own absence from town. If he were in town but prevented from being present at the comitia by attendance on some great person or by other necessary business he might appoint one of the elects to take his place there. He was to do all he could to expel unlearned impostors not only from London but from the whole realm, using for this purpose letters the formulae for which were inserted in the Annals for 1555[1]. Unless some weighty cause prevented, he was to read the penal statutes out at all ordinary comitia in the presence of all the fellows.[2]

The pro-president should if possible be the senior fellow, or failing him one of the elects. He might be appointed to act as the president's substitute in his absence, or to deal with urgent business which the president could not dispatch in person, but in the latter case he could act only in consultation with the president or consiliarii, and in both cases the pro-president's office was to be temporary. This clause superseded a somewhat less ample statute of 1543.[3]

The two consiliarii were to be chosen by the elects from their own number. They have sometimes been referred to as members of the council, but they were not councillors, for there was no council; they were the president's counsellors. They were always to be at hand to advise him in comitia, and if ever they were absent they were to declare on oath what weighty cause had kept them away. They were to decide any controversies between the president and the fellows. If they disagreed, the majority of the elects were to decide. Their title and function seem to be definitely Italian: the doge of Venice had six similar *consigliarii*. In the nature of the case their advice to the president would be unlikely to leave traces in the records, and in fact there were few occasions in the history of the College when they took any overt action.

Next came the censors, as the four officers appointed under the Acts of 1523 and 1540 were now called. They were to be Englishmen, either elects or fellows, chosen by the elects. They were to enquire about all practitioners of medicine both native and alien in London, in the suburbs and throughout the kingdom, to examine, correct and govern them, if necessary to prosecute them at law, to learn what were their methods of treatment, to judge medicines, to burn or throw away those that were vitiated and to report recalcitrant apothecaries to the president and College. In this and several other places of the statutes the censors are called 'censores literarum, morum et medecinarum'. There is nothing obscure about the medicines, and the *mores* no doubt meant professional conduct, but what, we may ask, was intended by letters. The Paris faculty apparently had a *censeur* who had to do with the censorship of books, which was one of its functions from 1542 to 1730,[4] but

---

[1] See below, p. 117.   [2] See below, p. 102.   [3] Annals, 1555.
[4] Delaunay, p. 338.

the College was not empowered to do this by any of the English licensing laws until 1687.[1] It may have intended to do something of the kind under its general powers, perhaps only in relation to publications by its own members. The name 'censor' is uncommon in England as the title of an office; but it is used in Henry VIII's foundation of Christ Church, Oxford.

One other officer, or rather a servant, is named in this part of the statutes, the caduceator, who may already have been called in English, as he was later, the beadle. His Latin title came from his duty of carrying the silver caduceus before the president. He was to be an honest man inaccessible to bribery. Besides looking after the property of the College, making the rooms ready for meetings, writing out notices of them, summoning the fellows individually, and generally making himself useful, he was to be present at all comitia, funerals, and feasts. Greater responsibilities must have arisen from his further duties: he was to seek out all impostors, whether physicians or empirics and to warn the president and censor of their names. He was also to burn the vitiated drugs.

Dr. Caius was a firm believer in ceremonial and he was one of those who brought back from Italy the liking for emblems which proved to be congenial to English taste and lingered here almost until the eighteenth century. In the statutes the clauses relating to the officers not only give the wording of the oaths appropriate for their admission, proportionate in length to the dignity of each office, they also regulate precedence. The president came first. He was treated with all due deference and he was addressed as 'your excellency', which, however, was not then such an exalted expression as it has since become. Indeed the beadle was to address each fellow as 'your excellency' in the written summons to comitia. On all College occasions the fellows preceded the licentiates and within each rank the order was that of seniority in the College. Except on these occasions they followed their seniority as graduates, not even the president departing from it. The consiliarii and censors had no precedence in virtue of their office, but the elects appear to have had the first places. In academic institutions it was usual, as it still is in some of them, to admit a new head by formally handing him some such objects as a book, a key and a seal. Until 1556 the College of Physicians had no such observance,[2] and Dr. Caius both devised the ritual and provided the instruments, which he regarded as

[1] See below, p. 356.   [2] Annals, *s.a.*

symbols of the virtues, for this and all other formal appearances of the president. He saw to it that a book of the statutes was made up and ornamented with silver.[1] He presented a cushion, and the graceful caduceus, a silver verge with a cluster of serpents, which is still used. To the Cambridge college which he augmented and which bears his name he gave one like it, though smaller. Whether the College of Physicians possessed a common seal before this time is not known, but must be regarded as very probable. It did, however acquire one now, in the shape of the *vesica piscis*, showing the seated figure of St. Luke with doctor's cap and nimbus, reading at a lectern. A niche of renaissance design enclosed the figure and below it was a shield of arms. This was charged with a hand grasping the fingers of another hand, a simplified version of the device of a hand feeling a pulse which appears in the arms granted to the College by John Barker, garter king at arms, in 1546. Round the seal ran the inscription 'Sigillum Collegii Medicorum Londini'.[2]

We return to the statutes. There were to be quarterly ordinary comitia, on the morrow of Michaelmas, on St. Thomas's day, on the days after Palm Sunday and St. John Baptist's day. in addition there were to be extraordinary meetings as required, but only for urgent business. No one was to leave before voting unless he received permission. Nothing was to be said except in Latin. In order not to interfere with the fellows' opportunities of earning fees, elections, examinations and admissions were to be held in the quarterly meetings, but examinations might be held at other times by agreement with the fellows.

The arrangements for passing and rescinding statutes were rigid. New statutes in the future were to be extremely few and were to be sanctioned by an oath or a fine, with a minimum of a silver groat, the value of which was stated at 5*d*. To pass a statute there must be at two separate comitia a two thirds majority or, if fewer than six were present, a simple majority. For abrogation there must be a three quarters majority on three days with some intervals between. Unless more than three were present a statute could not be validly passed or revoked until a majority of the absentees, on a subsequent summons, confirmed what was done.

Looking at these constitutional provisions as a whole, we may say that the fellows had filled in the outlines of their charter in such a

[1] Annals, *s.a.*, 1557.
[2] For further particulars of the seal see note at end of this chapter.

IV. The Earliest Seal, the Caduceus and the Silver Ornaments of the Statute Book

way as to do their business much as other small societies did at that time. There was no standing committee and no system of handing work over to committees: the full corporation kept all decisions of policy in its own hands, and if anything was to be delegated, the intention evidently was that it should be delegated to the officers. The functions of the officers were limited, and except the elects they were chosen only for one year. The ruling few were these elects, who chose the president from among themselves, in secret session, and filled the vacancies in their own number, thus controlling future elections as well as that of the current year. The president could not be removed during his term of office, but he was to be watched by his *consiliarii*; on paper his powers were narrower than those of many other heads of societies, and we may guess that in practice his authority would depend on his personality. The censors had regular duties all the year round, which might be heavy if they were men of energy. Unfortunately we know little about the elections to offices until the late seventeenth century. It is only occasionally that we can tell whether it was hard or easy to fill them, whether there was any competition for them, whether they attracted the abler and more ambitious of the fellows, and if so exactly what it was that made them attractive.

Next after the constitutional provisions comes the long and important group of statutes which were designated penal in 1543 but out of respect for the doctoral dignity, ethical in 1563, and ethical or penal in this manuscript. Any fellow who, being in town and not detained by illness or imprisonment, failed to attend comitia was to be fined 16*d.* unless for a cause allowed by one or both of the consiliarii. Absence from the presidential election comitia entailed a fine of 3*s.* 4*d.* For unseemly contention in comitia the fine was at the discretion of the president and consiliarii. If the president permitted any breach of the statutes, the consiliarii were to make an announcement in comitia but he was not to be deprived. On the election day or within eight days thereafter the president was to render to the elects an account of the receipts and expenditure of the previous year. Any elect who refused to serve the office of president was to be fined 40*s.*, unless he were a physician to the sovereign. A consiliarius who was not available to advise the president and did not give an adequate excuse on oath was to pay 20*d.* Refusal of the office of censor cost 40*s.* For revealing anything said in College the penalty was 3*s*. 4*d*. No fellow was to accuse any other of ignorance or malpractice (*maleficium*), on pain of paying 10*s*. to the College. The offended party was to seek a reconciliation privately or to refer the matter to the president and consiliarii.

So far the penal clauses follow familiar lines. Now come those of medical interest. No fellow who was called in by a patient was to cause a physician already attending him to be sent away, nor, except in case of urgency, to change the treatment without his agreement; but later he might give his treatment either alone or with the other physicians. When several persons had met over a case, discussion of the patient's condition was to be carried on with the greatest moderation and only when all outsiders had been excluded. Any who called to himself in a case a person who had not been examined and licensed according to law was to be fined. A fellow was not to make a bargain with a patient for the price of restoring him to health, but to be content with a moderate fee in proportion to the patient's condition and his own labour, except that when patients dealt meanly with physicians it was permissible to bargain with them on subsequent occasions. In this matter of fees a power of correcting injustices was reserved to the president and consiliarii or in their absence to four of the elects.

After this comes a sentence which has no justificatory phrases: 'No fellow will in any way practise alchemy or use in treatment the so-called quintessence.' The seven following lines have been erased.[1]

The next rule is that no one is to teach medicaments to the populace nor to reveal to them the names of medicines lest the people be injured by their misuse. He who should bargain with apothecaries to receive any part of the price of the medicines he prescribed, or should prescribe more expensive medicines in order to buy the apothecaries' favour in procuring cases should be held to have broken his oath and should pay 10*s*. to the College. No fellow was to consort with those apothecaries who themselves practised medicine or served practitioners who had not been examined and approved according to the law. Refusal to pay any fine was to be deemed a breach of the College oath.

The ethical statutes run on without a break but those which now follow have no special medical reference. As in all guilds, fraternities and colleges the fellows were to attend the funerals of their colleagues and their colleagues' wives. The fine for absence was 1*s*.

---

[1] For conjectures about their possible contents see below, p. 179.

and the same penalty was incurred by failure to contribute to the funeral expenses. A fellow who showed the College statutes to anyone who was not a fellow was to be fined 5s.

The next provision may easily be misunderstood. It is that if a fellow entered religion (the monastic life) or holy orders after election he was not to be summoned to the College lest it might seem to recall to the practice of medicine one whom religion and ecclesiastical law had excluded from it. Nor, the statute proceeds, did the College regard it as right (*honestum*) for a cleric to treat among other things the affairs and diseases of women. For the same reasons if a cleric or monk desired admission it was to be denied him. Although the grounds alleged consist of objections from the ecclesiastical point of view, it may well be thought that this was a polite or perhaps crafty device for justifying a measure which arose from anti-clerical feeling or from a fear that the clerical physician might prove a false friend. It is, however, unlikely that such reasons would prevail in the reign of Queen Mary, at least with Dr. Caius, who was a conservative in church matters, and a devoted admirer of the priest Linacre. There may have been some motive of prudence, such as a desire to shield the College from religious dissensions, but the most likely explanation of the clause is that it means in good faith what it says. That this is possible is shown by a clause in the Ordinances of the Cambridge Guild of Holy Trinity. This was a purely religious and charitable guild. Its Ordinances of 1377, long before the great religious troubles began, were approved by two minor ecclesiastical authorities and finally by the bishop of Ely. Yet they lay it down that if any ecclesiastic, especially one in holy orders, be admitted to the fraternity, he is to hold no office and to take no part in managing the property of the guild, since it is not fitting nor lawful for a cleric to involve himself in secular business.[1]

Two final paragraphs emphasize the disciplinary purpose of these rules. The fines were those for the first offences, for a second they were to be doubled, for a third trebled and for a fourth they were to be increased at the discretion of the president and consiliarii, on whom severity was strongly urged. Anyone who did not obey their judgement but protested or resisted was to be deemed to have broken his oath. For this the offender was to be excluded from the College and to undergo such further punishment as the

[1] Toulmin Smith, p. 265 n. There are close parallels in the *scuole grande* of Venice.

president and consiliarii should decide, until he had made satisfaction for his delict and returned as a suppliant to his obedience and the favour of the College. The penalty of expulsion for breach of the oath was not peculiar to the College and was known among the City companies; indeed it was not uncommon for societies in different parts of Europe to enforce discipline by expelling offenders and re-admitting them on conditions.

It is hard to believe that in a small and intimate body of respected or even distinguished members authority faced delinquency quite as sternly as the wording of these statutes implies. Dr. Caius himself appeared in other connexions as a disciplinarian and as a difficult man to work with or under; he did not run away from encounters with the academic and religious innovators of Cambridge. Some of the fellows and officers of the College were certainly of a more pliable temper, and we may guess that the weakness of human nature were sometimes viewed indulgently. During the first phase of the College history the records do not tell us whether the penal statutes were ever put into effect, but we shall see that in the succeeding period they were invoked on several occasions. The problem of the gap between the letter of the law and its enforcement arises in many spheres in the sixteenth and seventeenth centuries, and we meet it again in the next of the College statutes, which is a long and detailed one on the form of examinations. It sets up an exacting standard, and it shows what the College considered to be proofs of adequate medical education. We ought however to suspend our judgement on the question what level of performance actually sufficed to secure admission.

In its general outline, if not in every detail, this section dates from 1541–2 when Edward Wotton was president: the Annals tell us that the statute on the fourfold examination was then voted for the third time. There were four subjects in which the examination was based on books; for the fifth and most important, the 'use' and practice of medicine, no books were prescribed. A person who was known to the College and whom all believed to be highly skilled was only to be examined in this. An unknown applicant or a known person whose learning needed to be scrutinized before he could be admitted was to be examined four times and at intervals of three months. The first test was to be in the knowledge of medical theory (*speculatio*), the second in the signs used by the physician and in the causes and symptoms of disease, the third in methods of treatment and the fourth in materia medica. If, however, the applicant had lectured at Oxford or Cambridge in any of the first three subjects, there was no need to examine him in it, but he was to be examined the more carefully in the fourth subject. For each subject books of Galen were prescribed by their Latin titles. It was evidently intended that they should be studied in Latin, but no particular translations were named. The quantity of reading is formidable though the statute denies it. Seventeen treatises are mentioned, including some of the longest, but the list for the fourth subject, after specifying two, ends airily 'and others of that kind'.

There are still some educational systems in the world which promote an amazing knowledge of texts, such as the Muslim system which begins with learning the Koran by heart, but these works of Galen are much longer than the Koran, and it seems remarkable that a physician should have been expected at the end of three months preparation, even if it was only revision of what he had learnt at the university, to have at his command the whole contents of the most obscure among them. We know that in later times the student could avail himself of such aids as epitomes and cram-books. A meritorious author, the imperial physician, Oribasius, had provided something of the sort for Galen as early as the fourth century and in the sixteenth more were available. When its library was catalogued in 1660 the College possessed two of these, and for anything we know they may have been there for a long time.[1] One of them was printed before the foundation of the College, and there may have been fellows all along who deigned to use it, if only as a means of finding their way about in the complete works. But the College demanded, or so it appears, a genuine knowledge of the original, and this contrasts strangely with the almost off-hand enumeration of subjects for the fifth and bookless examination in use and practice: the conditions for purging and bleeding, the use of soporifics or narcotics, the positions of the internal organs and their medication, the use and measuring of clysters.

The conduct of the examination was regulated minutely. In the presence of the fellows, at least five in number, the president was to pick out, not advisedly but at random, three questions from three different places in the set books and to show them to the applicant, who was then to be shut up in a place where the same

[1] Those of Symphorien Champier (Valence, 1501) and Andreas Lacuna Secobiensis (Basel, 1571).

works of Galen were, but without an index. Some hours were allowed for considering and reconsidering the questions, after which the applicant was to return and read out clearly to the assembled College his identification of the passages and his 'distinctions' in answer to the questions. The fellows were to judge whether he had found the right place, understood what he read and reasoned about it well. Any fellow who wished might throw doubt on any point or formally dispute; but the fellows were not to be morose or difficult. Answers merely culled from the concluding summaries of Galen's works would not suffice. The right answers would pass even if they were found elsewhere than in the right contexts, except at the first examination. In that an error of this kind was to lead to rejection for that time and re-examination as a last chance three months later. The principle was laid down that a man for whom three months were not sufficient would have no hope of passing after six. The standard for passing was that failure to identify one question out of the three did not mean rejection, but failure to answer even one correctly and with understanding did. The result was to be decided by a simple majority in a vote taken by ballot.

The statute exhorts the College to be severe in the examinations, for two reasons, first lest it should be burdened with an excessive number of would-be entrants,[1] and secondly to make it universally known that no one would become a fellow unless he were learned in the theory and practice of medicine and had either taught it in a university or practised it for at least four years. There was to be no respect of persons. The examiners were seated and the candidate stood.[2] This, no doubt, was not meant to emphasize his suppliant position but came from the universities, where the candidate stood to dispute against an opponent; but in one way this examination was fundamentally unlike that of the universities. The fellows of the College had not been the applicant's teachers, and so, though they may have been more formidable and remote, they were less likely to be affected by personal considerations, and they may have been more impartial. Perhaps, as the examiners were not active teachers, they were more likely to be conservative and to stick to what they themselves had been taught. At any rate this different relation between candidate and examiner arose accidentally because there was no university in London.

[1] This does not necessarily imply that the College had any idea of restricting its numbers; it may only mean that frivolous applications should be discouraged.
[2] See below, p. 411.

Having passed the examination the applicant must first swear what country he was of, in case he might receive a royal summons, then he must show letters testimonial from the university which had granted his doctorate, especially if he were a foreigner. He must pay for the use of the College £4 if a foreigner and 40*s.* if an Englishman, besides 3*s.* 4*d.* to the president for sealed letters testimonial, and 3*s.* 4*d.* to augment the salary of the beadle. He was then to be sworn in, and his oath, besides covering his College duties, contained some of the Hippocratic ethical precepts and bound him to read the five first books of Galen *De Simplici Medicina* and the eight *De Usu Partium* within a year. This should mean that he was to lecture on these books. In the modern sense he had read them already, for he had been examined in them. Where and to whom was he to lecture, and if more than one fellow was admitted in a year were they all to do it? Unfortunately there seems to be no record of any such lectures. If not already a doctor the new fellow was to swear that he would take the degree within two years or three at the most. If he failed to keep this promise he was to be fined 40*s.* the first year, £3 the next, £4 the third and so on in arithmetical progression.[1]

Since four completed years of practice was a condition of admission as a fellow, a special status was created, with the name of candidate, for those who had not completed this term. After passing the examination they were to receive a licence to practise for four years, but on condition that they were to associate learned and experienced physicians from the College with themselves. They were to pay 20*s.* if they were Englishmen, £2 if they were foreigners, and the two fees of 3*s.* 4*d.* as before. Their oath bound them to call in a fellow in any difficulty, and it also echoed the Hippocratic prohibition against recommending harmful treatment.[2] They were to attend the College for all ordinary comitia if summoned and between times if the president so ordered, and to give an account of their successful or unsuccessful work. At the end of their four years they were to be examined again and then to be admitted on payment of the balance of the fees. But they were not to be too young. No limit of age was laid down, but the statute says that young men and those of foreign birth, even if qualified for admission

[1] This oath does not contain the pledge relating to apothecaries referred to in the City Ordinance of 1525, for which see above, p. 79, but does contain the first of the provisions of the penal statute regarding apothecaries.
[2] See above c. II, p. 32.

by learning and character, were to be admitted only to practice and not to the College; but they were to have the same letters testimonial as fellows and, unlike the candidates, they were to enjoy the privileges of the College. The two kinds of letters are set out in full but there are no details of the privileges.[1]

Feasts have a paragraph to themselves. The fellow and the candidate on admission had, like many other entrants into societies in those days, to entertain the College to a frugal and fitting repast to the value of 40s. or more if they so desired, and, if the president and consiliarii thought fit, after the feast strangers might be excluded and College business done.

Two paragraphs follow about the empirics. The College is not only to punish them by imprisonment and fines, but also to delate them to the senators and pro-senators (whatever that may mean) of every province, town or franchise (*custodia*) where they reside, in letters of which the form is given. The form is dated November 1557 and the empiric is described as a Fleming; it does not incite the senators to take any action, but merely apprises them that he has no right to be exempted as a physician from civic duties. The second paragraph relates to commissions against empirics, and it is so worded as to imply that the reader already understood their nature, though no form of commission is given. The paragraph relates to the commissioners' oath (no gain or private interest but purging the *respublica* of unskilful physicians), and to the president's fee of 6s. 8d. for the writing and sealing of each commission.

The last provision is that twice a year, at the Easter and Michaelmas comitia, the whole of the Statutes were to be read out to the College.[2] To read then audibly would take the best part of an hour. Some such practice as this was followed in various guilds and societies in England and on the Continent.

The statutes are primarily rules by which the College is to abide in its business and in its social relations. Even the exhortations and

---

[1] There are chronological and other oddities in the letters. The first, for a fellow, is dated 24 November 1556, but it states that the College has admitted him on 22 December 1556; the second, dated 17 April 1556 states that the candidate was admitted on 22 April 1556. The fellow seems to be imaginary, but like Caius he was a Norwich man and a doctor of Cambridge and Padua. The candidate is a Yorkshireman and an Oxford doctor. Caius seems to have left a trace here of his delusion that Cambridge was older than Oxford.

[2] That this statute was added after the completion of the main body of statutes appears from the fact that it is the only one which speaks of 'Sanctus' instead of 'Divus' Michael. It goes further than the statute on the office of president, which prescribes the reading only of the penal statutes.

expressions of general principles have to do chiefly with these matters, but it is possible to draw some reliable inferences about the relation of the College to the world about it. Unlike the authors of the charter of 1518,[1] the codifiers of 1555–63 regarded the College not as an organization of the profession in London but as an organization within the profession in the whole country. There was indeed no notion of an organized profession. The physicians formed a profession in the sense that they had their education and their ethical standards in common, and the College, saving the privileges of the universities, claimed the right to decide who were to practice and who were not. The College could inflict penalties for malpractice in the London area and make rules of ethics and etiquette for its fellows, candidates and licentiates. There was no provision for keeping a register of all the practitioners whom it licensed. They were not to form a body capable of common action even in London. In their daily work, except when they were accused of offences, the College was to be not an authority but an *élite*. It defended them against unauthorized competitors and cheating apothecaries. Only to that extent did it serve their interests.

In this position, even without the tendency to exclusiveness, the College was bound to develop interests of its own distinct from those of the physicians as a whole or their patients as a whole. It had business to manage which did not concern the licentiates in London or the provinces. It had a dignified and no doubt enviable social life to which they were not admitted. In the sixteenth century people commonly took the superiority of aristocracies for granted and submitted to it, at least so long as it was not flagrantly used for selfish ends. In relation to the rest of the medical profession, and still more in relation to the surgeons and apothecaries, the fellows were an aristocracy. Like all aristocracies they had an advantage in the competition for power, influence and preferment. But they were an aristocracy of merit and therefore they would be respected as an aristocracy only if their merit was believed in. They were not supported by a deep-seated sentiment like that which maintained the aristocracy of birth. They were not individually appointed to their places by an authority outside them and above the whole kingdom, as the servants of the Crown were. They were self-selected, and that meant that they were surrounded by men whom they had relegated to an inferior status, or excluded from the

[1] See p. 61 above.

profession, or excluded as they excluded the surgeons and apothecaries, from certain particular professional functions and rewards.
There were disappointed men and ambitious men who might
easily become enemies, and the future of the College would depend
on its success in acting justly and creating confidence in its justice.

Note on the College Seal and Caduceus

(See p. 94.)

This seal was used until 1737 and is not known to exist now; but
impressions of it survive on several documents which were issued by the
College and have returned to its possession. The resemblances of design
and lettering show that the seal is closely related to that given by Caius
to his Cambridge college in or about 1558: photographs in Caius, *Works*.
The *versica piscis* is a Christian and medieval form which a renaissance
designer would hardly have adopted independently. At Caius he followed
the shape of the medieval seal, which is preserved; at the College of
Physicians he may also have followed an earlier seal not known to exist
now; but he may have adopted this form for some other reason, for
instance because he was using it at Caius.

In the Cambridge edition of Caius's works Dr. John Venn prints at
pp. 15–16 two of his letters to Gonville College each of which contains
a reference to the seal of that College. In the first it is returned to the
painters to be amended in certain points, which seems to me to show that
what is meant is not the actual seal but a sealed document. Instances of
this usage are given in the *Oxford English Dictionary* and it probably
still survives: it occurs in the College Annals on 11 May 1688. In this
instance it looks as if Caius is referring to the letters patent for his augmentation of the college, of which he was to see to the decoration as the
College of Physicians should have done for its charter and failed to do in
1518. The second letter may also refer to the letters patent, though
possibly to the metal seal. Caius intends to fetch it; he wishes a better
workman to have it in hand than Rowel, and he does not know how the
pattern will please him.

There are other medical seals with figures of St. Luke. The circular
seal of the Collegium Medicorum Lugdunensium is reproduced in E.
Poncet *Documents pour servir à l'histoire de la médecine à Lyon* (1885), p.
40. It has a figure of St. Luke and the traditional date of the foundation
of this college, 1500. It is itself of later, probably seventeenth-century
date, and Poncet holds that the college was founded in 1576. This agrees
with the view expressed above p. 65. The pre-Reformation vesica-shaped
seal of Trinity Hospital, Edinburgh has a seated figure of a man with no

cap, seen from in front, reading a book at a lectern: see the illustration in J. D. Comrie, *History of Scottish Medicine*, 2nd edn. (1932), i. 241.

Mr. Gerald Taylor of the Ashmolean Museum, Oxford has kindly supplied his expert opinion on the caduceus. 'I believe that the design is entirely English. The staff is not unlike those of the two small City maces here: the four serpents are variations on the scrolls used on the stems and covers of cups, and the medallion head corresponds very closely to those on the heads of maces of the time—smaller perhaps—or as the boss in the centre of a cover of a cup or tiger-ware jug, or of a rose-water dish. It seems to me just the sort of simple design that an English silver-smith, unacquainted with the form of the Classical and Italian caduceus, as shown in connexion with Mercury, would have made, adapting standard "idioms" to a new purpose. Therefore it is quite likely that no paper design was ever used.'

Table of Fines in the Earliest Statutes.

Failure to attend comitia	16*d.*	
Failure to attend election comitia	3*s.* 4*d.*	
Refusal to serve as president	40*s.*	
Absence of consiliarius when needed	20*d.*	
Refusal to serve as censor	40*s.*	
Revealing College talk	3*s.* 4*d.*	
Accusing a colleague	10*s.*	
Irregularities when called in by another physician	?3*s.* 4*d.*	
Irregularities when in consultation with several physicians	3*s.* 4*d.**	
Summoning unlicensed practitioner	6*s.* 8*d.*	
Bargaining for fee	3*s.* 4*d.*	
Revealing name of medicament	3*s.* 4*d.**	
Corruptly bargaining with apothecary	10*s.*	and perjured
Consorting with apothecaries unless approved, after warning.	10*s.*	
Absence from funeral	12*d.*	
Failure to contribute to funeral expenses	12*d.*	
Divulging College statutes	5*s.*	
Failure to proceed to doctorate	40*s.*	for the first year, increasing annually by 20*s.*

Unseemly contention in comitia, at discretion of president and consiliarii.

* Payable to the president.

9

VII : DR. CAIUS AND RESOLUTE ACTION

THE Latin *Annales* of the College, the principal source of our knowledge of its early history, and down to 1666 more important than all the other sources put together, were begun in his own handwriting by Dr. John Caius who became president in 1555. When he took office he found that among other deficiencies the College had no account-book, and that its book of *acta* had no title and its statute-book no arrangement or consistency. He put all this to rights and entered up in the Annals not only current business but what little he found in the College papers about previous years. The result is that from then until his final resignation of office in 1572 we know far more than we do for the former period but we know it from his point of view. However much allowance we make for that, there can be no doubt that he shaped the activities of the College. He was president from Michaelmas 1555 to May 1564, eight and half terms with a break of one year in 1561–2, and then for a last term in 1571, after which, on account of his services and his age he was given leave to absent himself from all comitia except (if he were in London and his health permitted) the regular quarterly meetings and others of special importance. In the following June he resigned the headship of his Cambridge college and on 29 July 1573 he died in London. It may be that the elects wanted a change of president in 1561 but they may have been disappointed with the result in 1562 and they may have been the more willing to re-elect Dr. Caius in 1571 because a strong hand was needed again. The energy which the College displayed from 1555, or even from 1553 when he became censor, was detonated by him.

His place among the worthies of England is secure and his life has often been written.[1] He was born in 1510 in Norwich, one of the principal provincial towns, and educated at Cambridge. There is nothing to indicate when or why he turned his attention to medical studies, but at the age of twenty-nine, ten years after going

---

[1] The most reliable general account is that by J. Venn in *The Works of John Caius*, ed. E. S. Roberts (1912), the best estimate of Caius as a zoologist that of C. E. Raven, *English Naturalists from Neckam to Ray* (1947), pp. 138–53.

up to Cambridge, he left England to study medicine at Padua. He seems to have acquitted himself exceptionally well, and after rather less than two years of study he took his degrees as *artium et medicinae doctor*. At that time the famous Belgian Vesalius was professor of anatomy at Padua and his book *De Fabrica Humani Corporis*, soon to be published, must have been near completion. Vesalius indeed became famous not so much for the actual changes in anatomical knowledge which he brought about as for convincing many people that anatomy as Galen left it was capable of improvement from direct observation. John Caius lodged for eight months in the same house with this man of the morrow, and this is a revealing fact, for throughout his literary and active life he never gave any sign of accepting Vesalius's innovation; he did what he could to disparage it. It is typical of his adherence to the old medicine that, when he taught in Padua, as he did for about a year after taking his degree, he lectured on dialectic, using the Greek text of Aristotle. Four more years of travel followed in which his chief purpose was the examination of texts of Galen and Hippocrates. At Basel he made the acquaintance of Conrad Gesner, the great collector of zoological facts, and of Gesner he became a friend and fellow-worker. Caius was already the author of a short general medical treatise[1] when he returned to England at the age of about thirty-four or thirty-five.

Two years later he became a fellow of the College of Physicians, and this probably coincided in time with the beginning of his very successful and lucrative career in practice. He was physician to King Edward VI and afterwards to his successors Queen Mary and Queen Elizabeth. He never married, and in 1557 he set to work on the splendid benefaction which raised Gonville Hall, of which he had been a fellow, to a higher rank as Gonville and Caius College with its special provision for medical education. At the request of the college he consented to be its master, thus bringing upon himself unhappiness in his relations with the fellows, especially because he clung to all that he could preserve of the older religious and academic world; but he firmly imprinted his personality on its buildings and customs.

There are many resemblances between his career and that of Linacre, whom he devotedly admired, but Caius's life was more public and more varied. It is difficult to say how he stands as a

---

[1] *De Methodo Medendi* (Basel, 1544).

writer, and in particular no detailed estimate seems to have been made of his work on the classical medical authors. For his own first treatise he gives most of the credit to Galen and his own teacher Giovanni Battista Montanus, but he claims some degree of original-ity or at least of re-thinking.[1] So far as their subject is concerned, his other medical works, the two treatises in Latin and English on the sweating sickness, do deserve to be praised as original, for they give the first clinical descriptions of an epidemic disease by an Englishman. They made an impression on the English mind, for instance in the passages about the sweating sickness in Francis Bacon's *History of Henry VIII*, and that is significant even if they do not point the way to effective epidemiology. To zoology he gave the first methodical book on English dogs, again not notable for anything in its scientific approach and not a dog-lover's book, but useful. He also included some good new observations along with some mere copying in his treatise on rare animals. His antiquarian works on Cambridge are not contemptible, though in parts they are cheerfully fabulous. Altogether he was an able and industrious author, lacking the patience or the critical doubt which would have made him a high authority on any of his subjects.

With great natural endowments, a deep respect for learning, a high professional reputation and indefatigable energy, he entered on his offices in the College of Physicians full of determination to make the most of its still unfulfilled opportunities. Inside the College discipline seems to have been strict. In 1553 John Howell of All Souls, who had become a licentiate two years before, was expelled because he had not kept his promise to take his doctor's degree within the statutory time and for other ethical breaches of his oath. He took the degree and was restored in 1556, penitently and willingly promising to obey the president, to think and speak well of the College and of medicine, not to make forbidden bargains with apothecaries, not to damage anyone's reputation, not to show off, not to cause factions and divisions in the College, to pay a fine of 22s. 8d. and to give a dinner to the president and fellows. The chastened doctor only survived for two years. In July 1558 after three warnings Christopher Langton was expelled for rashness, for levity and for foolishly contending with other fellows in the presence of witnesses when visiting patients, for his ridiculous pride and vainglory which dishonoured the College, and to make

[1] *De Libris Propriis* in *Works*, p. 73.

good measure for certain unspecified marks of incontinence. He was never re-admitted. A third fellow incurred censure and his case is important.

In 1559–60 Dr. Wendy accused John Geynes, an Oxford doctor since 1535 and in other respects agreeable and well-conducted, of shamelessly asserting to the vulgar that Galen had erred. Geynes repeated the assertion before the whole College assembled in solemn comitia. He was ordered to submit in writing within a month all the passages of which he had made this allegation. This he politely declined to do, whereupon the president set on the officers of the sheriff of London to force him to comply or to hale him off to gaol. Under this compulsion he put in a document containing twenty-two passages, in which he professed to handle Galen as Galen had handled some of his predecessors. The document has unfortunately perished, and all we know about its contents comes from Dr. Caius. Apart from derogatory adjectives he tells us little except that Geynes had taken some of his points, without understanding them all, from an ill-conditioned Louvain doctor called Brachelius.[1] The College discussed the document and Geynes could not defend it. He honourably owned himself beaten; he admitted in writing that Galen had not erred in the twenty-two points, and it would appear that he orally confessed in detail to his own sins in the matter. After all this he was examined and he was admitted to the College on 15 November 1560. He was appointed censor the very next year under the new president Richard Master and he was censor for the short remainder of his life. In 1562 he was named elect. He died of the plague at the siege of Le Havre in 1563.[2]

John Geynes should be honoured as the first fellow of the College of Physicians to die on active service. Does he also deserve sympathy as a victim of persecution, the more shameful because his heresy was purely medical and could never have been the subject of a charge until the creation of the College? On the personal aspects

[1] His full name was Hieremias Driverus Brachelius and Driverus was his surname, Brachelius being the indication of his place of birth. In some of his many books the variants Driverius, Triverius, and Thriverius appear. In 1660 two of his books were entered in Christopher Merret's *Catalogus* of the College library, his commentaries on Hippocrates, *De Ratione Victus in Morbis Acutis* (1538) and on the *Aphorisms* (1552).

[2] Caius wrote in the Annals 'Portum gratiae voco quem portum novum vocant' which means 'I give the name of Havre de Grâce to the place which is called New Haven'. 'New Haven' seems to have been an alternative English name for Le Havre. See *Journal of James Yonge*, ed. F. N. L. Poynter (1963), pp. 32, 35–36, Yonge seems to have written 'Dieppe' by mistake in the latter passage.

of the case little can be said. There is no question of a youthful indiscretion, since Geynes was a doctor of more than twenty years' standing; but we do not know whether he delivered a considered attack on Galen or blurted out his criticisms irresponsibly. In the eyes of the College his offence was double: indoors it was heterodoxy but out of doors it brought the chosen intellectual foundation of the medical art into question if not into contempt. It is easy to understand that this apparent betrayal of the profession caused trouble. That the intellectual offence was met not by mere disputation but by the threat of force was also in accordance with many characteristics of the times. The College was the only separate and isolated body in England which was charged with preserving the purity of doctrine in one particular subject, and it adopted the methods of repression which had always been customary in the universities and in ecclesiastical institutions.

In the middle of the sixteenth century, after the upheavals of the Renaissance and the Reformation, European thought was in a tumult. Sceptics were questioning everything that had been traditionally accepted, but credulous writers swallowed much that had been traditionally repudiated. On both sides there was exaggeration and confusion, and furthermore the two tendencies, sceptical and credulous, were not simply opposed to one another. For many of its exponents occultism was a search for true causes which would do away with the necessity of invoking miracles as explanations. Neither the orthodox nor the heretics were the sole forerunners of the scientific spirit as we know it. There were naturalists and anatomists, as there were textual students of Aristotle, Dioscorides and Pliny, who patiently corrected one thing or another in the received account of nature. They recorded the results of observation and experiment, but without going on to subvert the structure which they were undermining. Dr. Caius was one of these. He not only knew Vesalius and worked for Gesner; in his own work on epidemiology he was original. But the other kind of originality, that of the alchemists and the impatient wonder-workers, also used observation and experiment, and also started on some of the tracks that led to a purer and simpler science.[1]

---

[1] For two independent accounts of this intellectual ferment from different points of view but largely coinciding in some of their conclusions see L. Febvre, *Le problème de l'incroyance au XVIᵉ siècle. La religion de Rabelais* (1942) and M. H. Carré, *Phases of Thought in England* (1949), c. vi, with the reservation that some of the qualities ascribed by Febvre to sixteenth-century thought are also traceable in both earlier and later times.

By the time of John Geynes, Galen was under attack from both sides. Paracelsus included Galen's works in his famous bonfire as early as 1528, and he started the long controversy in which the respective merits of chemical and Galenic medicines were fought over. In the second edition of his wonderful picture-book, which was published in 1555 Vesalius advanced from the cool *constatation* of the 1543 edition on the anatomy of the heart to an explicit doubt. Geynes's one authority, so far as we know, was not Vesalius in either of these editions but Driverus, whose many books appeared from 1531 to 1551, one of them indeed being reprinted at Leiden as late as 1621.[1]

The College took action against many classes of irregular practitioners and it is not always possible to place an individual in his proper class or classes.[2] First were those who had not satisfied the requirements of the law but who had some qualifications, which might even be good. In 1553, for instance, John Syminges, Hector Nuñez, Martin Corembeck, and Caesar Adalmarius were fined for practising illegally, although Caesar was a doctor of Padua itself, and Nuñez had a bachelor's degree. Yet within a few weeks the foreigners were admitted, not merely to practice but to the College. The two Englishmen joined them there two years later as Oxford doctors, and Syminges lived to be president. By his second marriage in 1576 he became the stepfather of a child who grew to be the incomparable John Donne.[3]

A more remarkable case is that of Thomas Penny. He was a Cambridge doctor and stood high in reputation as a botanist. In January 1571 he failed in an examination in the rudiments of medicine but he continued to practise and was imprisoned. He was a puritan and the puritan leader Sir Walter Mildmay, chancellor of the exchequer and afterwards founder of Emmanuel College, wrote to the lord mayor demanding that Penny, as his servant, should be released. It seems possible that the service in question was that of personal physician. Penny was released, but on condition

---

[1] The *Universae Medicinae Methodus.*

[2] C. Goodall, *The College of Physicians founded and established by Law* (1684) gives an account of the proceedings against empirics. Down to 1672 he depends entirely on the Annals except for the story of Grig, the poulterer of Surrey (p. 306) which he takes from Stow's chronicle. But Grig was punished by the privy council and the College was not concerned.

[3] The entry in the Annals seems to mean that only Corembeck, and not also Syminges as Munk read it, had studied at Bologna. For the life of Syminges see B. W. Whitlock in *Notes and Queries*, xcix (1954), 421 ff., and cciv (1959), 257 ff., 348 ff.

that the College might proceed against him in the court of the exchequer, which was the only place where the chancellor's servants could sue or be sued.[1] The College seems not to have availed itself of this unpromising opportunity. In August Penny was examined again and failed. In 1572 he was still in practice and highly esteemed as a physician.[2] He had long ceased to consider himself a clergyman but he was still in Holy Orders. Nevertheless in 1582 he gave his admission dinner as a fellow of the College.[3]

It would not be unduly charitable to include among those unlicensed practitioners who had some qualifications one of the two protagonists in Dr. Caius's most spectacular controversy. In 1552-3 six men were examined, presumably as applicants for licences. They were all rejected and one of them was fined £20 for malpractice. Four of the six, including a priest and a Frenchman, are heard of no more, but two become famous. Simon Ludford was an apothecary in London: born in Bedfordshire he had been a Franciscan friar, the last resident in the Oxford friary when it was dissolved and so an educated man. David Lawton was a coppersmith. Neither of them showed the least proficiency in medicine or 'philosophy' or the liberal arts, but Lawton was the worse of the two. When asked to decline the word *corpus* he answered 'hic, haec, hoc corpus' and he said that the accusative was *corporem*. Both were unanimously rejected. Two years later they were both admitted to the degree of bachelor of medicine by the university of Oxford.[4] This would have grieved Dr. Caius even if he had not suspected, as he did, that they obtained the degrees by influence if not by bribery. In the name of the College, and it seems with its assent, he addressed a spirited letter to the Oxford vice-chancellor and convocation. Drawing their attention to the purpose of universities and the wickedness of licensing unskilled physicians, he called on Oxford to reverse its decision. His letter was read in convocation and was answered by a condescending refusal. This in turn was read to the College, and, as Dr. Caius tells us, annoyed everyone; but opinion was divided about what to do next. Some were for hitting back, others were for remaining silent and not kindling worse animosity. Neither side had its way but the College agreed

[1] Sir William Holdsworth, *History of English Law*, i (1922), 239.   [2] Raven, p. 166.
[3] There is no record of his election. This and perhaps other parts of the story most likely belong to the years 1573-80 for which there are no Annals.
[4] This was after the resignation of Dr. John Warner, the first regius professors there, and thus in a period when Oxford had lowered its standard: see above, p. 69 n. 2.

on a plan for turning the enemy's flank. As it happened Cardinal Pole, the papal legate and archbishop of Canterbury, had issued a commission for purging and otherwise reforming the two universities. In July 1556 the College sent the commissioners a strongly worded report of the occurrence, and asked them to rule that in future Oxford should admit no one to a medical degree who had not studied the liberal sciences, especially dialectic, for a due period of time in some university, then applied himself to philosophy, taken his degree in arts, and finally qualified in medicine. By the commissioners' order this letter was read in a crowded convocation in Oxford, and the university was informed that it had taken to itself men of no learning and was not to take such liberty in the future. The commissioners would prescribe at their leisure the regulations for study and degrees. So the first commissioner, Nicholas Ormaneto, datary of the cardinal, told Dr. Caius. Before the commissioners arrived in Oxford, the College, in a flattering letter, begged for the support of the lord chancellor, Nicholas Heath, archbishop of York, against patrons of impostors about whom the president was ready to give information. Heath had migrated as an undergraduate from Oxford to Cambridge, where he became a fellow of Clare, and evidently Caius intended to delate Oxford to him. The letter was handed to him at Greenwich on Christmas Day 1556 by the three court physicians, Caius, Wendy and Huys, and he received it graciously. Before that, however, Dr. Caius was horrified to learn that the university of Oxford had petitioned for the right to examine and punish unqualified practitioners there and for seven miles about. Dr. Huys assured him that this petition was not granted, but Dr. Caius, with an eye to possible revivals of the claim, put it down in writing that he himself had added at the end of 'that statute' words reserving the authority and privileges of the College.[1]

While the big guns were being laid and primed the two originators of the disturbances followed diverging paths. Lawton the coppersmith was punished by the College in 1555–6 and with that disappeared from history. Simon Ludford, headed off from the Oxford doctorate, betook himself to Cambridge. In April 1554 a letter denouncing him was addressed to that university not by the College

---

[1] I do not understand this statement, which does not seem to refer either to any parliamentary statute or to anything in the *Statuta Antiqua Universitatis Oxoniensis*, ed. S. Gibson (1931), where Pole's statutes for the medical school are given on pp. 378–9.

but by its three most eminent Cambridge members, Caius, Wendy, and Huys. They did not scruple to hint that their own munificence to their *alma mater* in the future might depend on its good conduct now. Caius at least was more than a merely potential benefactor, but the university had its pride. Its dignified reply refused to interfere with the normal working of the examination system which already had Ludford under consideration, and politely reminded the three sons that its privileges must be respected. They replied at considerable length, and, for whatever reason, Ludford did not obtain the Cambridge degree.

The best part of the story is still to come. At an extraordinary comitia on 7 April 1563, in the seventh presidency of Dr. Caius, Simon Ludford, doctor of medicine of the university of Oxford,[1] was admitted to the College of Physicians. Besides his entrance fees he paid the fine of £10 imposed ten years before when he made his first appearance before the College, but he paid with spontaneous alacrity, and so the College gave him back £3 6s. 8d. And three times, in 1564, 1569, and 1572, he was censor.

If there were other not wholly unqualified practitioners among those inhibited by the College, they were most likely among the foreigners, who accounted for at least seventeen or eighteen in a total of between seventy and eighty in this period. They came from France, Italy, Spain, Flanders (which perhaps covers some other provinces of the Netherlands besides Flanders proper), Brabant, not to mention Scotland. Perhaps Valentine the Egyptian was a gipsy. Some of the Frenchmen and Netherlanders may have worked only among the London colonies of their own countrymen, and may thus have been only legally in the wrong, but we do not know that this defence was put up. Charles Cornet, a Fleming, was condemned in 1555 and made to set up notices of the fact in all the corners of the City. He was imprisoned; but he would not desist from his ill-doing, and in this he was protected by Hugh Weston, dean of Westminster, and Sir Roger Cholmley, who was a judge and the founder of Highgate School. The College resorted to the court of chancery and mobilized its friends against Cornet. These were some of the magnates, the royal physicians, and also Mr. Roper (perhaps the son-in-law of Sir Thomas More) and Mr. Vaughan. Cornet's medicaments were publicly burnt at Westminster; he took sanctuary first at St. Martin's le Grand and then in West-

---

[1] The date of this degree was 26 June 1560.

minster Abbey, but the College dug him out in spite of Cholmley and the dean, and his partisans at St. Martin's were imprisoned. In 1569 Gerard Gossenius, a Brabanter, claimed to be a doctor of Louvain but said that he had lost his certificate on his flight from the tyranny of the duke of Alva. He undertook not to practise during the short remainder of his stay in England.

The foreign empiric was indeed a familiar type, like the foreign doctor, and some of the impostors even falsely pretended to foreign birth or training or travel: it was part of their conjuring outfit. The main characteristics of these guerilla healers have persisted through the centuries and they were fully developed by the sixteenth century in England. They were international like the medical tradition of which they were the perverters; there was a western tradition of quackery. Even the names that were applied to them illustrate this: 'mountebank' and 'charlatan' are of Italian origin, 'quack' itself comes from the Dutch, and the English 'Merry Andrew' is the name of a cosmopolitan type. They were graded from familiar friends of the courtiers down to parasites of the poor, but they had common characteristics. On the whole they seem to have carried on their business very openly. A good many advertised their services in printed circulars of which the earliest to survive comes down from 1525.[1] Effrontery indeed was a necessity to them: they not only aped the regular physicians and surgeons; they also challenged them. They made high claims. They boasted of their cures; they sold panaceas; they cured the incurable; they vociferated in imposing terminology, sometimes pseudo-scientific, sometimes pseudo-mystical. Knowing how easily most people forgive inconsistency, they borrowed phrases and procedures from alchemy, astrology, religion and the current fashions of occultism. They often professed to offer free treatment to the poor, but they always had something to sell, and they sold with their own variety of cheap jack's patter. Sometimes their remedies were secret; sometimes, more cunningly, they revealed the formula at a price. They lived by their wits, and those of them who practised with any success had wits to live by. They depended on exploiting the patient's confidence, and among the qualities by which they won it there were no doubt sometimes genuine gifts by which they could cure at least some troubles.[2] The

[1] In the Library of the Royal College of Surgeons.
[2] The literature relating to these gentry is not of high quality, but some use is made of original authorities in such books, as C. J. S. Thompson, *The Quacks of Old London* (1929).

case against them was that they were ignorant, mercenary and fraudulent, and it could often be proved by evidence of fact. The College collected such evidence against some of those who appeared before it, though in law it only needed to prove that they had not been licensed. Even if they had some skill and some knowledge, they had never been tested by anyone who was entitled to judge and they had never bent to the yoke of professional ethics.

Besides the criminal impostors there was a heterogeneous body of men and women of whom some did equally undesirable things in less showy and enterprising ways, while others could scarcely be distinguished from the well-meaning amateurs who, in that age of home medicine helped out their neighbours with charms or herbs and poultices. It is not surprising that a person of any description accused before the College might produce supporters. Then as now it was possible to effect cures without a licence. More than that, the charlatan's patient is not always and altogether a victim. He easily becomes an accomplice. He may resort to the irregular because he already has a grudge against the regulars, or at least is disappointed in them; he can easily catch something of the charlatan's presumption, and be led on to conspire with him in contempt of discipline, science, and knowledge. A fee paid to a quack is a wager on his reputation. The College was to find that some of the quacks could count on support from greater men than the dean of Westminster and Sir Roger Cholmley, and this too was in the nature of things. The great are sometimes free from common prejudices but sometimes they are wilful and enjoy exerting their power in favour of those who gain their approval.

These were probably not the motives of Sir Walter Mildmay, the chancellor of the exchequer, when he furnished the English wife of Elisaeus Bornel, a Westphalian, with a letter in 1569.[1] Bornel was in prison for practising not only ignorantly but with the aid of magic, and the College refused to release him until he paid his fine and costs although he was needed as a member of the staff of an ambassador about to return to Russia.[2] In the same year Dr. David Lewis, judge of the court of admiralty, had to be appealed to when an empiric named William Rich went on with his illegal practice although he had been committed to the Marshalsea by the

---

[1] The Annals say that the letter was from the lord treasurer, but as there was no lord treasurer in 1569 Mildmay is probably meant.

[2] Bornel had studied at Cambridge. In Russia he became involved in plots and died after torture: F. G. Clemov in *Proceedings of the Anglo-Russian Literary Society* (1898).

College. The enforcement of the law met with constant hindrances of this and other kinds, but there can be no doubt that Dr. Caius set out with the determination to make it effective. In the eventful first year of his presidency the College decided to extend the effort to the provinces. A circular letter was drafted, addressed to all justices, mayors, sheriffs, bailiffs, constables and other ministers and officers and all others whom it concerned, requiring them to assist a person named in it in the execution of the laws under which the College acted. The draft was approved by two serjeants-at-law, William Rastall, the editor of More's works, and Walpole. Two hundred copies were printed and commissioners (*inquisitores*) furnished with them were sent out to oblige the unlicensed by personal bonds and sureties to submit to examination by the College, and to have the obstinate imprisoned. Unfortunately we do not know how many went, or whither, or with what success. Some facts from later years suggest that the outcome was not satisfactory. In 1569 Dr. Corembeck alleged that Dr. Walker had been guilty of accepting bribes for admitting certain empirics to practise medicine in Norwich and Norfolk. Dr. Walker refused to obey the beadle's summons. Seven months later the College fined him 40s. for this and a second refusal, and wrote to Dr. Corembeck empowering him to have the empirics sent to the College for punishment. Perhaps they never came. Dr. Walker at any rate had got off lightly.

To some extent, though apparently only to a small extent, the action of the College against empirics was supported by opinion outside it. There were, as we shall see, apothecaries and aggrieved patients who helped the College or ingratiated themselves with it by appearing as witnesses. It may, however, be set down as a weakness that there was no general popular feeling on the side of the College. It was probably not very widely known, and it took no steps to justify itself to the populace. It could have encouraged its members to write books or pamphlets, and it could even have provided some kind of occasional lectures or addresses for the more educated among the citizens of London; but there was no obvious example to suggest any such propaganda. The College was a small body acting through the constituted authorities, and no one can be blamed for not inventing a more liberal and realistic conception.

Another serious weakness was that pressure against the irregulars was not continuous. Dr. Caius started out with ten offenders fined and a dozen admonished in his first presidential year, besides a first general warning to the apothecaries; but in the very next year the numbers fell and he admitted that more would have been punished if he had not been engaged on the making of Linacre's monument for St. Paul's and the re-foundation and endowment of his own Cambridge college. One or two of his later years as president perhaps approached the level of the first, but during his long absences in Cambridge the energy of the College seems to have flagged. In 1561–2 Dr. Caius's tenure was interrupted for one year by that of Dr. Richard Master, but he was a physician to the queen, and so was scarcely able to put in a couple of appearances at the College, for which reason, as Dr. Caius wrote in the Annals, in that year there was an invasion of empirics of every nation from all sides, and it was a toilsome business to cope with them in the succeeding years. It is noteworthy that he attributed the swarming of the empirics to this cause alone. In spite of the distance of time we may say that he exaggerated the effectiveness of the coercive machinery. He himself had written in the previous paragraph that Master's presidential year saw the worst epidemic of smallpox he could remember, and was therefore favourable to the irregular practitioners, and that the next year, when the queen herself and some of the ladies and gentlemen of the court took the disease, was as bad. When Dr. Caius was restored to the presidency for a second time after the three years in which Dr. Francis, Dr. Syminges, and Dr. Caldwell ruled, a resolution was passed that all those who practised medicine without having been admitted to the College should be diligently examined and punished. This again seems to throw the blame on the laxity of the College officers. But a wider view was needed. Social conditions regulated the supply of quackery and the demand for it, but no one explicitly recognized this. The College operated on the small scale of seventy or eighty convictions spread over seventeen years, including those of several recidivists and a few women who carried on the business of their convicted husbands. This amounted to a very short casualty list for the hordes of illegal practitioners.

Apothecaries and surgeons who trespassed on the medical preserve were known men with fixed addresses, so that it was comparatively easy to proceed against them, but they were members of companies which might afford them protection and would certainly be on the watch for any encroachment on their privileges by an overzealous prosecution. In the case of the surgeon Verselius[1] two apothecaries appeared as witnesses, behaving like satellites of the physicians, but one of them, John Turpin, may have been the Turpin who committed the same offence in 1555. Two or three others had been charged along with him then. When they were admonished the wardens of the apothecaries were present and through them all the apothecaries were included in the admonition. This seems to have been an intimation that the law would now be enforced strictly, whatever laxity there had been before. Next year the wardens of the apothecaries were summoned to the College again and with them the wardens of the surgeons.[2] Through them those they represented were forbidden to practise medicine, to reveal the names of medicaments or to give back prescriptions which they had received, because that often led to harm.[3]

An ancient City company might not comply readily with the notions of a new professional authority, but the College had means of asserting its position. On 28 July 1558 the two wardens of the apothecaries and all the apothecaries of the City and suburbs attended at the College and were enjoined, when they dispensed *pharmaca*, to display the several ingredients which were to be ground together for six or eight days in their shop-windows, so that the physicians passing by might judge the goodness of the samples. The wardens gave their judgement that medicaments sold by spicers should be open to inspection by the censors equally with those of the apothecaries. They ruled it unjust to sell bad materials which had been bought in good faith along with good materials. The assembly also listened to a letter in pursuance of which it had been summoned. The letter was given under the signet of the queen herself at her manor of St. James five weeks before. She mentioned the Acts of 1540 and 1553, and the great inconveniences that were like to have chanced lately to one of her nobility by ignorance of the seller of certain wares. She commanded the College to enforce the Acts and she gave it authority to summon the wardens of the Grocers and all the apothecaries, to forbid them to sell poisonous or potentially dangerous drugs except under a physician's written order or to persons of good intent whose names were to be noted, with the time of the purchase.

[1] See below, p. 121.
[2] That is to say those of the surgeons of the Barber Surgeons' Company.
[3] The entry is not clear, but seems to convey that those rules had been broken by one spicer, three surgeons and four others, presumably apothecaries, who are named as present.

Some people are impervious to warnings. In 1559 three apothecaries and the employee of one of them were reprimanded, some for selling and supplying pills without the consent of physicians, the others for wrongly (*male*) preparing scillitic vinegar. Edward Stephens or Stephenson, one of the former group who is also described as a broker, obstinately refused to obey the president's summons and was sent to the Fleet prison. Dr. Caius allowed him to appear and to plead for release. He was brought by a servant of the Fleet and some of the apothecaries came to support his plea. In the presence of these persons, of the beadle and of Lord Cobham[1] he fell on his knees of his own accord before the president and begged the queen's pardon for disobeying the president of her College.

This did not end the trouble with apothecaries and in 1562/3 the College promoted a Bill in Parliament to give the College the admission, censure and correction of apothecaries, especially the search of their wares, reserving to the Grocers everything relating to food-stuffs.[2] The apothecaries objected; the citizens of London were indignant; the matter was sent to a committee, but it went no further before the session of parliament was prorogued.[3] This was a definite check. Dr. Caius noted in the Annals that the royal Physician Walter Cromer had failed in a like attempt in the reign of Henry VIII. There had always been citizens and even men of higher station who were prepared to resist any attempt to restrain the apothecaries from prescribing pills and potions. The College had to reckon with a hostile body of opinion, and its relations with the Grocers' Company cannot have been good.

The incidents involving surgeons were fewer, but equally serious. In 1555 three surgeons were punished, presumably by fines, and a fourth was admonished not to transgress in the future. In 1569 two citizens complained of a surgeon named James Alcocke. The first had been given a potion which made him worse, the second alleged that he was a victim of *mala praxis* and that he had been charged a

---

[1] It appears that throughout the sixteenth and seventeenth centuries when the officers sat to exercise jurisdiction they were deemed to be holding a court and therefore the public had to be admitted. For references to this rule about courts see Lord Wright's note in D. A. Winstanley, *Early Victorian Cambridge* (1947), p. 140.

[2] *Commons' Journals*, i (1742): 26 January 1562/3 first reading.

[3] Ibid. p. 22 February 1562/3, second reading and committed, the only member of the committee named being the recorder of London; Annals February and March. There is no reason to connect the lapsing of the Bill with the plague, which did not affect the prorogations until 10 April 1564.

fee of 30s. in ready money. The outcome is not recorded. In the next year there was a more troublesome offender. James Francis Verselius was a surgeon who, according to the evidence of two apothecaries, had practised medicine for ten years, and he was fined £20. At the instance of certain noblemen, however, a majority of the College let him off two-thirds of this fine, on condition that he should sign a bond for £100 not to practise medicine in the future. He refused to sign and grudgingly paid his £20 to the president.

On 24 March 1572 Dr. Caius enjoyed his last public triumph. Verselius succeeded in bringing the general issue raised by his conviction before the high commission.[1] The issue was whether it was lawful for surgeons to administer internal medicines in cases of sciatica and syphilis or for any kind of ulcers or wounds. The commissioners were the bishop of London (Edmund Grindal), Sir James Croft, a privy councillor, Sir William Cordell master of the rolls, Thomas Wilson, master of requests, Peter Osborne, who held among other offices that of clerk of the faculties,[2] (?Thomas) Wilbraham and others. They sat at Guildhall and Allen, the lord mayor, sat with them. The commissioners brought forward many arguments on the side of the surgeons, but Dr. Caius who had been summoned by the lord mayor in his own name and that of the commissioners, maintained the contrary and the commissioners decided the general question unanimously in his favour. They requested the College, however, to remit Verselius's fine. Sir James Croft acted for Verselius in this matter; but he was told that the money had been spent and that it had been lawfully come by. Verselius dropped his claim.

The College was not only an engine of repression. It also contributed positively to medical education. We saw that this was no part of its original mission, but that there was a possible reference to lecturing in the Statutes and that the Barber-Surgeons' Company

---

[1] I regard this as a session of the ecclesiastical high commission for the following reasons. No special commission for trying this case seems to have been issued. Dr. Caius wrote in the Annals that the disputation originated from a complaint of Verselius to the queen's commissioners. At this time various complaints which were scarcely or not at all ecclesiastical in their nature were heard by the high commission, but the licensing powers of the bishop and archbishop made this almost an ecclesiastical question. The procedure on this occasion was like that of the commissioners. They met wherever they pleased. The bishop and the lord mayor were commissioners *ex officio*. The commission for 1570 is lost, but Osborne, Wilson and Thomas Wilbraham are known to have been commissioners at other times; Croft and Cordell were suitably qualified. Finally, the loss of the commission's papers will explain the absence of any record of the event. See R. J. Usher, *The Rise and Fall of the High Commission* (1913), pp. 35, 55, 345 ff., 362 n. 1.   [2] See above, p. 78.

provided anatomical instruction for its members.[1] Soon after his return from Italy Dr. Caius began to be present at the dissections in Barber Surgeons' Hall, and he continued his attendance for nearly twenty years. He gave instruction revealing the treasures of Galen which was highly appreciated. It is not known whether he was officially in charge of the demonstrations and paid for his work.[2] In 1564/5 when Huyck was president and Syminges was acting for him as pro-president, the College of Physicians obtained a grant of four corpses yearly for dissection.[3] The fellows undertook to perform the dissection publicly in the College in rotating order of seniority, but in 1570 when it came to the turn of Dr. Lopez he was thought likely to refuse and was told that he might buy himself off for £3, which he did. One of the two Richard Smiths who were fellows, Smith of Oxford, was appointed in his place. In 1572 the Cambridge Smythe who came next in seniority, had his turn. These anatomy lessons are described as public. This does not necessarily mean more than that they were open to all members of the College, though they provided a spectacle so acceptable to the taste of the first Elizabethan age that we may suppose as many distinguished strangers were invited as the cramped accommodation of the College could contain. Of the instruction itself nothing is directly known. Although they held that surgery was a part of medicine, none of the London physicians seems to have acquired skill in it, but their anatomical study, which no doubt included physiology, though to that degree theoretical was of high quality. It was unquestionably to the good that this instruction was given. Throughout the whole existence of the College from that time this good work went on, growing in quantity and scope as successive benefactors endowed new courses of lectures. Occasionally the lectures were the vehicles for disseminating new discoveries of the greatest value. More often they were instruction in what was known and accepted. Always they were the best of their kind in London, and this should be remembered to the honour of the College.

Dr. Caius's other great contribution to the development of the College was that he planted and watered two kinds of activity

---

[1] Above pp. 85, 101.

[2] The contemporary authorities are quoted by Venn, pp. 8–9.

[3] This is not in the Annals but the charter of 24 February 7 Elizabeth is printed by Goodall. Dr. Caius had been president until the preceding May and was probably active in procuring the charter. In the following August there was a similar grant of two corpses for dissection at Caius College.

which he regarded as essential to its purpose, the ceremonial and the social. The insignia which he devised are still in use; the dinners, of which he gave the first in his own house in St. Bartholomew's Close, are still enjoyed. Let no man say that the College could have done without them. They helped to build round the business of licensing and inspection a sense of community which might have arisen but, to judge by many analogies, could scarcely have grown strong without these supports. In the sixteenth century these social relaxations went unrecorded. We do not know how convivial they were or how decorous, nor whether any guests came in from outside, but we can see indications of a development with which they may well have been connected. The College, which so far as we know had begun mainly if not wholly, as an instrument for carrying out its chartered duties, was becoming an entity by itself, to which gifts could be made,[1] with interests of its own. Not only had it a certain prestige but it conferred prestige on its members. Membership, and the various offices, especially that of president, were still burdensome, but they were desirable. Those who held them were respected, perhaps envied, the more so because entry was not easy.

As we move forward in time we come to know more about the men who composed the College, and, although we still know little, the picture is clearly that of a group of men with antecedents and education which provided many links between them. The two foreigners at court, the surgeon Guersie and the physician Lopez were a small separate element. Among the twenty Englishmen who were admitted or on the way to admission in this period we find only four who had studied abroad, one at Padua, one at Grenoble,[2] one at Bologna and one at Venice; after the religious schism foreign travel was more difficult in itself and less readily permitted by the English authorities. At least seven had been fellows of Oxford or Cambridge colleges. Two or more were physicians' sons, and one, Henry Wotton, as the son of a former president of the College. All had been at Oxford or Cambridge, though not quite all seem to have taken degrees there. The distinction between fellows, candidates and licentiates was firmly established by the end of the period.[3]

[1] William Bullein, known as a medical author, gave a gold chain with a polished stone and sundial; but it was sold in 1571 for £12 as useless to the College.

[2] Peter Daquet.

[3] The information about licentiates in the Annals is meagre. In 1556 Ralph Standish was licensed for one year. In 1559 William Leverett, the first extra-licentiate appears, to practise in Newark; in the same year Robert Dalton to practise in the diocese of Durham. John Luke (1561) is licensed to treat eyes by external means.

Esprit de corps is esteemed by the English as a binding and energizing force, but suspected by the French, who invented the phrase, as an impediment to co-operation with other units in larger formations.[1] For the present the College was the only medical body in England which evoked this sentiment. The faculties at Oxford and Cambridge were small and were not the centres of the personal loyalties of their members, who also had their universities and colleges to think of. The great hospitals were still scarcely more than embryonic: Roger Giffard, who was probably elected to the College between 1566 and 1570, was more notable for his fellowships at Merton and All Souls than for his appointment as physician at St. Bartholomew's. The College was a solitary institution. Since its foundation it had become in more senses than one exclusive. It had virtually excluded the licentiates. By its system of examinations for membership it had made itself intellectually exclusive, which was indeed necessary for raising the standards of the profession. In all probability it was becoming socially exclusive. In the stratified society of the time that was inevitable; but it set a limit to the possibilities of action for the future. In a sense the limit had been imposed long before by immemorial tradition. The healing arts were divided among three bodies, the physicians, surgeons and apothecaries. Of the three the physicians were the most elaborately educated and the College, a select body among them, championed their claims to certain specific superiorities over the other two. If all three were to move together, either in the advancement of knowledge or in the provision of more and better-trained practitioners, these superiorities would have to be exercised generously and imaginatively. At the end of Dr. Caius's time the surgeons and apothecaries had been humiliated, and it was for the future to decide how co-operation with them should be organized. Much depended on the capacity of the College to invent a solution or a *modus vivendi*.

---

[1] After writing this sentence with military examples in mind I came across the passage of M. Raynaud, *Les médicins au temps de Molière*, (1862), p. 19, where the Paris medical faculty is charged with 'l'esprit de corps, dans ce qu'il a de plus étroit: c'est a dire l'esprit d'exclusion, de chicane, d'entêtement et de routine'.

VIII : THE ELIZABETHAN COLLEGE, 1572–1603

FTER the valedictory entry about Dr. Caius there follow eight years for which there are no Annals and for these years only a few isolated facts about the College can be gathered from other sources.[1] There is no reason to suppose that any Annals were kept. When they begin again with the Michaelmas *comitia* of 1581 they are more orderly and fuller than before.[2] No doubt this was because in that autumn the College made sure that they should no longer be the president's responsibility but that of a special officer. The *regestarius* was to keep the *regesta*,[3] the records of things done: they probably called him 'register' in English and gradually turned over to 'registrar' long after that form came into common use in the seventeenth century.[4] He was to receive 40s. a year, besides a fee of 3s. 4d. for every licentiate, candidate and fellow admitted and the same amount from every person fined by the president and college or by the censors, on each occasion when he paid either the whole fine or an instalment. He was to be fined 1s. if ever he were absent from the comitia and failed to arrange for another of the fellows to act as his substitute. The first holder of the office was Dr. Roger Marbeck, the son of the Windsor organist who 'noted' the Book of Common Prayer. His duties turned out to be heavier than was expected,[5] and in May 1582 his share of fees was raised to half-a-crown in the pound for every licence to practise and for every fine. Dr. Marbeck seems to have done his work admirably and his terse Latin minutes are compatible with a sense

---

[1] When the Annals began again Dr. Atslowe had £60 13s. 8d. of the College money in his keeping, and this suggests that he may have been president or have taken charge of the money in a vacancy of that office. He is referred to as president and there is a reference to the detaining of College money in the document printed on p. 129 below.

[2] For their value as an authority see Appendix to vol. ii below.

[3] This word is not actually used in the Annals.

[4] The earliest sign of 'registrar' that I have found in relation to the College is in Latin: Dr. Collins is 'registrarius' on 23 July 1683, but 'registarius' again three days later. On 30 September 1690 'registrarius' reappears. But 'register' was almost invariably used throughout the eighteenth century.

[5] He may well have kept the vanished Book of Ordinary Examinations mentioned in the Annals, 25 June and 30 September 1601.

of humour; he was appointed for life, and held office for twenty-five years.

Another important office was created in 1583: one of the fellows was to be made treasurer. At that time the College was coping with a piece of business for which it had to raise money specially and supervise the expenditure carefully, the extension of the building.[1] The old system by which the president did everything put too great a burden on him. The new office was constituted on the lines which are familiar everywhere, except that the treasurer was responsible not only for the money but for all the property of the college, and, along with the president, for looking after any legal proceedings that it engaged in. His stipend was 40s. and he was to receive 6s. 8d. from the admission fees of each fellow, candidate or licentiate. The treasurership soon began to change hands from time to time. The first holder, Dr. Baronsdale was elected for one year, which was followed by three others; he came back into office after serving as president, and in the meantime there had been five other treasurers under Queen Elizabeth, one of them, the illustrious William Gilbert, serving for two single years with a long interval between.

The College settled down into methodical and businesslike habits, but it was not out of tune with that adventurous age. The reliable Dr. Marbeck was in the Netherlands with Leicester in 1585-6 and with the admiral Lord Howard at Cadiz in 1596. He, Dr. Gilbert, Dr. Browne and Dr. Wilkinson were the four physicians from whom the privy council required the president to choose two for the fleet which was awaiting the Armada.[2] Dr. Mouffet went to Normandy with Essex in 1591 and Dr. Atkins sailed with him in 1597. There had been a licentiate who went to Russia as early as the reign of Edward VI[3]; now Dr. Robert Jacob, strongly recommended by the queen as an *accoucheur*, made himself useful at the court of Ivan the Terrible. Dr. Mark Ridley had two long spells in Moscow in and after the reign of Boris Godunov. We can imagine good talk at the College dinners. These were elegant (*lauta*) but that is almost all we know about them. Sometimes they were held in the College, sometimes in the house of the president or a fellow; once two of the fellows gave their party in the house of the veteran fighter Sir John Norris.[4] Those who could not provide a dinner paid

---

[1] See below, p. 150.
[2] *Acts of the Privy Council, 1588* new ser. xvi, (1897), p. 5.
[3] Ralph Standish.   [4] 28 September 1591.

money instead, to the amount of £6 13s. 4d.: the only one of whom we know by name that his house was unsuitable and too small was, alas, Dr. Marbeck.[1] That the dinners were appreciated is shown by the failure of a proposal to divert the money set aside for them to the building fund.[2] Looking round the tables in the late fifteen-eighties someone may have reflected that, before they began their medical studies, Dr. Marbeck had been provost of Oriel, Dr. Christopher Johnson had been headmaster of Winchester and Dr. Reuben Sherewood had been headmaster of Eton. Such a reflection would not have been so surprising as it would be now. Medicine was still a study to which an educated man could betake himself without conjuring up new aptitudes, and academic headships were often relinquished for other pursuits. The three late converts fitted easily into the College as it now was, a small section of the increasingly consolidated upper professional world. There were some sons of doctors: Thomas Fryer, elected soon after Henry Wotton, was the second fellow's son[3]; there were sons of the married clergy, Thomas Jeesop and Mark Ridley. William Gilbert's father was recorder of Colchester. Some of the fellows came from landowning families, for example Dr. Bayley, Dr. Doylie and Dr. Moundeford. The more successful physicians moved in influential circles, whether at court or as affluent men among their neighbours. John James, Thomas Lake and Thomas Mouffet sat in parliament[4]; Dr. Thomas Jeesop was a justice of the peace in Dorset.

If the College shared in the prosperity of the time it also knew the dark side of Elizabethan life. In the routine work of granting licences and checking unlicensed practice it became aware of the hardships suffered by protestant refugees from the Netherlands and France. The Englishmen who suffered were on the other side. In the year of the Spanish Armada John Halsey, an Oxford master of arts was detained in London by orders of the queen and the high commission and supported himself by illicit practice. He offended again in 1595. The troubles of Dr. Caius's last years came at the time when the authorities began to use force in earnest against resistance to the Elizabethan settlement. This pressure met with resistance at home and abroad and then became more severe.

---

[1] 25 June and 12 July 1587.   [2] 22 November 1522.
[3] There seems to be no evidence of relationship between Joseph Jeesop, admitted in 1597 and Thomas Jeesop admitted before 1589.
[4] Sir John E. Neale, *The Elizabethan House of Commons* (1949), p. 302, says that two physicians sat in the parliaments for the reign, but gives no names.

Thomas Vavasour, who was or had been a licentiate and practised in York, was believed to have harboured Edmund Campion: he was held in solitary confinement in the castle at Hull. Dr. Atslowe was twice upon the rack. Dr. Good was imprisoned for holding secret correspondence with the queen of Scots. Dr. Fryer did not suffer like his father but compounded for a yearly sum of money for his refusal to go to church. As he died possessed of the manor of Harlton in Cambridgeshire, which he had bought, he was not ruined. We have seen that there were two fellows, close contemporaries, called Richard Smith, one from Oxford and the other, who became president, from Cambridge. He of Oxford was a staunch catholic and left the country to live in Douai: his place as an elect was declared vacant after he withdrew from London. The grimmest case was that of Dr. Roderigo Lopez, the first man to be appointed physician to the refounded St. Bartholomew's. He had been Leicester's physician and he became one of the queen's; but he was a converted Jew of Portuguese origin,[1] and so he was drawn into a network of Spanish and Portuguese intrigues in which the ill-fated Essex was entangled. It was widely believed in those days that princes had as good a right to defend their states by assassination as by war.[2] Physicians were more useful than bravoes for disposing of highly-placed and well-protected opponents. In 1594 Dr. Lopez was hanged, drawn and quartered for high treason and he was almost certainly guilty.

In the face of these compromising associations the College could not escape interference from the government. In or soon after 1572 the following memorandum was drawn up for the eye of someone in office, and the marginal notes give precision to the accusations in the text.[3]

---

[1] Roth, pp. 140–1.

[2] For the history of this ethical doctrine and for examples of doctors who acted as its instruments see W. Platzhoff, *Die Theorie von der Mordbefügnis der Obrigkeit im XVI Jahrhundert*, Historische Studien (1906.)

[3] The list is printed in *An Impartial Enquiry into the Legal Constitution of the College of Physicians* (1753), p. 44 n. and the substance of the memorandum on pp. 98–100, with reference to R. Seymour (pseudonym of J. Mottley), *Survey of London*, i (1734), 156. They are also in the 1754 edition of vol. i of J. Stow, *Survey of London*. The original is in Brit. Mus. MS. Lansdowne 21, and previously belonged to John Strype, the ecclesiastical historian, which suggests that it may have been addressed to the bishop of London or the archbishop of Canterbury. Clement died on 1 July and Syminges was elected president at Michaelmas 1572; but the blank in the Annals makes it impossible to fix a latest date for the paper. Dr. Travers of Chester is not known to Munk.

British Museum MS. Lansdowne 21 (fos. 123-4)

Disorders in the Colledge of Phisitions in London to be Reformed

Presidents. Caius often, Simings Caudwell Astlowe who was also chosen the second time after his troubles.	That the president, censors, electes and other theyre officers are not sworne to the quenes majestie at theyre admission, as in other corporations they are wherbie it commythe to passe, that papistes have continually occupied the cheefe roomes.
Astlowe Gyfford from Martyn Colledge.	That men expelled theyre universities for religion by this meanes have from tyme to tyme ben receved into the colledge and therby (?maintained) in theire credyte.
Fryer of Godmanchester. Coldwell. Turner. Italy.	That eyther they do wholie reject, or not without muche importunitie admit any, whome they thinke to be well affected towards the true religion nowe renewed.
Smithe Oxon. Fryer Oxon.	That such as have gone beyond the seas to take the degree of doctor because they would avoyd the othe of the supremacrie ministered according to the statute in our universities have shortly upon their returne ben admitted without any othe ministred unto them.
	That suche as have been imprisoned for religion and other greate matters, have kept them selves in office at their owne pleasures (contrary to the colledge statutes and theyre othes) and deteyne in their handes the colledge goodes, disdainyng to make any accomte of the same.
Clement	That some of the electes who have fled for religion out of the realme have bene kept in theyre offices, and stoutlye defended as cheefe members of the colledge being at Lovaine untill they dyed: that other honest true subiectes might be kept out of the same roomes.
The last election stolen by Astlowe, Simings, Cauldwell and Smithe.	That they make pryvate conventicles of a fewe to bringe to passe theyre purposes and elections whiche ought by the colledge statutes to be donne on quarter daies and the whole companie being therunto called.
	That the college statutes are generally unperfect and partly papistic.

The Names of the Phisiconis of the Colledge of London

D. Simings president
D. Cauldwell
D. Good
D. Astlowe
D. Smythe Oxon.
D. Gyfford
D. Fryer
D. Wootton
D. Travers of Westchester

D. Huyike
D. Masters
D. Walker
D. Smithe Cantabrig.
D. Baronsdale

D. Foster candidatus   D. Spiringe a stranger candidatus

Strangers of the Colledge

D. Julio
D. Martyn Corymbacke
Mr. Hector
D. Lopus

The Electors (who are perpetuall officers of the colledge) are these

D. Huicke
D. Masters
D. Symminges
D. Good
D. Caudwell
D. Astlowe
D. Walker
D. Smythe Oxon.

No purge followed this denunciation, though the inactivity of the years with no Annals may have some connexion with it.

In 1584 William the Silent, the leader of the Netherlands revolt against Spain was shot dead by a catholic fanatic, and therefore English statesmen took an unprecedented step to protect their queen. Burghley and Walsingham drew up for the privy council a bond of association, to be voluntarily signed by noblemen and others, by which they swore to resist or avenge anything that should tend to the harm of the queen's person. The privy council and the office-holders in and about London immediately joined in, and copies were sent to the lords lieutenants of counties, the mayors of towns and others. The College of Physicians received a copy and it was read in comitia on 10 November. Two only of the fellows who were not present, Dr. Atslowe and Dr. Smith of Oxford were out of sympathy with the Church of England. All the fourteen who were present took the oath including Dr. Fryer. They did indeed scrutinize the text and add a condition, that they adhered in so far as the association was in agreement with the word of God and the laws of the realm. But this does not necessarily imply that they supposed it fell short in either respect. They may only have been guarding against a possible future eventuality. Some government or law court might hold that subjects ought not to take so much upon themselves. Voluntary associations and the doctrine of the social contract were characteristic of the opponents of royal authority on the continent. In England they were unfamiliar, and it was an innovation for those in authority to give countenance to them.[1]

On one other occasion the College received an official communication on a similar matter, and in this too it was treated as an ally in maintaining the established order, though an ally needing a reminder of its responsibilities. In 1587/8, between the execution of Mary queen of Scots and the Armada, the government watched the catholics with special vigilance. The archbishop of Canterbury was now Whitgift, who in his Cambridge days had taken part in the raid on Dr. Caius's store of popish gear. With other members of the ecclesiastical high commission he now wrote to the College from Lambeth requiring them to send him the names of all true and pretended physicians and surgeons in or about London who refused to frequent divine service. They also enjoined the fellows to be more careful in future elections, and in granting licences, to make sure that those they chose were well-affected to the established religion and to the queen's ecclesiastical supremacy.[2] In reply the College sent a list of its own fellows and licentiates, and in addition the names of those it tolerated or connived at, that is such as it knew, having made a suitable trial of their sufficiency. It did not venture upon a catalogue of Roman Catholic empirics. For surgeons it very properly referred the commissioners to the surgeons' own

---

[1] The text of the Association is given in full in the Annals. It has often been printed in collections of constitutional documents. The absentees from the meeting were Dr. Walker, Dr. Astlowe, Dr. Smith *Oxoniensis*, Dr. Jeesop, Dr. Bayley, two recently admitted fellows Dr. Hall and Dr. Turner, Dr. Penny, ?Dr. Caldwell who died in that year and the two foreigners Hector Nuñez and Lopez.

[2] Printed in *Historical Manuscripts Commission, 8th Report*, p. 227.

company.[1] It said nothing about the concluding admonition and it was left in peace.

That it now had an assured place among the institutions of London is proved by the frequency with which, as we shall see, influential people approached it with requests of diverse kinds. For its own members it was a place of social resort. A rule was made about adornments to hang on the walls: any fellow or any foreign gentleman not of the College might put up his coat of arms or his portrait if he paid £10, and anyone who had served three years as president might do it without making any donation.[2] This may be a sign that the spirit of a club was beginning to develop, and that spirit may have something to do with the policy of the College about its numbers. In the unofficial list of 1572 or later there were eighteen fellows and two candidates. At some earlier point a total of twenty fellows was fixed by statute.[3] A doubt arose about the interpretation of this limit, and in 1584 it was decided that the royal physicians should not be counted in the twenty. They were to be admitted provided they asked for admission and were Englishmen, but twenty fellows could be admitted beside them.[4] This number was, however, exceeded. In 1590 the limit was raised to thirty including the royal physicians,[5] and there actually were thirty fellows already. The earliest nominal roll preserved in the College dates from 1589.[6] The names are arranged tidily in order of seniority, first twenty-eight English fellows, then the two foreigners Nuñez and Lopez, then the eight candidates. When the limit was raised to thirty it was provided that, by agreement of the president, consiliarii, censors and seven other fellows a deviation might be permitted if it preserved the force and sense of this rule, and the case for this soon arose. The next two lists, for 1595 and 1597, show thirty-one fellows, because, as is noted, Dr. Ridley was in Russia.[7] All this is intelligible and fits in with the picture which we shall see of an

[1] The answer refers to the surgeons, 'as an entire body of them selves and utterly exempted from our societie and privilege, wherby we are not to deale with them and their incorporation'.

[2] 5 April 1596. The custom of giving portraits and putting up coats of arms was already known in universities.

[3] In the eighteenth-century case of Rex v. Askew et al. (for which see below, vol. ii) this by-law was stated not to be then extant but to have been passed on 1 February 1555. No authority can be found for this date which is that of the statute on admissions mentioned above, p. 90 n. 1.

[4] 25 June 1584.   [5] 27 April 1590.

[6] In the second volume of Annals, fo. E at the beginning.

[7] Annals, ii. fos. 113ᵛ, 129.

expanding profession,[1] but in 1599 there came a new statute reversing the process. The number of candidates was fixed at six.

The reasons for this are obscure, and the spirit of exclusiveness, if it was among them, was probably reinforced by other and more defensible considerations. For imposing a limit of numbers in the first instance there may have been various main reasons: the premises in Knightrider Street were modest, and some of the routine, such as the summoning of fellows individually to the comitia, was only suitable for a small body. Keeping the number always full might mean that an awkward waiting list would grow up. Some very desirable recruit might have to wait for a vacancy to be created by the death of a fellow. On the other hand keeping a few vacancies open might mean that whenever one was filled an invidious choice had to be made between several applicants. What had been a qualifying examination, in which the applicant simply had to reach a suitable standard, might become a competitive examination in which he was compared with others. As election conferred a status which was coming to be valued, besides some material privileges and exemptions, the examiners would be exposed to pressure from the influential friends of candidates.

Most of these difficulties did in fact materialize, and the College tried to steer a course between them. The status of candidate created a reservoir of doctors ready for admission when vacancies occurred or when they had completed the four years of practice required before admission. In 1582 a new statute passed a preliminary stage, laying down that no one should be included among the candidates until he had completed one year's practice and paid an annual fee of £8 (the usual fee of the licentiate at that time) and that no one should be admitted a fellow unless he had been a candidate, but this did not apply to those who had been professors (*doctores cathedrae*) in an English university, or had taught medicine publicly in one of them for three years, or had been doctors of medicine for seven complete years or were royal physicians.[2] Then came the admission of two middle-aged Cambridge doctors who had not been candidates.[3] which was followed by a letter of protest from a candidate, Dr. Mouffet. This brisk piece of Elizabethan prose

---

[1] See below p. 162.
[2] 7 December 1582, 4 September 1584. Two years later, rather unaccountably, it was found that the candidates had fallen out of the habit of paying their fees, which were said to be 40s. a year, and they were to pay in the future. 13 April 1584.
[3] Edward Dodding and Thomas Randall, 25 June 1584.

annoyed the fellows and they ordered the registrar to copy it into the Annals. At the previous meeting, so the letter alleged, the president and College had sworn that Dr. Mouffet should have the next vacancy for a fellow. Now he heard but hardly believed that others were to be put in before him. He challenged the College to deny his sufficiency. Then he wrote some sentences which imply that it was the custom to pay calls on the fellows before an election, as it was in the Paris faculty and as is still done by candidates for election to some academic bodies abroad: 'Doth any man except that I have not visited the College for that place? Let them remember that I did three yeares since: and yet indeed I visited not 2 or 3 of them, being such manner of men as I would not vouchsaffe to speak unto, nor to bid them God speede. Doth any one feare lest I stepping in to your society, will marre their musick and jollyty? If he be a papist, he hath cause to support it, for I hate him with an unfained hatred because he is an enemy to the truth of God and so to our prince.' After some thundering appeals to God and his justice, Mouffet concluded with a quotation from Plautus.[1]

This was disturbing. Mouffet was only a little over thirty, but he could not be ignored. He was not only a strong protestant; he had published two medical books, and in one of them, on the application of chemistry to medicine, he took the side of Paracelsus against Galen. But he was a friend of Thomas Penny and worked with him on natural history; he knew Sir Philip Sidney and he was a protégé of Sidney's brother-in-law and sister, the earl and countess of Pembroke, in whose time Wilton House was 'like a college'.[2]

Before anything further happened to the candidates another question arose. It had become common for Englishmen to leave Oxford and Cambridge without completing the full course which was expected in earlier days by the College, then to go abroad and to take their doctors' degrees in unknown regions, in less time and at less expense than they could have done in England.[3] It was to be feared that such less well-qualified doctors would crowd out those who had not merely incorporated but finished their studies at home. It was decided first that anyone admitted a licentiate, candidate or fellow who had only a foreign doctorate should pay

---

[1] 23 July 1584.   [2] Aubrey, i. 311.
[3] Since Dr. Caius's days the College had admitted fellows who had graduated in Heidelberg, Basle (Mouffet's second university), and Nantes. The first two were protestant universities. In his statutes for Caius College the doctor recommended Padua, Bologna, Montpellier and Paris.

triple fees; secondly, that any Oxford or Cambridge doctor who had not put in seven years in studying arts or as a bachelor of medicine should pay double, and thirdly that any should pay double who had taken his doctor's degree in another university than that in which he had spent seven years in arts or as a bachelor of medicine.[1] Thus the inferior physicians would be taxed but not excluded. None of the seven doctors who were present when these rules were made, with the possible exception of Hector Nuñez, had studied in a foreign university. A few years later the question was raised again by an incident concerning one Saul[2] and in 1595 it was decided to write to the university of Leiden to persuade it to be more careful (*cautior*) in granting doctors' degrees. Leiden was the youngest of the medical faculties of Europe and the most easily accessible from England. The first student inscribed his name in its books in 1578, and he was an Englishman, John James. By 1595 he was already a fellow of the College, as were four other Leiden graduates.[3] Two of these, James himself and Dr. Nowell, were present when this decision was taken.[4] In teaching Leiden was already doing well; its professors, Bontius, Forestus, Heurnius and Pavius were celebrities; its library and garden were exemplary, but it did grant the title of doctor easily, and the Leiden graduates who were fellows had reason to be concerned for the reputation of their own degrees.

The domestic question of the candidates came to a head in 1587/8. It was decided then that in all admissions, other things being equal, the seniors were to be preferred to the juniors, and that four should be admitted at that time[5]; but when the admissions took place the number was no less than eight, since it was resolved five days later to admit all the candidates.[6] So Dr. Mouffet had his way at last.

On two occasions recommendations were made from outside to influence elections. In 1586 Walsingham wrote that the College

---

[1] 23 October 1585.

[2] The Annals for 22 July 1591 tell us that he confessed to practising only among his friends and promised to refrain for the future, but on 7 August 1604 they mention that he was a foreign graduate. His name is not in the very useful annotated alphabetical list R. W. Innes-Smith, *English-Speaking Students of Medicine at the University of Leiden* (1932).   [3] Drs. Farmery, Osbourne, Nowell, and Paddy.

[4] 16 July 1595. The letter is not entered in the Annals.   [5] 23 February.

[6] 28 February, 8 March. One of the candidates, Robert Preest is not noted as admitted at this or any other time and he does not appear in the list for 1589; but he frequently attended the comitia from Michaelmas 1588 and appears in the list for 1595, so that the number admitted in 1587 was in effect nine.

had broken a promise to Dr. Jacob by admitting others over his head. He transmitted the queen's commands that it was to admit the doctor without gainsaying before he departed for his second visit to Russia.[1] The College complied with scarcely any fuss. In 1595 it yielded to the instances of Lord Buckhurst that Dr. Thomas Twine should be licensed to practice and that he should be admitted as a fellow as soon as there was a convenient opportunity. Though both Twine and his patron lived until well on in the reign of James I such an opportunity seems never to have occurred.

The College as a body disposed of its business in a sufficiently workmanlike way. There were comitia on the average rather more often than once a month: the largest number of meetings in any one year was twenty-one in 1601; nineteen was reached twice; the smallest number was eight in the plague-year 1591 and there were two other years with as few as nine. Friday was a common day, but except for those which followed dinners we do not know what time of day was usual.[2] As we shall see there were also some meetings of committees, and the censors held meetings of which the records are lost. The attendance at the comitia was reasonably good. In 1583 only seven fellows joined the president at Christmas, so at the following Easter a stern rule was passed that any fellow absent without excuse from the solemn quarterly comitia must pay a fine of 6s. 8d. and go to prison if he failed to pay.[3] Ten years later the June comitia were too thin to do any business,[4] and in 1595 two fellows were fined 5s. each for absence when they were needed for a particular item on the agenda[5]; but the College did no worse in this matter than many other societies. Usually it met in its own rooms, but when it dined at the house of the president or a fellow it stayed there for its meeting. Besides those who became presidents there were other fellows, Drs. Nowell and Clarkson, who had meetings in their houses and, perhaps for special reasons such as building work at the College, some of these meetings in private houses seem to have been on days when there was no dinner. The procedure seems to have followed the normal English ritual. Except for elections, however, we do not know whether a vote was taken when opinion was divided. Human nature asserted itself in the matter of the reading of the statutes. Scanty attendance was used once as an

[1] 15 March 1586.
[2] The dinner-hour may have been about eleven or about twelve: see *Englishmen at Rest and Play*, ed. R. V. Lennard (1931), p. 205.
[3] 13 April 1584.   [4] 25 June 1594.   [5] 4 July 1595.

excuse for omitting it[1]; then it was proposed only to read a quarter and decided only to read a third of the statutes at any single meeting[2] but that did not put an end to dispensing with the reading altogether on occasion.[3] For the sixteenth century the standard of decorum seems to have been very creditable. When Dr. Hector Nuñez was taxed with breaking the statute which obliged him to take his doctor's degree he lost his temper and said that Dr. Smith of Cambridge was like a slave in Terence. This lapse cost him 40s. but Dr. Smith paid 10s. for answering back.[4]

We have already mentioned some changes in the statutes; others will be dealt with later, including the general revision which was first talked of in 1590[5], referred to a committee in 1596,[6] and pursued its leisurely course to a final vote in 1601.[7] Here we may mention a few miscellaneous points which arose separately before the revision. In 1583 it was decided for the first time to abrogate the statute which made the president absolutely irremovable. It was held to be unjust and wholly unreasonable, and no doubt it was so, though if the need had ever arisen in all probability the Crown or the court of chancery could have found a way round it.[8] After the Michaelmas dinner in 1591 a confused debate started up about the grammatical interpretation of the statute about the election of the president, but by Christmas, even as it would seem after dinner, everyone was satisfied that the required majority was a majority of the elects who were present and not of their whole body.[9] At the following quarterly comitia it was decided that the office of an elect should be vacated if he departed from London and the seven-mile limit and kept house elsewhere for a year.[10] Lastly statutory regulations about dress were considered. Agreement was reached on scarlet for feast-days and solemn meetings, purple for other occasions, and on caps, either woollen or silk, or of other suitable material, for comitia, funerals, anatomical demonstrations and 'honourable' consultations. There was to be a half-crown fine

---

[1] 1 October 1582.
[2] 22 December 1586, 28 April 1587; *Statuta Vetera.*
[3] 30 September 1587, 28 February 1587/8, 6 April 1601 (the last date being during the revision of the statutes).
[4] 22 December 1582, 2 January 1582/3. On 7 April 1582 there was a violent scene between Dr. Nowell and his father-in-law (not a fellow) but the president reconciled them.
[5] 25 June: see also 28 April 1587 for the need of a tidy copy of all current statutes.
[6] 23 December.   [7] 25 June, 31 July, 30 September.
[8] See above, p. 61 n. 3.   [9] 30 September, 25 December.
[10] 20 March 1591.

for having no cap. But consideration of other articles of dress was adjourned.[1]

Like all other bodies in those days the College was sensitive about its privileges. These included exemption from taxation for warlike purposes, apparently derived from the exemption from watch and ward. In 1585 the College supported Dr. Forster in his claim that he was not liable to pay such a tax.[2] In 1587 letters were sent to the archbishop of Canterbury, the earl of Leicester, the lord treasurer and Sir Francis Walsingham to enlist their support in defending the privileges.[3] The occasion of these letters was the queen's intervention on behalf of John Banister,[4] but this was soon followed by another provocation, which led the College to send a deputation to Walsingham, an order from the lord mayor to furnish certain weapons and armour by a stated time. The Armada was fitting out in its Spanish harbours, but the secretary of state rebuked the lord mayor.[5] In 1595 there was an inconclusive discussion about sending some of the fellows with a letter to the lord treasurer asking for the College to be exempted from demands which had been made and such as should be made in the future for payments for military purposes.[6] After another four years the lord mayor and aldermen again demanded payments for warlike preparations. Groups of fellows waited on the lord treasurer, the lord admiral, the lord keeper and the secretary of state, and apparently won their point.

It may have been detrimental to its relations with the College that the City attempted to collect these taxes; but by this time there seem to have been few relations between the two and nothing resembling friendship. In 1583 the lord mayor and aldermen approached the College with three questions concerning precautions against the plague. First, what number of physicians did it consider would suffice to deal with the cases of plague only. Secondly, which out of all the physicians of the city were best suited to deal with this matter. Lastly, what annual stipend would the College recommend as becoming and proportionate to the physicians' dignity. The offer of a stipend marked a change of mind on the part of the City, which had maintained nine years before that those who could afford it should pay fees, and attendance on the poor should be paid for from the City stock. If the College wanted to do its utmost for the

---

[1] 25 February 1596/7, 21 May 1597.
[2] 31 January 1585, from the subsidy granted by 27 Eliz. c. 29.
[3] 22 December.   [4] See below p. 154.   [5] 19 March 1587.
[6] 26 June.

public health and was strong enough to put aside all other considerations, this was a notable opportunity; but its reply, in the summary that we have, seems to give a minimum of help. In so large a city as many as four physicians would be needed; every one of the fellows of the College was adequate and might safely be appointed; as to the stipend the College could lay down nothing definite, but hoped the City would be generous to those who undertook this dangerous duty.[1] The City did appoint physicians, but the situation probably got out of control. The eminent surgeon John Banister had a son-in-law, Stephen Bredwell, who seems to have practised physic without a licence before and throughout the epidemic. His wife caught the disease in the next serious epidemic in 1593. After it was over the College handled him civilly and admitted him to practice.[2]

Not long after the plague year 1583, Dr. Turner gave notice that he would retire from his office as physician to St. Bartholomew's, and the College wrote in good time to the governors, who were a board of aldermen, citizens and freemen of London. It recommended Dr. Wotton, and it recommended him not only for his merits but in his capacity as a fellow: 'And albeit so noble and well governed a cyty as this is, is rather to geve than to take example by any other what so ever; in all other honourable cities and townes in all Europe where the like hospitalls are maintained the phisition is alwaies provided out of the body and society and college of the phisitions of the same city'.[3] This bold generalization may have impressed the aldermen; they promised the appointment to Dr. Wotton, but Burghley, Walsingham and Sir Walter Mildmay intervened with a recommendation of Dr. Timothy Bright and he it was who received it. He was not a fellow of the College, and the aldermen may have thought that the College had twice manifested a desire to monopolize City medical appointments.

After Dr. Bright's appointment the College asserted its rights in what we might now regard as an unsportsmanlike spirit. Although

[1] 5 May 1583.

[2] F. P. Wilson, *The Plague in Shakespeare's London* (1927), p. 21 says that in 1583 the College appointed a 'certain and convenient' number of physicians for the counsel and cure of the sick, and that they were required to give their whole attention to the infected. This book gives an excellent general account of the part played by the privy council and the City in measures against the plague. For Bredwell or Bradwell see the book *Physick for the Sicknesse Commonly Called the Plague* (1636) by his son of the same name, pp. 30, 48 and Annals, 1585, 1594, 1599.

[3] Letter of 7 January 1584/5, printed from the Annals in Sir N. Moore, *History of St. Bartholomew's Hospital* (1918), where the whole incident is described on pp. 429-33. See also p. 320 below.

he is chiefly remembered as the inventor of the first modern system of shorthand, he was respected in his day as a medical author; he taught in Cambridge, and he was closely associated with Burghley, the chancellor of that university, whose medical knowledge he praised. But he had no licence to practice except a Cambridge licence, and that did not extend to St. Bartholomew's in its London suburb. The College summoned him, perhaps with the intention of politely admitting him to practise there. When he repeatedly ignored the summons it committed him to the Fleet Prison. We do not know whether he was actually incarcerated, and if so for how long, but most likely he never went.[1]

In its everyday business of licensing the College seems to have concerned itself during this period wholly or almost wholly with the London area and scarcely at all with the provinces. No more emissaries went out and no more letters to sheriffs and mayors. Licences for the provinces only were granted by the president and three elects[2]; but the right of the universities to license for provincial practice was not disputed. Whether the College also recognized that the bishops had such a right it is impossible to say at present because there seems to be no evidence that any of them tried to exercise it during these years. On one occasion, however, a certain Robert Tanner was accused of practising in London and produced a licence with the seal of the archbishop of Canterbury. He said he had obtained it through Mr. Hartwell, that is Abraham Hartwell who was secretary to Whitgift, and that he had been examined and admitted by Mr. Aubrey, that is William Aubrey, the vicar general.[3] The College judged him to be wholly illiterate, as well as ignorant and arrogant, and forbade him to practise. In London and for the surrounding seven miles it did indeed claim to be the sole licensing authority. Dr. William Butler of Cambridge was the best-known provincial doctor of his day,[4] but he did not dare to visit his patients when they were in London until the great Burghley had persuaded the College to overlook the trespass.[5] This claim of the College was

---

[1] 10 November 1587; Sir Geoffrey Keynes, *Dr. Timothie Bright* (1961).

[2] 30 September 1585 for the requirement of fees.

[3] Aubrey, i. 55. Leonard Po also had an archbishop's licence: R. R. James, 'Licences to Practise Medicine and Surgery issued by the Archbishops of Canterbury, 1580–1775' in *Janus*, xli (1936), 97 ff.

[4] See *Dictionary of National Biography*. For an example of his country house practice at a distance from Cambridge see the exciting story in Joan Wake, *The Brudenells of Deane* (1953), pp. 78–80.

[5] Burghley's letter of 13 February 1592/3 and the reply of 2 July 1593, both in the Annals.

upheld by the judges early in the next reign.[1] It was limited to the London area: this must be the meaning of the phrase 'within the limits of our privileges'.[2] Freedom was accorded outside it to some who were forbidden to practise in London.[3]

Licences were sometimes conditional: they might be limited to the treatment of certain specified diseases, or the licentiate might be obliged to call in a fellow for the more serious cases. They were never limited in duration. The College had no staff to administer any system of renewing the licences from time to time, but it learnt from disagreeable experience in the case of Leonard Po that even a conditional licence might be useful to an offender after it had been forfeited. An important change was therefore made in a new statute of 1596. In future everyone admitted to the College or to practice was to give his bond for £100 that if for any just cause he were expelled by the president, consiliarii, censors and a majority of the fellows in town at the time he would surrender his sealed licence without delay and refrain from practice within the limits of the privileges of the College.[4] This, however, was not strict enough. In 1599/1600 it was resolved that in the future neither a candidate nor a licentiate should receive any licensing document: the names of candidates should be entered in the Annals and those of licentiates in a book in the College.[5]

The licentiates had to pay an annual fee to the College, which some of them found a hardship,[6] and they had to attend meetings and anatomy lessons which few of them enjoyed; but their privilege was valuable. On occasion some magnate like Essex would support an applicant for it.[7] The College seems to have thought in 1595 that the number of licentiates was growing too large[8] but we do not know in what way it could be excessive, and the sentence may have some other meaning. On the whole the licentiates gave very little trouble.

The work of licensing could not be kept altogether distinct from that of censuring and punishing those who could not be approved. The same work *examinare* was used for the testing of applicants for licences or for fellowship and for the questioning of those who were

---

[1] See below p. 210.   [2] Statute of 5 April 1596.
[3] John Not, 1586; James Mossan, 1592/3.   [4] Statute of 5 April 1596.
[5] 17 March. This was contrary to the charter of Henry VIII and was not included in the revised statutes of 1601.
[6] In the earlier years £8 seems to have been usual and in the later 40s., but there was no fixed tariff.
[7] His letter of 17 April 1584 in the Annals.   [8] April 1595, *s.n.* Twine.

accused of offences. It is not always clear which kind of examination was intended, and certainly the latter sometimes glided over pleasingly into the former. Nine men who were charged with illicit practice were sooner or later allowed to continue unhindered. Three of them were foreigners who probably worked mainly among their fellow-exiles. Guillaume de Laune was a Huguenot refugee preacher, a doctor of divinity and a man of good character but with no appointment to any church. He had studied medicine in Paris and Montpellier, apparently from 1558 or thereabouts. From 1582 to 1593 the College often had to consider what fees he could be reasonably expected to pay.[1] Daniel Celerius was a German. He started badly by incurring a fine for unlicensed practice and by rudeness to Dr. Doylie; but the earl of Huntingdon wrote a letter for him and he was licensed.[2] Raphael Thoreus or Thorey was a Dutchman and a Leiden doctor. In 1593 he unwisely treated an Englishman who died, and he was threatened with prison. Three years later he was charged again but in the end he was licensed and practised very successfully. There were two Germans, a father and son, whose story perhaps illustrates the ill-defined position of the aliens. From 1581 to 1587 Godfrey Mossanus was fined three times for illicit and ignorant practice and so forth.[3] In 1592 his twenty-eight year old son applied as a doctor of Cologne for a licence for London. He was put back for four years to read Galen and to practise in his provinces.[4]

The five Englishmen who obtained their licences after appearing as defendants were decent men who gave way either to impatience or to conceit. Peter Turner, a Cambridge graduate and a Heidelberg doctor, was the son of that 'medical dean of Wells' who was by far the most distinguished English botanist of his time. Christopher Atkinson had his doctor's degree from Oxford. Stephen Bredwell was not a graduate but he was not unlearned and he had special claims.[5] Thomas Rawlins of Clare College occasionally gave trouble

---

[1] For two others of his name in the next generation, an eminent apothecary and a fellow of the College see Munk.

[2] His unlicensed practice began in 1580; he was excused further payments in 1597.

[3] He may be identical with 'one Moses' who is said to have been fined £20 in 1580/1 by Goodall, p. 316: Goodall gives the regnal year and may have made a small mistake in it.

[4] 'in iis locis in quibus liberum est illi practicare'. His name Jacobus Mossanus Vesius may conceivably be translated James Mossan of Wesel. He published an English translation of Christoph Wirtzung (Wirsung) *Praxis Medicinae Universalis* (1598), of which the original is in German.

[5] In 1585 he was studying medicine and admitted that he had occasionally attended his father-in-law's patients: Annals, 27 November. See above, p. 139.

after gaining his licence, not only professionally but on the score of religion[1]; but ultimately he became a fellow. The most curious case was that of Richard Palmer. When he was a Cambridge master of arts of several years standing he admitted that he had practised in London for about six months without a licence.[2] He lived to be not merely a fellow but president.

What the College did was to sort out the London healers into three classes, those whom it received as fellows, candidates or licentiates, those whom it connived at, and those whom it tried to inhibit. The second class seems to have been very small. Simon Balsamus of Milan confessed to practising for a living, but he was allowed to go because he was a religious refugee.[3] One Willis, a bachelor of arts, protested that he only treated his friends and without charging them fees. He was thought to have practised for not a few years but he made a fair show when he was examined and nothing further happened.[4] A few months later, however, the College enforced its rules against a Cambridge graduate who had practised for years after a fashion but apparently showed less knowledge. It was obdurate even after he took his doctor's degree.[5] Twice it gave way to pressure. Richard Scott was scarcely able to answer anything and was mulcted in a small fine, but on the petition of unnamed friends of high rank it was agreed to tolerate him if he paid £3 a year.[6] Bartholomew Chappell was fined for illicit practice but, after producing letters from Lords Burghley, Chandos and Hungerford he was accorded an examination, in which he failed. For the sake of Burghley it was decided to tolerate him on condition that he always called in one of the fellows to his cases; but he offended again, was forgiven after an appeal from the countess of Warwick, and finally had to be treated as a mere offender.[7]

Except for these concessions to expediency the College seems to have kept conscientiously to a line between severity and indulgence. It was importuned by powerful friends of irregular practitioners, but it very seldom failed to be firm. Only a few of the outsiders understood the point of view of the College. One of them was Sir Robert Cecil, Burghley's son, who had perhaps learnt from bitter experience.

---

[1] See the Annals for 31 July 1601 and 18 April 1602 and the letter of Archbishop Abbot printed in Munk, i. 121 n.
[2] 30 March 1593/4.   [3] 30 April 1602.   [4] 6 August 1596.
[5] Ethelbert Spencer: 3 December 1596, 2 April 1599.
[6] 30 January 1589/90, 25 September 1590.
[7] April–November 1595; 6 August, 14 October 1596.

When the College thought he would stand up for an impostor, Cecil gave his assurance that although he had employed her in the past, he made no objection to any steps they might take against her.[1] Alderman Sir Lionel Duckett begged off an offender on condition that he should submit to any penalty imposed by the College if he again practised illegally.[2] The celebrated Dr. Dee persuaded the College to overlook the past errors of a certain Chomley, a chemical distiller; but Chomley was bound over for the future.[3] When John Harris, a Norman, totally ignorant of medicine, was imprisoned after practising in England for twenty-two years, the French Ambassador undertook that he should never do so again.[4]

On the other hand there were more than a dozen defendants who received some support or protection from high quarters. The most alarming intervention was that of the queen herself, by whose orders Sir Francis Walsingham, as secretary of state, wrote to recommend a poor woman named Margaret Kennix, a foreigner of Sea Coal Lane, who had a special knowledge of simples for the cure of diseases and wounds, and maintained her disabled husband and family by practice, especially among the poor. In a second letter Walsingham demanded the removal of the prohibition which the College had imposed on her. He hinted that the College had done as much for the queen's predecessors and he threatened that if they disobeyed now they might procure more inconveniences to themselves than perhaps they would be willing should fall out. The College sent a deputation with an absolutely unyielding reply.[5]

Some years elapsed before the secretary on his own authority courteously, if rather briefly, asked for the release from the Counter in Wood Street of John Not, from whose treatment he himself had received good. This Not had been required to give sureties and the College now told Walsingham that it would be satisfied with his own small bond. They mentioned with aversion that he claimed only to have treated for the pox. His patient Walsingham gave him no further protection, but he continued to be troublesome, and the secretary found another *protégé*.[6]

---

[1] 17 September 1602. This notorious lady, Mrs. Woodhouse, underwent an examination on 3 July 1596, displaying wonderful ignorance but claiming to have cured many bewitched persons.
[2] 23 December 1583.   [3] 1594.
[4] 18 March 1685/6, 20 July 1586.   [5] Letters of December 1581 in Annals.
[6] 5 and 12 February 1584/5, 17 and 30 September 1586 and letter of 2 October, 10 November and 1 December 1587: the new man was Paul Buck, for whom see below, p. 146.

It would be tedious to relate all the meddlings of Lord Hunsdon, the queen's cousin, and of his son who succeeded him as lord chamberlain, of Essex, Derby, Herbert and lesser lords and gentlemen. They added to the difficulties of a task which was repellent enough without them. Altogether the College handled over a hundred cases of illicit practice from 1572 to 1603. The easiest were disposed of at a single hearing; the worst dragged on for years. On 28 January 1582, in the active period after Marbeck became registrar, the College discussed what methods it could devise for driving the empirics out of practice, and it decided to retain William Fleetwood, the recorder of London, as its adviser, giving him an annuity of £3 for life. The arrangement was concluded in an exchange of elegant Latin compliments. Although Fleetwood might well have to deal with College business in his capacity as a judge, this does not seem to have been any part of his motive or theirs: he was *ex officio* also the legal adviser of the City. The advice which he gave to the College seems to have proved satisfactory, for the same arrangement was continued in 1602 with his successor, afterwards Sir John Croke.[1] Fleetwood may have approved the regular procedure by which the College began with an admonition and went on first to lighter and then to heavier fines and bonds, with imprisonment as an auxiliary. Sir John Popham commended it from the bench.[2] It seems to have been wise in itself and wisely applied, but ten years after Fleetwood's appointment there was need for another general discussion about the empirics ending in an unanimous resolution to proceed against them by prosecution.

They conformed to the permanent types. There were nineteen women. Perhaps the most dangerous was Thomasina Scarlet who often administered antimony.[3] She was twice committed to prison. There were several other women whose ministrations appeared to be lethal. Most of them were indigent; they were apt to take payment in kind; some of them argued and one absconded. They were not treated harshly. Among the men there were a few misguided persons of education and even of distinction. Henry Holland was the

---

[1] In a case noted on 3 November 1586 Fleetwood was consulted along with two other counsel, an attorney named Thomas Antropos being employed; in one noted on 8 May 1590 with one of the same two counsel, namely Mr. Daniel, who may very well be the Mr. Danyell, serjeant at law, who received an annual retaining fee of 40s. from St. Bartholomew's Hospital in 1593/4 and succeeding years: Sir Norman Moore, *History of St. Bartholomew's Hospital* (1918), p. 225.

[2] See below, p. 156.

[3] There are entries relating to her in 1588, 1593 and 1598.

vicar of a City parish, an author, but too anxious to help his friends.[1]
Simon Forman was the leading astrologer, but he had read only
one book on physic, Cockis, in English.[2] In the lower ranks also
there were a few busybodies, and a few part-time performers such
as a silk-weaver, a choirman of St. Paul's, a brush maker, a dyer,
a tallow-chandler and a grocer who killed his man.[3] But there was
a hard core of pretentious empirics. Roger Powell put up bragging
advertisements on the walls and professed to be backed by various
eminent people.[4] Paul Fairfax produced what appears to have been
a bogus degree-certificate from Frankfort.[5]

Three men soared like falcons above these crows and magpies.
Francis Anthony's career was only beginning: we may leave him to
a later chapter.[6] Paul Buck was a goldsmith, an irrepressible talker
who said he had read Paracelsus and Erasmus. He was imprisoned
in 1589. The Lord Mayor let him out of the Wood Street Counter and
the censors were instructed to take legal action against the gaoler.
Buck refused to renounce his practice and was sent back to gaol.
Walsingham came to the rescue with a letter, but the College was
unmoved. A pause of two years ensued before Buck's next appearance, and not long afterwards the lord admiral moved up in support. Essex joined him. In 1596 Buck was fined £5; but in 1599 it
was necessary to fine him £3 more.[7] He did not appear before the
censors for the last time until 1612.[8]

Even more slippery and far more successful was Leonard Po,
deacon, *Lincolniensis*. He began in the same year as Buck and he
began better. He was found on examination to be wholly unlearned
and without knowledge of any branch of medicine, but Essex stood
by him from the start, and in 1592, having disobeyed all injunctions,
he put in a letter signed by seven members of the privy council.
The College began to lose its unanimity. In 1594 Po was examined
again, with pitiable results: he owned to knowing no Latin and no
Greek; but Essex wrote again and the president, Dr. Giffard,
spoke up for Po, though in vain. At last it was agreed to let him
treat certain specified diseases on condition of calling in a fellow for

---

[1] 1598. The parish was St. Bride's, Fleet Street: G. Hennesy, *Novum Repertorium
Ecclesiasticum Parochiale Londiniense* (1898), p. 12.
[2] These two are both noticed in the *Dictionary of National Biography*.
[3] Thomas Burnet, 17 July 1590.   [4] 3 September 1591, 10 January 1595.
[5] 30 September, 6 and 23 December 1588.   [6] See below, 201.
[7] 6 June 1589 to 7 March 1599—thirteen entries. 18 December 1589—25 June 1601—
more than twice as many.
[8] See below, p. 234.

all others and paying £4 a year. Two years later he had broken his undertaking. The treasurer set the law in motion[1]; but on 8 May 1598 things took a fresh turn. Po was expected to appear, but he was suffering from *morbus anginosus* and could not come. Nineteen of the College attended: they evidently expected something important. They agreed to call off the legal proceedings entirely and to refer the whole final adjudication (*moderatio*) of this controversy to a strong committee of four, Dr. Forster, Dr. Gilbert, Dr. Langton, and Dr. Paddy. If these four failed to agree, Dr. Smith of Cambridge was to decide between them. At the quarterly comitia in June sixteen were present.[2] Leonard Po presented himself and it was decided to postpone consideration of his fine of £20 and his imprisonment to the usual time and place on the following Friday. On the Friday there was a discussion *pro* and *con*. Nothing was decided by vote of the College, but the censors passed a sentence on Po which was written down in English by Dr. Paddy: for *pessima praxis*, which had resulted in the death of one Scull by vomiting and scouring, he was condemned to lie in the Counter in Wood Street at the pleasure of the president and censors. His licence was revoked. Yet 'upon some honourable meanes made to Mr. President' they would accept good behaviour on his part and a vote of the majority of the College as grounds for the renewal of the licence and remission of the imprisonment. There was another long discussion in comitia in November. Po had shown his old letter of protection from lords of the council to the several keepers of prisons, and he was appearing publicly in the streets. The College decided to ask the *nobilium senatus* (not the house of lords but the privy council) to allow them to act against Po notwithstanding these letters. They moved carefully. Three fellows prepared alternative drafts of the petition, and five were chosen to present it. Separate deputations of two were charged with interviewing six individual councillors beforehand.[3]

---

[1] An undated letter of Po to an unnamed nobleman asking his leave to sue Dr. Moundeford, the treasurer, for slander appears to belong to this stage of the story: *Historical MSS. Commission, Salisbury Papers*, xiv (1923), 94.

[2] The absentees were Dr. Smith and two other royal physicians, Dr. Marbeck, who had leave of absence, Dr. Smith of Oxford, five who were in the country (including Dr. Mouffet) and four others of whom Dr. Forster was one.

[3] The president, Dr. Baronsdale, was to go with Dr. Smith of Oxford to Lord Buckhurst; Dr. Browne and Dr. Paddy to Essex; Dr. Marbeck and Dr. Doylie to the admiral; Dr. Wilkinson and Dr. Moundeford to Archbishop Whitgift; Dr. Gilbert and again Dr. Doylie to Sir Robert Cecil, secretary of state; Dr. Nowell and Dr. Atkins to Lord Fortescue.

The petition was read at the council board and Po was heard in person. His letter of protection was openly obliterated and rescinded, but the controversy between Po and the college was committed for decision to seven commissioners.[1] There were the three royal physicians, Dr. Smith, Dr. Browne and Dr. James, the two clerks of the council, Thomas Smith and William Waad, and two men of law, Herbert, master of requests, and Francis Bacon, queen's counsel. Bacon had published his book of essays in the previous year, and one of them was about regimen of health. The affairs of the College now came under his eye, that 'delicate, lively hazel eie' of which William Harvey said enigmatically that it was like the eye of a viper.[2] It was not the last time that Bacon passed judgment on the physicians.

Dr. Smith brought the written decision of the commissioners to the College, and the College accepted it without dissent. Po was to acknowledge his offences and the justice of the punishments inflicted on him by the College. He was to pay a penalty of five marks, to enter into a bond of £100 for his future good and honest carriage. He was to surrender his licence, but on his fulfilling the aforesaid conditions, it was at once to be restored.

Here was Leonard Po in licensed practice again though without his safe-conduct. Two whole years went by before Dr. Bright brought a new charge of malpractice against him, and nothing seems to have come of it; but in June 1601 he was fined £5 for malpractice in one of his fatal cases. There was no Essex now to appeal to: his career had ended on Tower Hill, but Po could always make friends among the aristocracy, and to such purpose that in the end, as we shall see, he was admitted a fellow of the College.

At the end of Queen Elizabeth's reign there was evidently no hope of extinguishing illicit practice in London. It was impossible for the few recognized physicians to ensure that no one else in that swarming and disease ridden city should ever prescribe a potion or a clyster. That was one of those laws which define an ideal, not an attainable aim. At the practical level charlatans who could rely on powerful backing could snap their fingers at the College, but, except for them, it had gone some considerable way towards

---

[1] The letter appointing the commissioners does not give them that name. It is printed in *Acts of the Privy Council*, new ser. xxix, 1598–9 (1905), p. 352. It adds some details to the account in the Annals, for instance, that Po took exception to some of the physicians who accused him.

[2] J. Aubrey, *Brief Lives* (1898), i. 72.

establishing the sort of equilibrium that normally exists in civilized countries between the police and the criminal elements. Crime is not abolished; sometimes it gets out of hand, but on the whole it is kept within bounds and away from sight. This is not a reproach to the College. Although no close comparison can be made, there is no reason to believe that it had thus far been less successful than the authorities, whatever they were, which were entrusted with the same function in other European countries. The physicians, however, were not the only people lawfully concerned with healing, and their relations with the surgeons and the apothecaries were more important to the public than their relations with the quacks.

IX: SURGEONS, APOTHECARIES
AND SCEPTICS, 1572–1603

FOR the art of surgery the College had a genuine concern. Its fellows continued to lecture at the Barber-Surgeons' Hall and to take turns, or occasionally to be excused from taking their turns, at the winter dissections in Knightrider Street. In February 1581/2 the College accepted a gift of £40 a year jointly offered by Lord Lumley and its own fellow Richard Caldwell for the stipend of a lecturer on surgery.[1] Caldwell had been president in 1570–1; he was approaching seventy years of age and he was a landowner in his native county of Staffordshire. The revenue was to come from a rent-charge on his lands and on those of Lord Lumley. He was personally interested in anatomical teaching. Several years earlier he had offered a smaller benefaction, £10 a year, as an endowment for an anatomical lecturer at Barber-Surgeons' Hall. For reasons unknown this offer was not taken up.[2] He translated the text which accompanied the anatomical tables of the Florentine 'Horatio More', published in London in 1585, after Dr. Caldwell's death, and used as a textbook by the Barber-Surgeons.[3] Lumley was a rich and highly-connected nobleman, the owner of a famous library. There is nothing to show how he was acquainted with Dr. Caldwell or why he joined in this project; but both of them had been suspected of complicity in catholic political activities.[4] The College had begun the year with a balance of £108. 18s. 6d. in hand besides a considerably smaller sum owing to it. It immediately decided to add to its building so as to accommodate the lectures worthily and to devote £100 to the purpose. In March 1583/4 it decided, apparently enlarging its plans[5] to build a suitably capacious theatre, with a *cathedra*, for dissections.

[1] The amount, £40, is not given in the Annals, but in Baldwin Hamey's list of benefactors in Brit. Mus. MS. Sloane 3914, fos. 62v–63. For the reluctance of Caldwell's son to pay his share see the Annals for 1590, 1593.

[2] South, p. 143, Minute of 1579.

[3] South, p. 184 : 500 copies were given by the son or nephew of Dr. Caldwell, who edited the book and in his preface of 1585 expressed his regret that the Barber-Surgeons neglected the Lumleian lectures. [4] See above, c. viii, p. 129.

[5] It seems from the entry of 22 November 1582 that building was already in progress then, and by 14 November 1583 Dr. Caldwell had received £120 from the College and expended £153 on the buildings.

The stipend of the lecturer was substantial, double that of the physician at St. Bartholomew's Hospital and the first lecturer, Dr. Richard Forster, was an able man who afterwards rose to be president. He lectured every Wednesday and Friday from ten to eleven, for three quarters of an hour in Latin and a quarter in English, and he covered the whole of anatomy in a six-year course. He was not appreciated as he deserved.[1] On 17 and 23 July 1584, after well-grounded complaints of the fewness of those who heard the lectures, it was decided that all candidates, all licentiates and, for the first year after their admission, all fellows admitted in the future must attend diligently. The fine for absence was 1s., rising to 2s. 6d. if not paid within a week; but in each term it was permissible to be absent four times. The candidates could hope for promotion, and the fellows for release after a year, but the rule seems hard on the licentiates who were apparently bound to attend for life or to pay, and imperfect in not requiring the fellows and candidates to hear the full course. As early as 27 November 1585 the rule had to be reaffirmed, and it was added that if anyone contumaciously refused to pay the fine he was to be for ever incapable of becoming a fellow. A month later this statute was read out, but only two of the candidates and one licentiate were there to listen.[2] In the spring the College proceeded to a stronger measure. Ostensibly it was taken to improve the attendance at the lectures, but it seems not impossible that there may have been a further motive. No fellow or candidate or licentiate was to summon or admit any surgeon for blood-letting, scarification or any other surgical business unless that surgeon had frequented the lectures as often as his business permitted. It is true that the last words offer a wide loophole; but this rule, if seriously enforced, might have given the College a degree of control over surgical education and practice. Whether it had any effect or not, the old problem was still unsolved in 1600 when it was proposed[3] that the candidates and licentiates, and the newly-elected fellows, in their first two years, should present themselves at the College in each of the four terms of the year to give an account of their past attendance and of their intentions for the future. In the general revision of the statutes in 1601 compulsory attendance was retained but made less burdensome.

[1] R. Holinshed, *Chronicle* (1587), iii, 1349.
[2] Dr. Turner, Dr. Jacob and John Martin.
[3] 'unanimi consensu sic statutum et conclusum est pro prima vice', 26 June 1600, but no further entry.

In 1602 at the Christmas comitia Dr. Forster, now president of the College, resigned the praelectorship and the College submitted three names from which Lord Lumley was to choose his successor. All three were 'sufficient'—Dr. Dun, Dr. Davies and Dr. John Giffard—so Lord Lumley chose the one whose sufficiency was best known to him, Dr. Dun, who was also the senior. Sad to say in the following April when the statutes were read before the licentiates only three of them attended, one Englishman, one Frenchman and one Dutchman.[1] The laxity in attending the anatomical lectures was again reproved, and at an adjourned discussion in April the beadle was given a list of the defaulters and told to collect their fines. However good the Lumleian lectures were in the reign of Queen Elizabeth the attempt to compel attendance failed.

More than twenty surgeons were accused of encroaching on medical ground, perhaps as many as twenty-six, and they were difficult to deal with. There were three who seem not to have appeared for examination.[2] There were eight who confessed to administering internal medicines, though three of them said that they had acted on the advice of some physician. One of these eight was Peter Chamberlen, of Huguenot refugee origin and already eminent in the specialism which his family were long to adorn, that of the *accoucheur*. He had prescribed a diet for the *morbus gallicus*, but like those others whose behaviour was submissive he was treated leniently.[3] Three, however, although they confessed, behaved by no means meekly. John Lumken owned to having treated dropsy, gout and other serious diseases over a long period of time. A very severe letter about him was sent by a gentleman named Arthur Gorge, who was probably the sea-captain, author and public man afterwards Sir Arthur Gorges. Lumken said he would produce an equally strong letter in his favour from the same writer, and that is the end of this incident, though it is by no means the last we hear of Lumken.[4] Edward Owen was more troublesome. In 1590 he confessed to giving the usual purgatives, alleging that a physician had prescribed them. Six years later he was lurking in obscure places and failing to obey summonses for new offences. After a threat of imprisonment he promised to pay the usual first

---

[1] Rawlins, Delaune, Thoreus.

[2] Edward Field, 1595; Petrus (Piers), 1599; Browne, 1602.

[3] Christopher Beauter or Beawter, 1589; Thorne, 1589/90; Owen, 1590, perhaps the same as Edward Owen for whom see below, p. 152 Peter Chamberlen, 1600; Bayley, 1602.   [4] 1589. See below, p. 195.

fine of 40s., but in 1598 and 1601 there were serious complaints against him and at last, when he once more failed to answer a summons, it was decided to make an extreme and perhaps an unwarranted use of the rights of the College by arresting and interrogating his servant.[1]

Owen, although a surgeon, comported himself like an ordinary quack, taking advantage no doubt of the opportunities which his profession opened to him, and something of the same sort may be true of eight other surgeons, five of whom were imprisoned until they paid their fines for illegal practice.[2] Their medicines were much the same as those of the erring apothecaries, and some of them practised uroscopy. Some were accused by fellows of the College. One seems to have been specially dangerous. In 1587 Peter Piers, surgeon, of the county of Kent denied that he had practised unlawfully. It was alleged that eight years earlier he had given to Mr. Laborn, a surgeon, a pill in the proportion of 3 grains of antimony, 30 grains of turbith simple, and one and a half of mercury sublimate; that he had written a description of it with his own hand for Mr. Laborn's book; that he had administered it frequently to patients, and that, according to the evidence of witnesses, many had died of it. Here was a novel issue. For the first time there was a charge relating to antimony, highly prized by the alchemists as a remedy, condemned in 1566 by the Paris faculty as a poison. Piers denied everything and was committed to prison until he should clear himself by the testimony of those to whom he had administered the pill. Unfortunately that is the end of this chapter in the story of Peter Piers. He is not heard of again until 1600, when he was convicted of malpractice, fined £5 and committed to the Counter in Wood Street with another charge, arising from a grave matter, still to answer.[3] But two points in the fragmentary chapter can be elucidated. Mr. Laborn's book was apparently some book which he kept for recording prescriptions; there is no reason to suppose that this allusion has anything to do with publication in a printed book. The effect of the pill cannot be estimated precisely, since it seems uncertain whether pure antimony is meant, but the action of the College was justified.

[1] 17 August 1602.
[2] John Gyle, 1582; Sebastian Leager, 1583 perhaps a surgeon since he was also accused of *mala praxis*; Peter Piers, 1587; John Grove, 1595; Jinkinson, 1596; Joseph Smart, 1596; Johnson, 1601/2; Richard Gyle, 1602.
[3] The case of Mr. Luke, for which see p. 155 below. On this occasion Piers is described as of Ratlief, 'Petrus de Ratley'.

There were surgeons who shamelessly flouted the jurisdiction of the College. In 1587 John Banister came back from sea-service and settled in London. Earlier he had practised both surgery and physic in Nottingham and no doubt practised both now. He was summoned and said that he could not come because he had the queen's orders to apply himself to curing Mr. Lidcot.[1] The College had to put up with this treatment from a leader of his craft. In the next year it sent the beadle to summon a much less conspicuous surgeon, who answered that he had to be off to the queen's court and had no time to spare, also that 'he marvailed much how the president dirst be so sawcie as to send for him to the College'. On 15 February 1593/4 the College had before it a letter from the queen asking that Banister should be admitted to practise physic. It agreed unanimously, on condition that in any serious and dangerous disease he should associate some fellow of the College with himself in the case.[2] The cumulative effect of the individual cases led the College in 1595 to address a warning, not quite correctly, to the master, warden, assistants and the residue of the Company of Surgeons of London. After stating the powers and duties of the College in relation to the law this declared that among offenders against it there had been no few of that Company, but that for the most part the College had forborne either to punish or to molest them. Its lenity had led to unendurable inconveniences. It therefore requested the surgeons to see to it that such offences should cease. If they failed to show good will, the College would defend its privileges and deal with particular offenders according to the law and its own ordinance.[3]

The Elizabethan surgeons were a mixed collection, but they had among them such men as Banister and his friend Clowes, Gale and Read who had a right to resent any imputation on their professional spirit. Whether they welcomed this letter we do not know, but it seems to have been futile. It was not long before a surgeon, confessing that he had given many potions to Alderman Taylor, maintained that he did it in circumstances (*in casu*) pertaining to surgery. He spoke confidently and was fined £5.[4] In 1597–8 the Barber Surgeons' Company promoted a Bill in parliament which seems to

---

[1] I have failed to identify Dominus Lidcot.
[2] Surgeons were similarly often obliged to call in an officer of the Barber Surgeons' Company in dangerous cases.
[3] The full text is in the Annals under date 7 November 1595.
[4] Edmund Messenger, 1596/7.

have included a provision for the giving of internal remedies in certain cases. It was not passed.[1] In 1598 Dr. Paddy, not yet a royal physician or a knight, was fined £4 for carrying out a public dissection in the Barber Surgeons' Hall without leave from the president. The College remitted half the fine. Not until the last year of Queen Elizabeth did the College once more triumph over the surgeons as signally as it had done under Dr. Caius.

This success resulted from a little drama with two villains whom chance brought together, Simon Read and Roger Jinkins or Jenkins. Simon Read seems to have been an ignorant charlatan. In 1601 he was said to have given medicine to Lady Shelley and a Mrs. Cuckston of Westminster. Examined by the censors he declined to answer in Latin, and when allowed to give instead a written account of any one disease, he handed in a ludicrously ignorant answer. He was forbidden to practise, and on the decision of the censors was fined £5 and sent to prison. Thereupon Lady Howard wrote a letter on his behalf and it was decided to let him off entirely if he paid back the fees he had extorted and gave a bond for his future good behaviour. Eight months later, in February 1602, he was up again and confessed that he had practised in London for six years and had no other means of livelihood. Back he went to prison, with a fine of £20. There he found Jinkins, against whom proceedings had been initiated in the previous November.[2]

Jinkins was a surgeon, and, as he is referred to as Jinkinson and Jenkinson it is safe to identify him as the Jinkinson who was already a hardened offender. On three occasions spread over the years 1596–99 he had been convicted of the usual offences; he had been fined and threatened with prison. In 1600 a Mr. Luke died in the house of the worthy apothecary William Besse. His widow and her uncle Mr. Montague, who acted as her attorney, petitioned the College to enquire fully into the case. It examined all those who had been concerned, that is, besides Besse, the surgeons Bayley and Piers whom we have already encountered and three others, Martin, Fenton and Jinkins. These three had made a post-mortem examination, from which they concluded that Mr. Luke's death was due not to the malignity of any medicine but to a bad habit of body and a violent motion of nature. Besse and Bayley were each fined 40s.

---

[1] South and Power pp. 196–200. A Bill there mentioned as promoted in 1588 may have been of a similar character.
[2] 'Decretum est in ius eum vocare': 6 November 1601.

for their temerity in prescribing purgatives and emetics without the advice of a physician. Although Jinkins had informed against Besse after the post mortem, he was in trouble again in 1601 and confessed to prescribing purgatives for his surgical patients. Before he was sent to prison he boasted that he knew how to give medical treatment when it was needed.

Read and Jinkins were not content to languish in prison. They applied for a writ *Corpus cum Causa*, one of the recognized forms of the writ of *Habeas Corpus*, and it was granted by Sir John Popham, lord chief justice of the queen's bench. On 8 April 1602 they appeared in court with their counsel, Mr. Harris, and the College was represented by three of the censors. The judge questioned Jinkins and drew from him the claim that his practice had not been illicit because he was a surgeon and in surgery the use of internal medicines was often necessary. In such an emergency, said the judge, a physician should be called in and the surgeon might not play the physician. No surgeon as a surgeon might practise physic, no, not for any disease, though it were the great pox.[1] Harris contended that the College had no power to imprison but only to prosecute before other judges. Popham rebuked him and affirmed that the College had that power. Jinkins complained that he had been too heavily fined for his few offences and those done by the advice of others. The book of the Annals was produced, with its record of his previous convictions, and again the judge held that the College had acted justly. He added an excellent piece of advice: every prescription of a physician should be dated with the day and month and should bear the name of the patient for whom it was intended.

The College thanked the judge in an enthusiastic letter, and pressed on with its campaign. It had not indeed heard the last of the two villains. At the request of Popham himself, the reason for which does not appear, they remitted one-third of Jinkins's fine. New evidence against him was proferred in the following September, but he came to no harm.[2] Read was even luckier. The bishop of London had it in his power to grant him a licence for surgery; but Popham had explicitly said that none but the College could do so in London for medicine, so the bishop wrote a letter in favour of Read in consequence of which he was released from prison in May

[1] This disease was treated by surgeons because it had external symptoms.
[2] 23 September 1602.

1602, with his fine excused.[1] In the first three months of 1603, however, the College struck at three more surgeons. John Actour confessed but thought he was allowed to give medicines because he was a surgeon. Although Mr. Spencer a serjeant-at-arms interceded for him, he was fined and sent back to prison.[2] James Henley said that he had given his turbith pills to more than fifty people without endangering their lives and in any case that he had done no more than all surgeons did; he went to Newgate.[3] Was Ralph Barret more wily or more in the right? He admitted that he had given a purgative tablet for the pox, but he said that the surgeons' regulations which were publicly read at their meetings stated that without calling for the advice of a physician they might with impunity give medicine for that disease and the plague.[4] He was admonished as a first offender.

In fifteen to twenty cases apothecaries were accused. Two or three denied the charge of illicit practice, and suffered nothing more than a warning.[5] Four others admitted that they had given purgatives or other medicines, but got off equally lightly by maintaining that they had acted on the advice or prescriptions of physicians. One of them had treated Mr. Spilman of Lincoln's Inn, surely the eminent antiquary afterwards Sir Henry Spelman.[6] Another who had paid a fine of 40s. for illicit practice two years before, had attended Mr. Pett of Limehouse, presumably Peter Pett of the dynasty of shipwrights.[7] A similar defence was put up in vain by another apothecary who admitted administering a clyster, a bolus and pills: he was fined 20s. but found sureties and so avoided imprisonment.[8] Three confessed to illicit practice, of whom two were fined and one warned.[9] One was accused of charging £3 for useless medicine, but does not appear to have been summoned[10]; one appeared to face a charge which is not stated, but he removed himself without leave.[11] Only four of the charges were serious. In 1596 an apothecary was accused of extortion and of malpractice ending in the death of his patient;

[1] 5 May 1602.   [2] 31 January 1602/3.
[3] 21 January 1602/3.   [4] 18 March 1602/3.
[5] James Tatlock, 1589/90; Owen Jones, accused by the licentiate Mr. Bredwell in 1600/1, whom I guess to have been an apothecary; Lunx of Southwark warned in 1601 by the censors.   [6] Smith, 1601.
[7] Edward Barloe, 1585 and 1587; Edmund Phillips, 1588. William Clapham, 1599.
[8] John Chekley, who seems to be the same as William Chetley, 1595.
[9] Roger Gwin, 1584; Antley, 1595; John Parker, 1599.
[10] Denis Purcot, 1589.   [11] Trout, 1601.

but as there is no further record we must conclude that he was innocent.[1] Of the three convicted of serious offences one was involved as an underling in the fatal case of Mr. Luke where the chief blame lay on the persistent wrong-doer Jinkins.[2] Of the others, the only two apothecaries who earned a really black mark, one had given a fatally excessive purgative, the other was proved in spite of his denials to have sold purgative medicines and powders of his own composition and to have treated a case of syphilis.[3] There were also four or five cases, all but one of trifling importance, in which employees or former employees of apothecaries trespassed on the forbidden ground.[4]

The College may well have felt misgivings about its relations with the apothecaries so far as they were expressed in its police jurisdiction and there were wider matters pending between the two branches. In 1585 at the June comitia there was a discussion about the possibility of preparing and publishing one certain, uniform pharmacopoeia for the use of all the apothecaries of London. This was a matter in which England was notably backward. In order to make up prescriptions the apothecaries needed lists of herbs and other *materia medica*, and in the Middle Ages manuscripts of several such compilations circulated widely. In 1353 the antidotary of Nicholas Myrepsus, a thirteenth-century Greek, was set up as the compulsory standard in the statutes of the *épiciers-apothicaires* of Paris.[5] It affords one of the worst examples of inertia in the history of ideas. From the beginning it was ill-suited to the needs of western countries with their different flora; and by the middle of the sixteenth century botanists had moved far beyond it, but it was not until 1637 that a new national *Codex* was authorized in France.[6] In the meantime the invention of printing had made it possible to insist on a real uniformity of pharmaceutical standards. There had arisen, however, not any new work with an international circulation but a multiplicity of works each prescribed by some authority with merely local or regional powers. As early as 1498

[1] John Parkinson.
[2] Besse, 1600: see above, p. 155.
[3] Salthouse, 1591; Edward Coker or Cocker of Southwark, 1602/3, perhaps not identical with the Coker of St. Katherine's Street against whom there was a minor complaint in 1600.
[4] Richard Barker, 1587; ?Thomas Hobs, 1587 and 1588; ?Linch's servant, 1589; More's servant, 1589.
[5] It does not concern us whether there is confusion with Nicholas Praepositus.
[6] The Commission which produced it began work in 1623, and the publication in 1638 was in the end hasty.

the Florentine guild which included both physicians and apothecaries published the first of all printed *ricettarii*. By 1585 Mantua, Bologna, Rome and Bergamo had followed suit; other Italian cities were to do so.[1] The town-physicians of Lyon printed their list in 1561, and the apothecaries of Cologne were provided for four years later.

Some of these publications were known in England, and some of the fellows of the College knew enough about botany and had enough critical sense to judge that none of them deserved to be taken over as it stood.[2] It may be that they were unduly cautious. If they had been keen and confident they might have aimed at imposing a standard on the whole of England; but the limiting of their ambition to London may simply have followed from that loss of interest in the provinces which we have noticed already.[3] At any rate, when the question was mooted in the comitia, it was noted that this was evidently a laborious undertaking, and that further deliberation was needed. It was adjourned to the next comitia when all the fellows were to attend and each was to state his views freely so that something complete and outstanding could be attempted in such a laudable matter. Even at this stage delays began, and the Annals do not tell us whether the matter was even mentioned at the next comitia or for long after that. Nor do we know whether there was any connexion between this preliminary talk and the inditing of a letter from the master and wardens of the Grocers' Company which is entered on the day of the annual visitation of the apothecaries, 20 July 1586. The master and wardens were concerned at the sale of a treacle called 'Jeane Triacle' which they found to be unwholesome for adults and children, being indeed compounded by certain rude and unskilful men. Moved by Christian charity towards all good people, they besought the College to set down a 'recept' for the true composition of this treacle, which should be registered at Grocers' Hall. Anyone who was admitted to make it should take such an oath as the College might direct.

The letter was brought by William Besse,[4] whom it was proposed to place at the head of these sworn dispensers. Genoa treacle was not a novelty in England; Sir John Paston acquired some pots of it about 1466 from an apothecary who swore, not quite

[1] Ciasca, 337 ff.
[2] The College library catalogue of 1660 contains those of Bologna (1575), Bergamo (1580), and Nuremberg (1598).
[3] See above, p. 117.   [4] See above, p. 155.

convincingly, that they had never been opened since they left Genoa.[1]
There does not seem to be any reason except the one alleged (the
prevalence at the time of some inferior sorts of it) to explain why it
was now singled out from the other available sovereign remedies
of many ingredients. The College replied with friendly politeness,
giving William Besse a pat on the back, and sent the beadle with its
recipe put down upon mature deliberation and by common consent.

The project of a pharmacopoeia had no doubt been formed from
foreign examples. Another aid to standardized pharmacy was the
management of botanical gardens in conjunction with teaching
and practice. There was no new principle in the planting of herb
gardens: they were known in the Middle Ages everywhere; but in
1506 the bachelors of medicine in Paris began to make a small
annual payment for the upkeep of a teaching garden, and there
were several in Italy, Germany and elsewhere by the time when
the university of Leiden started one in 1577. In London individual
apothecaries had their gardens for business purposes and some of
them were well up in the botanical knowledge of the time,[2] but
it seems to have been without consulting them that the College
set up a garden of its own. On 12 July 1587 it decided to rent from
Lord Sackville a garden which he offered for sale, if he would
accept a rent of 40 marks ($£26$. 13s. 4d.) a year. On 6 October it
engaged a curator who undertook to stock it with practically every
sort of the rarer herbs. Well he might, for he was no less a man than
John Gerard, surgeon, the most prominent English gardener of his
time, who, if no great botanist, at least wrote the first published
catalogue of any garden and compiled the most influential of English
herbals.[3]

The garden would no doubt be useful if the plan for a pharmacopoeia were taken up in earnest; but it might also provide drugs
for use in practice, and it looks as if the apothecaries suspected that
there was some such intention. On 12 February 1588/9 they gave
the College a copy of a petition which they had submitted to the
queen. They asked that none except themselves should be allowed
to make up or sell any composite medicines. When the petition was
read out it appeared that there were certain things in it which
derogated from the privileges of the College. A committee of the

[1] *Paston Letters*, ed. J. Gairdner, ii (1900), 293.
[2] See Raven, pp. 115–17, 170, 192.
[3] On 22 December 1598 the College resolved to inspect a house and garden in the
Charterhouse with a view to moving there; but no action followed.

president, the registrar and three others was appointed to consider the petition and report to a later meeting. In the meantime the existing statute that none of the College was to compound medicaments or buy them in order to sell for a profit, was for the first time voted upon with a view to abrogation. From this it appears that the College did mean to invade the apothecaries' territory. On 25 June 1590 the abrogation was completed. This was the day on which it was resolved to revise the whole body of statutes, and the old restriction was not revived in the new code. From this time relations with the apothecaries became more and more uneasy.

The plan for a pharmacopoeia came to life again. On 10 October 1589 the president and fifteen of the fellows met in comitia. A scheme was agreed upon for better and speedier execution. Committees of two, three or four fellows were appointed to deal with ten groups of medicaments into which the whole subject was divided: the queen's physicians took as their province powders and confectionary (*tragemata*), the president and 22 fellows by name were allotted other groups.[1] As there were some things concerning the apothecaries which it was intended to correct, all were to present themselves with their written opinions on their tasks at the Michaelmas comitia. On 23 October a new committee of six, without the president or registrar, was appointed apparently to edit the whole work. Michaelmas came and it was decided to adjourn the *liber antidotarius* to the next comitia. On 13 December 1594—that is five years later—a new editorial committee of eight was appointed, including five of the former six. Upon this followed twenty years in which nothing further was recorded even if anything was done.[2]

The Annals of the College could not be expected to record more than its daily activities; they were never intended to relate the doings of physicians outside the College, and there was no place in them for general observations or for estimates of influences from outside. If there were formal or informal discussions about these things in the Tudor period we know nothing about them. We do, however, know a good deal about the facts of medical practice, and the reactions of the College to these facts seem to show clearly that the equilibrium which it now maintained between the various forces around it was an unstable equilibrium.

[1] The list is printed in Munk, iii. 373.   [2] See below, c. xii, p. 220.

In the first place the profession was growing. We still have no figures, but the records and the literature of the time give a definite impression that there were more physicians at work in London and in some, if not all or most of the regions outside it in the middle of the sixteenth century than at the beginning, and more again at the end than in the middle. This impression is confirmed from two sides. In the first place there were more physicians who engaged in special kinds of practice. The men-midwives, of whom we have encountered two, Dr. Jacob and Peter Chamberlen, were specialists in the full sense: they dealt with a limited range of physical conditions and they, or some of them, used technical means and knowledge which the general body of practitioners did not possess. This is also true of the few physicians who served with the army and navy, though perhaps not true to the same degree as it is of the surgeons, who did the main work for the fighting services.[1] Physicians as well as surgeons began to accompany merchant ships on their distant voyages and so to encounter both diseases and remedies which were unknown in Europe. They had no new science, and their practice was specialized only in the sense that it did not include some of the matters which came up in ordinary practice: but they were confronted by new facts and new problems. Here the College has been thought to have missed an opportunity. Richard Hakluyt thought of including in the last volume of his *Voyages* a pamphlet by George Whetstone or Wateson, published in 1598, on *The Cures of the Diseased in Remote Regions*.[2] He consulted William Gilbert, but Gilbert, rightly thinking Whetstone's work inadequate, suggested writing something himself or conferring with the College on 'some order by consent'. Nothing came of these suggestions, and English physicians did no important, original work on sailors' diseases for about a century; but in Gilbert's time it would have been a task if great difficulty to put together a work of any merit from all the available sources, which were in their nature imperfect and hard to evaluate.

At home there were now a few physicians who attached themselves specially to baths and wells. In 1562 Dr. William Turner, physician, botanist and divine, wrote a book in which he compared

---

[1] For the army see the documents of the period of Henry VIII printed in Bodleian Quarterly Record, vol. i (1900) and the useful summary in C. G. Cruickshank, *Elizabeth's Army* (1946), c. X, for the navy the excellent book of J. J. Keevil, *Medicine and the Navy*, 2 vols. (1957–8).

[2] See the annotated edition by C. Singer (1915).

the English with the German and Italian baths, but in England he mentioned only Bath. Ten years later a Poor Law Act mentioned Buxton along with Bath as a resort of many poor and diseased people.[1] About that time the earl of Shrewsbury was building special accommodation there for well-to-do patients, and there was to be a resident physician at least during the summer season. Before the end of Queen Elizabeth's reign new medicinal wells were in use in several places. Protestant controversialists wrote against the miraculous virtues of holy wells, and Dr. Walter Bayley, a fellow of the College who had been regius professor of medicine in Oxford, wrote a pamphlet on the waters of King's Newnham in Warwickshire. Thus there began a localized branch of practice, with its own problems in relation to quacks and advertising, its special remedies and in later times its particular approach to medical science.[2]

In hospitals there was still no equipment and no treatment which differed from what was available in private houses; until the nineteenth century no one went to hospital if he had a home where he could be treated. There were only a handful of hospital physicians in London and none outside it; but they had good opportunities for observation[3] and at St. Mary's of Bethlehem there had been continuous experience of mental illness for about 200 years, so that there was an inheritance of knowledge, though not yet of systematic knowledge, in this separate department.[4] The number of hospital posts of any kind does not seem to have increased in the Elizabethan period.

The modest beginnings of specialization seem to imply a growth in the total amount of medical service rendered, and so does the modest increase in the numbers of medical degrees and licences granted by Oxford and Cambridge. The benefactions of Linacre and Caius and King Henry VIII were not without effect. The

---

[1] The appointment of Dr. Robert Henryson as medical officer by the corporation of Newcastle-upon-Tyne, which is thought to be the earliest such appointment in England, can scarcely have been made until the seventeenth century, since his successor was Dr. Samuel Rand, for whom see Munk: J. Brand, *History of Newcastle-upon-Tyne*, ii (1789), 363.

[2] There is an excellent essay on this subject, covering the sixteenth and seventeenth centuries, by R. V. Lennard in *Englishmen at Rest and Play* (1931).

[3] This fact is recognized in the letter recommending Dr. Henry Wootton to St. Bartholomew's (see above, p. 139) 'that place hath oftentimes great and strange accidents and divers cases of importance not elsewhere usuall', but in mentioning it the College did not show disinterested regard for medical study. It offered its 'best advice and conference' in these cases if Dr. Wootton should be appointed, but not otherwise.

[4] E. G. O'Donoghue, *The Story of Bethlehem Hospital* (1914).

figures for doctors' degrees may indeed give a misleading impression. The first was conferred in Oxford as early as 1312[1]; the first in Cambridge in 1560–1 and the first in Scotland (at Glasgow) in 1470; but the degree of doctor of medicine was a rarity even in Paris in the fifteenth century, and even after it came into use there were well-qualified physicians who were only masters. Thus the rise of the Cambridge school was probably not as abrupt as would appear from the contrast between the single doctorate granted in 1500–41 and the sixty-three granted in 1542–89. In Oxford the number of doctorates is less easily ascertainable; but from 1571 to 1602 the total seems to be only twenty-four, or on a stricter reckoning, nineteen. The bachelors of medicine, however, who spent less time on the literary parts of the study, had the right to practise and in both universities they were more numerous than the doctors. Below them again were licentiates, most of whom did not proceed to degrees. Altogether it seems that the number of recruits to the profession from Oxford and Cambridge was substantially larger in the reign of Queen Elizabeth than in the same number of years immediately before it. Allowing for such factors as degrees by incorporation given to graduates of other universities, it may be estimated at somewhere about 300. This is not a great number, and it was spread over forty-six years, at the end of which a good many were dead or in retirement, but by itself and without reckoning other sources of recruitment it implies that the number of physicians grew. The medical faculties were small. That of Oxford had to share a beadle with the faculty of arts. But they had a place in the movement by which Oxford and Cambridge made it a main part of their business to train young men, not for the church but for the professions and for public and private affairs.[2]

This growth of the profession was not peculiar to England: the number of physicians rose in Paris as it did in London.[3] It seems

[1] Simon Moene, for whom see A. B. Emden, *Biographical Register* (1958).
[2] The chief sources besides the biographical collections are *Register of the University of Oxford*, ii, *1571–1622*, ed. A. Clark (1887–8), especially pt. 3, pp. 410–11, and for Cambridge *Grace Book B*, ed. Mary Bateson, pt. ii (1905), pp. vi–vii and *Grace Book Δ*, ed. J. Venn (1910), pp. 130–70, 383–440. For a general discussion see M. H. Curtis, *Oxford and Cambridge in Transition, 1558–1642* (1959), especially c. vi. Dr. Robb-Smith had very kindly shown me the new figures which he intends to publish in a full and close study of the Oxford school, in which the places where these physicians practised will be examined. Excluding the comparatively small numbers who incorporated from foreign universities, but including licentiates as well as graduates, the totals are for 1551–1600, 154; for 1601–30, 118; for 1631–50, 185. The last figure includes 46 graduates by creation of whom 25 were 'political'.
[3] Franklin, xi 123.

likely that various social changes of the time were favourable to the increase. England was more peaceable at home and much more prosperous than it had been, and this may have been a favouring condition; but in France it was not equally evident. Perhaps the prestige of the physicians was rising, and with it a preference for their treatment over that of the empirics and over home-made remedies. If this was so the College may have helped to bring it about by its championship of the accepted standards and by the distinction of its members in learning and social life. Direct proofs of this are not to be expected, and the tale told by the Annals is compatible with this possibility. But, whatever brought it about, the growth in the numbers of physicians did not result from any scientific discoveries or from any improvements in the medical art. Some discoveries were made, but as yet the College paid no attention to them. It also discountenanced changes in practice, those few which may be called improvements along with the rest.

Although there were individual fellows who broke away, until the statutes were revised in 1601 the corporate fidelity of the College to Galen was unimpaired. Dr. Giffard, when he was president, presented a copy of the first edition of the treatise De Sanitate Tuenda in Linacre's translation.[1] In the fifteen-nineties Galen is mentioned several times in the notices of examinations: it almost looks as if there was a deliberate stand on his behalf. A foreign graduate who aspired to a licence for London was put back for four years to practise in the country and apply himself more studiously to reading Galen.[2] The lot of Edward Jordan, a doctor of Padua itself, was not as hard as some. On 4 July 1595 he was given oral permission to practise, but on condition that he read the books De Temperamentis, Elementis, Facultatibus, Morborum atque Symptomatum Differentiis atque Causis and De Locis Affectis—five books—before Michaelmas. He complied and gave satisfaction[3] and ultimately became a fellow. Dr. Thomas Hudd of Cambridge in the meantime had been enjoined to read De Elementis, De Temperamentis, De Naturalibus Facultatibus and De Usu Partium[4]; but without a time-limit. He seems to be the same Dr. Hood who confessed later on that he had read Forestus and other neoterics, but not

[1] 30 September 1586.
[2] James Mossanus, 20 January 1592/3: see above, p. 142.
[3] 7 November 1595.   [4] 17 October 1595.

Galen because his books were too expensive.[1] For the time being Dr. Hood was forbidden to practise.[2] A middle-aged practitioner said that he had read all Galen and Hippocrates, but he showed no knowledge of Galen and it was only the support of the lord treasurer that gained him a conditional licence.[3] Lastly it was one of the misfortunes of Thomas Rawlins to fail in his examination and to be admonished to work harder, in particular at Galen.[4]

We do not know for certain that any of the fellows did more than keep up enough of their Galen to serve for examining, which was less than was needed for undergoing examination. Two of them in this period may have followed in the steps of Linacre and Caius by doing something for Galenic studies; but Alban Hyll's contributions have perished if they ever existed, and the Latin title of Walter Bayley's manuscript, also lost, indicates that it reviewed some of Galen's doctrines only to apply them to the brewing of ale and beer. It may have been indirectly due to the College that English translations of Galen were made from the Latin. As early as 1541 the printer Richard Copland put out a version of the *Terapeutica*. In 1574 John Jones, a provincial practitioner and a writer on medical baths, published a translation of Galen's *Book of Elements*[5] from the Latin, and in 1586 the eminent surgeon Thomas Gale gave his name to a translation of the *Methodus Medendi* executed by Dr. William Cuningham or Keningham, a man of some note. But the life was going out of these studies. The high hopes of the Renaissance humanists had not been fulfilled. The closer knowledge of Galen had led to no improvements of the physician's art. The association of classical scholarship with medical studies was indeed destined to last long after this, but its nature was continually modified by changes on either side. By this time classical scholarship had become more elaborate and stricter than it had been in the time of Erasmus; it was no longer possible to cover the whole of classical learning at a satisfactory level. As the standards of linguistic, historical and literary studies rose these absorbed attention at the expense of other branches and the humanists drew away from science and medicine.

[1] 25 February 1596/7: Forestus is the eminent Dutch writer Pieter van Foreest (1521–97). 'Neoterics' simply means modern writers, without any sense of disparagement.

[2] On 5 August 1597 he was, however, granted a conditional licence.

[3] Bartholomew Chappell, 17 October 1595.

[4] 23 December 1596: see also above, p. 142 and below, p. 188.

[5] The book is also included in the author's *Briefe, Excellent and Profitable Discourse* (1574). It is of no importance.

From them Galen was ceasing to count as one of the great thinkers and writers of antiquity.

The physicians still needed Latin for two practical reasons. It was still the main medium for the international communications of learned men. In some subjects books were beginning to appear in English, French, Italian, Spanish and German, but there were too few English readers to tempt physicians to address major works only to their own countrymen. The other practical reason was that Latin above an elementary level was the exclusive possession of the learned world. Reading and writing in Latin kept the physicians' secrets within a comparatively sympathetic circle. Proficiency in Latin or Greek helped the physician to rank as a man of learning with that intellectual prestige which was an element in the status of the profession.

This intellectual prestige was broadly based. There were fellows of the College who were esteemed for their Latin poetry, their knowledge of modern languages or other miscellaneous accomplishments, but their main strength lay in natural science. Edward Wotton and John Caius began a line of fellows, to which Penny and Mouffet belonged, who collected and published facts of natural history without originality but well enough to satisfy some of the needs of the time. William Gilbert's work on the magnet stepped clear of the confusions of sixteenth-century speculation into the open air of science, where relevance earns its reward. But there is a gulf between the scientific work of individual fellows and the official conservatism of the College in medical knowledge. Its members did indeed add to medical literature. Eight or nine of their names are to be found among the Elizabethan writers on the plague and diet and medicine in general; but almost all of them were mere bookmakers in the manner of the time, stringing together excerpts from previous writers with something from their own observation, perhaps shrewd, perhaps absurd but never in any serious sense scientific. There were others among their contemporaries who did the same sort of thing at least as well as they did, for instance Thomas Cogan, M.B., fellow of Oriel and high master of the Manchester Grammar School in his *Haven of Health* of 1584.[1]

The College as a body had not emerged from the sixteenth-century fog. When the astrologer Simon Forman was forbidden to

[1] Cogan made a contribution to the criticism of Galen: 'How much Galen is deceived if he spake generally of the mutton of all countries, experience prooveth in this Realme' (p. 114 in ed. of 1596). For the same subject see R. Burton, *Anatomy of Melancholy* (1621), pt. 2, sect. 2, subsec. 1, men. 1 subject 1.

practise he betook himself to Lambeth, which was under the jurisdiction of the archbishop of Canterbury, and the College wrote at
length to Whitgift reminding him of its ancient privileges (they
had become ancient by now) and begging him to withhold his protection. The archbishop came out strong:

Forman nether is nor shalbe countenanced by me: nether doth he deserve
yt any way at my handes. I have heard very ill of him: in so much as I
had a meaning to call him by vertue of the Commission Ecclesiasticall
for divers misdemeanours if any man woold have taken upon him the
prosecution of the cause against him. In which mynd I remain still. And
therefore use your aucthorytie in the name of God.[1]

But it was not because he was an astrologer that the College objected to Forman. At the very next Michaelmas comitia it chose as its
president Dr. Richard Forster, whose solitary publication was a
pocket almanack, *Ephemerides Meteorographicae*, of 1575, a belated
tribute to astronomy as the handmaid of medicine.

The College was divided over a case of magic. On 13 November
1602 a petition was read in the comitia from a little old woman
called Elizabeth Jackson who lay in prison under suspicion of
witchcraft. She believed that her accusers were Dr. Moundeford,
Dr. Herring, and Mr. Bredwell: she asked the College to examine
the three of them and consider her whole case. Dr. Moundeford
was away but the College examined the other two. A girl had fallen
sick. Dr. Herring said that he had gone with her parents before
the recorder at their request. He had gone as a spectator, not an
accuser, but he confidently affirmed that the girl was bewitched,
and he suspected Elizabeth Jackson. Mr. Bredwell told much the
same tale and added that whenever the supposed witch came in
sight of the girl a voice muttered through the sufferer's nostrils
'Hang her, hang her'. But many of the twelve fellows who were
present, and those amongst the first of them, men of great learning,
took the other side and stoutly maintained that the girl was not
bewitched but afflicted with some natural disease. Many neighbours
and friends of the old woman were in attendance and ten of them,
people of mature age from the same parish, spoke up for her. They
said there had been nothing against her for twenty years and they
asked for other learned men to be sent to see for themselves. Seven
doctors, including Dr. Herring, were deputed to go. At the trial

[1] Letter of 4 July 1601 after the entry of 25 June.

Dr. Argent himself gave evidence for the defence, and so did Dr. Edward Jorden, a licentiate and a notable writer on hysteria, but the unfortunate Elizabeth Jackson was sentenced to be imprisoned for a year and to stand four times in the pillory.[1]

Some of these learned men were among the enlightened few who were already beginning to doubt the very existence of sorcery. In the world outside the College there were sceptics who questioned not only this belief but many others, and among them the fundamentals of the medical art. There was, to be sure, nothing absolutely new in this; but there was a novel simplicity and directness. Scepticism now isolated its objectives and disembarrassed itself of its incongruous alliances. In 1531 a famous and travelled German physician, Cornelius Agrippa, in a book on the uncertainty of all the sciences, set out the contradictions between the medical classics, which were all accepted as equally authoritative, and threw doubt on the value of the art itself, as also of many other valued beliefs such as judicial astrology.[2] He rejected these, however, only in order to establish other principles, including those of religion. He corresponded with Erasmus and when he came to England he was the guest of Linacre's friend John Colet, the great dean of St. Paul's. In 1580 Montaigne published the first two books of his *Essais*, and the second book ends with a scathing polemic against the art and against physicians themselves, in which the arguments of Cornelius Agrippa are marshalled along with many others. Although Montaigne's manner is rambling and his temper professedly reasonable, the effect is concentrated and negative. The whole argument is meant to destroy, and to leave nothing standing. Not many Englishmen could read French, but one of them was Francis Bacon. In 1608 there came Florio's translation of Montaigne, and anyone in London could read the case against medical conservatism including Galenism. Among the fellows of the College there were a few who were already on the side of the sceptics. Dr. Hood was a writer of some note on geometry and navigation: we have observed his distaste for Galen.[3] Dr. Mouffet was a considerable naturalist, and a noticeable man all round, but a partisan of chemical medicines. One day his name was mentioned to the assembled president and

---

[1] For an account of the trial see R. Hunter and Ida Macalpine, *Three Hundred Years of Psychiatry* (1963), pp. 68 ff.

[2] *De Vanitate Scientiarum*, caps. 82–88. There was an English translation by James Sanford or Sandford of which the first edition appeared in 1569.

[3] Above, p. 165.

13

fellows in a context that shocked them. A charlatan was boasting under examination that after others had failed he had cured Sir Charles Morison of a tumour in the thigh. Dr. Mouffet, he said, had been astonished, and had protested that diseases were cured not by language and literature—*non linguis et literis*—but by *experientia*. The registrar wrote his marginal heading with disapproval 'Dr. Mouffet's judgment on an empiric'.[1]

A doctor who was later to become a fellow broke away from rigid Galenism in a piece of business on which the College was not consulted. The great financier Sir Thomas Gresham died in 1579 and on the death of his widow in 1596 the charitable provisions of his will came into effect. He left his capacious house in Bishopgate Street for almshouses and for lodgings to accommodate seven unmarried readers in seven academic subjects, one of which was medicine. The foundation[2] was to be governed by the City and the Mercers' Company, and detailed ordinances for the lectures were drawn up in tripartite agreements between these two authorities and the lecturers. It would seem that the regulations for the medical lectures not only had the approval of the professor of physic, Dr. Matthew Gwinne, but represented his own views. The physic lecture was to be given on the Mondays of eight-week terms, from eight to nine in the morning and from two to three in the afternoon. 'And for as much as the greatest part of the auditory is like to be of such citizens and others, as have small knowledge or none at all of the Latin tongue, and for that every man for his health's sake will desire to have some knowledge in the art of physick' the morning lecture was to be in Latin and that of the afternoon in English. The matter of the lectures was to be left to the lecturer's discretion 'yet it is to be wished that he herein follow Fernelius his method, by reading first physiologie, then pathologie, and lastly therapeutice; whereby the body of the said art may be better imprinted by good method in the studious auditors, rather than be disjointed and delivered out of order by exposition of some part of Galen or Hippocrates'.[3]

---

[1] 10 January 1594/5. The best translation for *experientia* would be 'trial'.

[2] I do not know whether anyone called it a college before Sir George Buc in his treatise on the 'third university' of London written in 1612 and appended to Howes's edition of Stowe's *Annales* (1615).

[3] J. Ward, *Lives of the Professors of Gresham College* (1740) pp. ii-iii, vii-viii, 19 ff. The ordinance quoted above seems to have been written in 1597, the year of the first occurrence of the word 'physiology' in this, Fernel's, sense noted in the *Oxford English Dictionary*.

Fernel was not a revolutionary; indeed he was a Galenist[1]; but in this the ordinance rather diverges from the spirit of the College, and not only in this. The citizenry were to be taught, and taught in English. Was this to be the beginning of popular medical education, and would the spread of sound medical knowledge strengthen the physicians in public esteem? Might it not, on the contrary, open the way for subversive teachings or encourage the surgeons and the apothecaries in their ambitions? There were many signs of impending change, and also of impending conflicts.

[1] For the degree of his originality see Sir Charles Sherrington, *The Endeavour of Jean Fernel* (1946), especially pp. 63, 70, 74, 81, 91, 101, 124–36.

X : THE *STATUTA VETERA*

AMONG the College records which were destroyed in the great fire of London in 1666 was a complete set of the statutes in force at the beginning of the reign of James 1. Fortunately the first historian of the College, Charles Goodall, had copied them all out and his copy survives.[1] It has been generally suppposed that these *Statuta Vetera* may be the revised code approved on 30 September 1601.[2] The date 1601 actually appears in them; it is substituted for the original 1556 and 1557 to bring up to date the forms of letters testimonial and the letter to mayors and other officers, and the statutes mentioned in the Annals as belonging to the 1601 revision are all included. There are, however, a few provisions which cannot be dated from the Annals, and there is one which seems to have been inserted after 8 April 1602, the date of Popham's judgement in the case of Jinkinson. A statute about the impostures of the surgeons ends by requiring the physician, in all his so-called bills and receipts, to signify and append the day and time of writing. If this statute had been in existence, it would have been superfluous for the chief justice to advise that this should be done.[3] In spite of the possibility that there are some trifling additions to the code of 1601, these statutes are however clearly those under which the College acted from that time or very soon after it. They show how its constitution and purposes had changed in the first eighty years or so of its life.[4]

The code shows signs of thorough revision in almost every respect, and hardly any flaws can be found in the drafting.[5] The language is improved; In a good many places it runs better than

[1] His copy is at the end of the fourth volume of his transcript of the Annals; from it was taken the only other existing copy, in a separate exercise book, by William Munk.

[2] Munk, iii. 337.

[3] See above, p. 156. Oddly enough the statute does not say that, as Popham recommended, the name of the patient should be given. It is perhaps a sign of carelessness that in this clause 'volumus' is not followed by the usual 'et statuimus'.

[4] In some places dealing with admissions to fellowships, but not consistently throughout, instead of royal physicians mention is made of physicians to the king or queen, which suggests that these passages were altered after the accession of James I.

[5] Under 'Juramentum Permissorum et Candidatorum' a short programme for the oath appears, although it has already been given in full under the heading 'Juramentum Candidatorum' with no mention of the licentiates.

before and some eccentric words disappear: the *caduceus* or *accisus* becomes a straightforward *bedellus* or beadle. The elects are no longer *electores* but *electi*. In the same spirit minor inconveniences of the old statutes are removed, especially where they were needlessly rigid. The dates for presidential elections and quarterly comitia are no longer absolutely fixed, a few days postponement is allowed for sufficient reasons. Some of the other changes, even if they resulted from actual disagreements over particular cases, may be regarded as essentially adjustments to enable the machinery to run smoothly. Such are the provisions that the office of an elect becomes vacant not only if he dies or is expelled from the College, but also if he leaves the City, bag and baggage (*cum pannis*) and is absent for a whole year otherwise than in the king's service.[1] Perhaps there is a little more than mere adjustment, an intentional abatement of the extreme respect for seniority, in a change of procedure for choosing a new elect: there must be a quorum of four elects, and the election is to be by majority vote; only in case of a tie are the seniors to prevail. In the clause about the election of the president there is another new provision which does rather more than fill a gap. If the person first nominated is not elected, then another name must be proposed and if necessary a third, a fourth or a fifth: the election is not to be broken off until someone is chosen. This rules out adjournments and wire-pullings which might have caused confusion and ill-feeling: it sounds arbitrary, but it was probably wise.

The president, as we have seen, is no longer irremovable.[2] If he offends against the statutes, the *consiliarii* are to declare it in comitia, but he is not to be punished except for a grave offence, such as peculation or squandering the College property, in which case a majority of the fellows present is to decide, but those present must include four of the elects, who are to vote with the rest. To the honour of the College it must be said that this enactment has never been invoked. One president, it is true, was admonished by his consiliarii, and another was discovered after his death to have committed irregularities which might, if he had survived, have led to punishment; but none has ever been deprived of his office.[3] Nor is there any sign that by making him accountable for his

---

[1] See above p. 137.   [2] See above, p. 137.
[3] See below, pp. 339, 370 for the cases of Dr. Daniel Whistler and Dr. George Rogers.

misdemeanours, the College wished to diminish the president's dignity. The only other provision which may have reduced his influence is that which says that in the elections of fellows he is to be the last to give his vote. The clause about his duties ends as its predecessor did with the phrase 'So great is the respect which we pay to the president's honour and authority'. In practice, of course, his functions were now reduced by the amount of those discharged by the treasurer and the registrar, whose statutes are included without alteration in the new code. The occasions when a pro-president may be appointed are defined more precisely than before: the president may name one if he is absent or ill or overburdened in the service of the sovereign or of some other great personage (*magnatis alicuius*) or by other business; but he must notify the beginning of his absence and the pro-president is not to do more than what is necessary to fill his place. The pro-president's full power to carry on current business according to the true sense of the statutes is explicitly stated, but it stops short of making or abrogating statutes.

The clause dealing with the *consiliarii* has undergone careful revision. In part this is like the common-sense tidying-up in other clauses. The *consiliarius*, for instance, no longer has to declare on oath the reason for any absence. But some sentences are added to the part which deals with controversies between the president and the fellows, and this seems to imply that the College had not been satisfied with its arrangements for preserving harmony. The original statute only said that in case of disagreement between the president and the fellows, the *consiliarii* were to settle the doubtful points, and if they disagreed among themselves the majority of the elects were to decide. The new clause says that if any private disagreement arises between fellows about any doubtful matter or about the true interpretation of any statute or such-like, it is desired that the whole business be quietly and calmly composed by the president, consiliarii and censors or a majority of them. In the same way if a disagreement arises between the president and fellows, then the consiliarii and censors or a majority of them are to act; and if no settlement can be reached by these means then the remainder of the elects are to be called in and the whole disagreement is to be settled by a majority vote of this larger body. The same procedure is to be observed for all private complaints of fellows, by which means it is hoped that quarrels, contentions and complaints will be avoided and this famous College will for ever be united in brotherly love and unity of will.

It will be noted that in all this the elects take no part as a body; except for their duty of examining and of choosing the president from their own number, they do not seem to have done any business collectively until long after this time. They lost one important function: henceforward the censors were to be elected by the comitia on the proposal of the president.

The changes affecting the comitia are as great as those affecting the College officers. It might indeed be a mistake to attach much importance to one of them, the disappearance of the rule that all proceedings must be in Latin. It is not until many years later that an English speech is recorded, and it would scarcely have been noted if it had not been exceptional even then.[1] If, however, this omission is significant, its tendency fits in well with some other changes: the comitia are acquiring an organization better suited for a growing amount and variety of business. The original statutes remarked with pleasing candour that physicians were liable to be busy at irregular times, and so, in order that they should miss as few opportunities as possible of earning fees (*lucri sui occasiones*) through College engagements, there should be only one meeting every three months except for an urgent reason or for a specially arranged examination. Now this passage also drops out. Instead it is laid down that the president may summon such solemn or major comitia if the character of the business requires it; that a quorum of twelve is required; except only that the president or pro-president may act with a smaller number if urgent business has to be done by royal command when there are not twelve members available in town. The quorum of twelve is again prescribed for alterations of statutes. But certain kinds of business may be done in minor comitia, meeting once a month or whenever they are urgently needed, at which it is silently implied any fellow may be present but for which only seven must be present except for a weighty cause, namely the president, the censors, the treasurer and the registrar. Examinations for entry or licence may at the president's discretion be held in either, but the jurisdiction over offences and such-like matters are to belong to the minor. This workmanlike division of the two kinds of meetings, comitia and censors' days as they came to be called, had already come gradually into use. It

[1] See below, p. 307.

continued to be the framework of College action for centuries, modified only by the addition of committees, first for the dispensatory, then for other special matters and later for general purposes.

In the earliest statutes the provisions about candidates began with an apologetic phrase: it was advisable to lay down a few rules (*pauca*) about them, and their oath was given in *oratio obliqua*, not in a formula, almost as if the precise words did not matter. The licentiates received very little notice and the name was used only for those who were allowed to practice by virtue of some qualification lower than a doctor's degree. In some places the name *exteri* almost seems to cover not only those who as foreigners were ineligible for the fellowship, but also foreign brothers, as the guilds might have called them, who did not aspire to it. This does not seem to have been intentional, but it does seem to imply something vague or transitional about the two grades. One thing was definite which was sometimes departed from in the eighteenth century: the word *collega* applied only to the fellows and did not include candidates. All the confusion disappears in the statutes of 1601. There is a clear line between candidates and licentiates (*permissi ad praxin*). The candidate is to pay £6 for his first year and 40s. for each of his other three. The three years may be shortened by special favour if there is a vacant fellowship, and if the candidate has to remain in that status longer than three years his fee drops to £1. The London licentiates have exactly the same obligations, but they have to pay £8 for the first year and £4 for each following year as long as they remain in practice. The minor fees and the doubling of fees for graduates of foreign universities are the same for both. It may be that when this discrimination against the licentiates first came in, the College feared that many physicians would be satisfied with the right to practice, which might create a difficulty in filling up its own numbers and consequently in discharging its duties. But there is no evidence for this. On the contrary, as we have seen, since at least as early as 1582 there had been competition to get in.[1] The candidates had an almost sure prospect of privileges, and they probably already enjoyed advantages in acquiring lucrative practice. By taxing the licentiates, the College seems to have used its powers for its own benefit.

---

[1] See above, p. 133.

The oath of the candidates and licentiates has become more explicit. It imposes attendance at the anatomical demonstrations, and abstention from the use of abortives and poisons and from speaking ill of fellows. There is a promise to delate empirics and impostors. The candidate or licentiate is not to associate openly (*familiarem se exhibere*) with empirics or unlicensed practitioners, nor in any way to frequent their meetings or gatherings (*conventicula aut conventus*) to the detriment of the College or of its good name. This seems to cover something different from consultations over cases, but nothing seems to be known about any associations or combinations among these people at that time.[1] Some new paragraphs about illicit competitors and undesirable practices appear towards the end of the statutes, between other provisions which have no logical connexion with them, in such a way as to suggest that they were shuffled in, either when they were adopted or later, to save the trouble of re-arranging the earlier sections. First there is an important passage with a heading which says it provides against the impostures of surgeons, though in fact it also hits at the apothecaries. Both of these classes, it says, but especially surgeons frequently bring the urine of sick persons to physicians, ask them to prescribe something after inspecting it, and then, on this pretext of consultation, keep the remaining course of treatment in their own hands, snatching all the fees except a pittance for the inspection. Therefore no fellow or candidate or licentiate is to impart any advice (*quicquid de suo consilio*) to such crafty impostors on the basis of inspecting urines unless he has been called in to advise as a physician during the whole remainder of the case and also from time to time during the illness has prescribed, in Latin and to an honest apothecary, such medicines as are required from day to day by the nature of the disease and other circumstances arising therefrom. Here the ancient division of the three branches is re-affirmed, but it is the physicians who are ordered to conform to it, and we shall see, though not until much later, that some of them found it more profitable to break this rule if the pittances they received were sufficiently numerous. For the present we may notice that, since the document is addressed confidentially to the physicians themselves, the rule is justified here only by their need for proper fees.

It is immediately followed by the recommendation, possibly interpolated here, which we have already mentioned as possibly

[1] See below, p. 263.

later than 1601, about dating prescriptions.[1] Then comes another clause against uroscopy, starting with a condemnation much more radical than that in the preceding rule. It is ridiculous and foolish to divine the nature or kind of disease or the condition of the sufferer by conjecture from the inspection of urine. All physicians are therefore admonished to be much more cautious in this matter than many or most of them (*plerique*) have been customarily in the past. All practitioners are forbidden to give any directions (*quicquam in medicinam prescribere*) to the ignorant persons and the females who carry round chamberpots unless they have previously known the patient well or seen him or at least are clearly and fully informed by those who ask their advice about the disease and the circumstances. So will the dignity of physicians be better protected, and so will they be better able to think out the most helpful remedies for the patient. Although both the justification at the end and the initial complaint are much stronger and more impressive in this rule against the irregulars than in the preceding rule against the surgeons and apothecaries, the two rules seem to belong together and not to be separated by any interval of time or any change of attitude. There is no means of assigning a precise date to them, so that they may go back as far as the interval between 1563 (the last date for the earliest statutes) and 1581 when the Annals begin again, but more probably they were written during the general revision.

Another statute, about the dissections, has such a tang of Dr. Caius about it that it almost seems to go back to that distant interval, and it was certainly in force in 1598 when Dr. Paddy was fined for contravening it, but here again there is no definite evidence.[2] All fellows admitted in the future are to perform this anatomical function scientifically (*artificiose*) and publicly at the expense of the College. The president is to decide on the year in which each fellow is to act. The place is normally to be the College, but the president and a majority of the fellows may designate a public place outside it. None of the fellows may undertake or publicly announce a dissection in any other place unless it is more than seven miles from London except that they may publicly anatomize at the Surgeons' Hall. This freedom is, however, subject to a condition. The master and two wardens of the surgeons must first seek the president's permission, and, as it is thought most just and reasonable that those who benefit from any of the fellows should display their

___
[1] See above, p. 172.   [2] See above, p. 155.

gratitude to the College, the surgeons are to honour their demonstrator by accompanying him from the street to the theatre. Nothing is known of any private anatomy teaching in sixteenth-century London except that of Nicholas Encolius, who died in 1552 and was a fellow.[1] We therefore cannot tell whether this statute was meant to check some existing activity or merely to prevent any such enterprise in the future. In either case there is no reason for ascribing it to jealousy; the fear of dangerously misleading instruction would be an adequate ground for it. Whether there was such a fear, well-grounded or not, we do not know. The dissections do not seem to have been directly profitable to the College, so if they wished to keep everyone out of the field except themselves and the Barber-Surgeons' Company, we must suppose that they were actuated by their general purpose of maintaining high educational standards.

The one notable sign of intellectual progress is that the prohibition of alchemy has disappeared from the statutes, and with it very likely the provisions which followed it but were deleted from our only copy of the original code.[2] It should be mentioned as a possibility that this deleted passage contained, perhaps not in exactly the same form, the substance of one or other of the two rules about uroscopy; but the order of the various paragraphs in the two codes seems to tell against this possibility.

The statute on examinations is recast, but in content it remains as it was.[3] There are now three tests instead of four and they need not be separated by intervals of time. They are divided according to the arrangement of Fernel, which Dr. Gwinne had followed at Gresham College.[4] The first is in the physiological part or the science and knowledge of medicine (*in scientia et cognitione rei medicae*; the concept of physiology is still indefinite) and in the very rudiments of medicine (*in ipsis rudimentis medicinae*); but the list of prescribed books is the same, except for some verbal changes, as it was before for the first examination. The second is now described as being in the pathological part, or in the causes of diseases, the differentiae of symptoms and the signs by which physicians know the essence of diseases. The books are the same as for the original second examination. The third test is in the use and exercise of medicine, that is in the manner of treatment (*in medendi ratione*):

[1] See above, p. 85.   [2] See above, p. 96.   [3] See above, p. 98.
[4] See above, p. 170.

here the books are those of the old third part, with the addition of the two prescribed for the now eliminated fourth part. For some reason in the list of subjects with which the syllabus ends vomitories have dropped out. The details about how the questions are to be chosen, how the candidates may prepare to answer, and what answers are sufficient are also omitted, so that the examiners were now less strictly tied in their procedure and may in practice have interpreted their duties more indulgently, accepting as satisfactory a less literal knowledge of the texts, though still demanding an intelligent grasp of the subject-matter.

The ethical or penal statutes show similar concessions to common sense. Not everything said in College must be kept secret but everything that is of any moment. The fines are increased because the value of money has fallen. A new key clause against consulting with unlicensed practitioners allows the president and censors, or a majority of them, to approve such action in emergencies. The penalties for accusing a fellow before outsiders are made much more severe, but bargaining with a patient though still reprehended is no longer subject to a penalty, and is permitted if the patient insists on doing it. It is no longer an offence to reveal the name or nature of any medicine to a layman but only of those which are more powerful and dangerous, such as purgatives. The barrier against priests is to shut out licentiates as well as fellows. The duty of attending the surgical lectures is limited to five years, and a lapse from it does not disqualify for election to a fellowship. Towards the end comes a new provision, which shows that the College, without intending to spread such knowledge outside its own doors or indeed even among all its fellows, thought it undesirable that a physician should use a secret remedy without revealing its nature to the appropriate officers. No one was to refuse to make a clear and open disclosure to the president and censors, if they required him to do so, of any secret which he customarily used in his practice. Every refusal, whether of a boasted master-secret or of any other hidden medicine was to be visited with a fine or imprisonment or both at the discretion of these five officers. The wording of this clause is unusual in that it does not say to whom it applies. It may have been aimed in the first instance at empirics who advertised their remedies, but it seems also to extend to licentiates, candidates and fellows alike. They may still have and use their secrets, though the expression about master-secrets (*ista si Diis placet praeclara secreta*) is sarcastic; but they must put themselves in the hands of those who have the right to punish them if there is anything noxious in the ingredients. We do not know whether anyone in the College had advanced so far as to believe that all medical knowledge ought to be freely imparted to the whole profession, which was certainly not the official view of the College until much more than a century later; but this statute clearly proves that the College was public-spirited enough to bar its own members from one insidious by-way to malpractice.

Table of Fines in the Statuta Vetera

Absence from comitia minora if summoned unless ill, in prison or at least 2 miles from City.		2s.
Refusing office of president unless physician to the king.		40s.
Refusing office of consiliarius or censor.		40s.
Consiliarius not ready with advice unless for urgent cause (to be stated).		3s. 4d.
Revealing secret.		10s.
Accusing colleague	first offence.	£4.
	second offence.	£8 and expulsion.
	restoration after third offence.	£10.
Not ascertaining treatment of first doctor.		20s.
Bad manners at consultation.		5s.
Consulting with empiric.		40s.
Revealing name of medicament.		40s.
Corruptly bargaining with apothecary.		40s.
Associating with discommoned apothecary.		10s.
Revealing statutes.		20s.
Absence from funeral.		3s. 4d.
Absence from anatomy demonstration.		1s.–2s. 6d.

XI: THE EARLY SEVENTEENTH CENTURY, 1603–25

IT has been written that there was a 'discovery of England in Tudor times'.[1] This discovery took place in the last thirty years of Queen Elizabeth. Among its monuments are Camden's great topographical work *Britannia*, published in 1586, and the first accurate set of engraved county maps, dedicated to the queen in 1579. Not only scholars and map-makers attended to the physical lay-out of the country: there were also statesmen who thought in terms of survey. Lord Burghley himself carried a map of England about with him, and by degrees public men of all kinds fell into the new attitude of mind. In 1626, for instance, Bulstrode Whitelock, newly called to the bar, persuaded his father, who was a judge, to make the necessary arrangements so that, as he tells us, 'I rode all the circuits of England to acquaint myself with my native country'.[2] These were early signs of a major change of focus which has led in the fullness of time to the organizing of all social activity on the basis of national geographical and statistical planning. Historians have traced its development in many departments of national life, especially in economic life. The local and municipal organs of trade and industry were gradually superseded or at least overridden by national institutions and a national policy, and this widening of horizons was accompanied by a corresponding change in the working ideas of business men. The old-fashioned artisan who hugged his trade secrets and his chartered rights had to surrender trench after trench before the advance of the organizer and his ally the statesman. Everyone knows that there has been a parallel change in medical provision. The guild mentality has yielded ground to the consciousness that the profession is one whole, to the pressure of ministers and parliaments, and to the universal spirit of the scientists who abominate secrecy. But this has been the work of centuries, and they have been centuries of conflict. None of the many interested parties has ever been satisfied for long with any balance which may have

---

[1] This is part of the title of a lecture by the late Robin Flower, dealing mainly with cartography, in *Proceedings of the British Academy*, vol. xxi (1935).

[2] *Memorials* (1853), i. 20.

temporarily reconciled the conflicting claims. From the time of this discovery of England these conflicts have occupied more and more of the attention of governments and of the public.

It is always unsafe to point to any definite fact as the first manifestation of a wide social change, but perhaps it would not be wrong to say that the first medical book, or the first English classic more or less on medical subjects, which adumbrates the idea of national medical services is Robert Burton's *Anatomy of Melancholy* of 1621. In the prefatory address Burton sketches his own Utopia, and, when he comes to these matters, through his whimsicality there gleams the calculating eye of the planner. He wants hospitals of all kinds not to depend on the unstable bounty of rich benefactors who rob a thousand to relieve ten, nor to be maintained by collections and appeals which will enable them to benefit some set number of people. He wants all those who are in need to be provided for, be they more or less in number, and from the public treasury. He advocates the foundation of colleges for many professions, and in the list the physicians appear, as do also druggists, alchemists and philosophers. He has a rule for the remuneration of those lawyers, surgeons and physicians who are 'allowed to be maintained out of the public treasure'. They are neither to give nor to take fees on pain of losing their places, 'or if they do, very small fees, and when the case is fully ended'.

The present writer has failed to find any evidence that anyone else in the reign of James I thought of the physicians in England in this way. They were still too few in numbers to be material for planning or for survey. The compilers of atlases and descriptions of the country had nothing to say about them, including for instance John Speed, though he had a son in the profession.[1] Nor were the physicians on their side interested in geographical distribution. It might be thought that the College had some such considerations in mind when it granted licences for provincial practice, for some of these are limited to specified areas. The earliest recorded grants belong to 1559: the first gives William Leverett the right to practise in those places where he had practised before his admission; the second licenses Robert Dalton in his own *patria*, that is the bishopric of Durham. The former is very vague and the latter very extensive,

---

[1] See the editions of Speed's *Theatre of the Empire of Great Britain*, which began in 1611. The Speeds became a medical dynasty, three generations taking medical degrees at St. John's College, Oxford.

but even more extensive is the licence granted in 1607 to Alexander Vodka of York to practise in the counties north of the Trent. As early as 1561 one applicant, the first of a good many, was licensed for the whole country outside London and the seven-mile limit. He already had a Cambridge licence extending *per totam Angliam*; otherwise some boundary might have been set; but on the whole matter it is safe to conclude that the College neither tried to prevent overcrowding nor attempted to fill deficiencies. Most likely it permitted the applicant to practise where he said he wanted to practise.

The growth of the profession had not indeed reached a point when there was any need to provide against the inconveniences of competition. The physician arrived in a country house or in the neighbouring town more as a missionary of an unfamiliar creed than as a recruit to a settled body of workers. The idea of a 'practice' which can be passed on from one incumbent to another, an independent and impersonal entity like a canonry or a business firm, still lay in the future.[1] One physician had followed another in the service of the sovereign or a great nobleman; we have already seen sons joining their fathers in the profession, and we shall soon come across more frequent instances of this, but in the reign of James I there seems to be only one instance in which we can say for certain that the son took over his father's patients, and that, significantly, lies on the borderline between legitimate medicine and quackery. It is the inheritance of Francis Anthony's son John.[2] The country was filling up with the physicians, and indeed their steady multiplication throughout the seventeenth century amounted to a major social change. It introduced a new element in the educated community, not only bringing improvements in health but enriching the minds and stimulating the public activities of Englishmen in general; for the present, however, there was ample room, and each pioneer could easily make his way to a tract of unfelled forest.

The only geographical fact of which the College of Physicians took cognisance was the contrast between London and the provinces. So it had been from the beginning: there was a lower standard for the country physicians.[3] In one of the lawsuits of this reign counsel for the College and also one of the judges, the rich Sir Thomas

---

[1] The earliest example of this use of the word 'practice' given by the *Oxford English Dictionary* is surprisingly late: 1898.   [2] See below, p. 203.

[3] See above, p. 77. The difference of procedure for licensing city and country surgeons by the Barber Surgeons' Company, though it arose from their relation to the country guilds, may also imply a difference of standards.

Walmsley, explained the reasons. In that age, the social order was supposed to rest on rank or 'degree'. The Statutes of Henry VIII intended that in London none should practise except those who were most learned and expert, 'more than ordinary', because London was the heart of the kingdom, where the king, the judges and other great ones lived, besides which its air was more pestiferous.[1] No one was dissatisfied with this discrimination. The College, as we shall see, occasionally complained that the bishops granted licences, and the universities both licences and degrees, too freely, but it was reminded more than once that its own powers were limited to the capital.[2] Its history was not indeed merely a part of the local history of London. In population, in extent, in wealth and in power London was growing, and its dominance over the country was growing in proportion. That alone would have given the College a higher national standing, and we shall see that it did acquire reputation in the kingdom generally. When the Elizabethan fellows who had country houses were buried in their parish churches their monuments mentioned their other honours, but in the seventeenth century it became the custom to mention the fellowship.[3] Some of their country neighbours must have understood the allusion, and at least in part this must have been due to the prestige of the College itself.

The Stone House in Knightrider Street served the purposes of the College for nearly a hundred years. It was small, but so was the society that used it, and there was room for a full comitia or a banquet.[4] What other purposes it served, beyond housing the library, we do not know. It may have served as a social resort where fellows met in casual intervals of their occupations. By chance there has survived a record of a consultation held there in 1607 between Dr. Ralph Wilkinson, Dr. George Turner, and Dr. Mark Ridley, all fellows of the College, in the case of Henry Clifford.[5] Possibly

[1] Harris and Walmsley in Bonham's case as reported by Brownlow and Goldsborough: see below, p. 209, n. 7.

[2] There is an allusion to Bath in the Annals for July 1624: Dr. Foxe reported that the physicians there wished to know what action they should take against apothecaries and surgeons who practised medicine.

[3] Among the earliest examples, if not the earliest is Robert Fludd (1637).

[4] Munk, iii. 321, n. 2 gives the measurements of the building in feet of assize, which means standard feet near enough to those of the present time: frontage 24, depth 24, width at the south end or back 22½.

[5] Sir Norman Moore, *History of St. Bartholomew's Hospital* (1918), p. 450. Another reminder that we depend on chance for much of our knowledge is the College

the fellows met there in consultation with licentiates or even with tolerated physicians. For the London life of the times the position was still conveniently central, and the shortness of the distance from there to the next abode of the College shows that the move was made only in order to obtain better housing. They moved in 1614 to a house which they leased from the dean and chapter of St. Paul's, at the west end of Paternoster Row in Amen Corner, near where the canons' houses now stand, and there they were to remain for the next fifty-two years.[1] Substantial sums of money were spent on altering the building, and though we have no picture or description, it is known that it provided amply what was needed. The publishers, then called booksellers and still keeping retail shops, were already congregating in that neighbourhood, and it was not long before the College complained to the lord mayor about inconvenience from their new buildings.[2]

The freehold of the old house was not sold; it was leased to a succession of tenants and so it brought in some modest revenue.[3] The new house was held on a lease, but the price was high enough to put a strain on the finances of the College for years to come. Two great ladies gave the handsome donation of £400, the king's cousin the Lady Arabella Stuart, who was a prisoner in the Tower of London, and Mary, countess of Shrewsbury, the companion of her offence and of her captivity.[4] The College still existed financially, as it always had done, from hand to mouth, so that it was necessary to raise the rest by subscriptions and loans from fellows. There was a special committee which seems to have squeezed the fellows fairly hard, and minor sources of income were exploited, such as compounding by a payment of £20 for not giving a dinner.[5]

The change of abode does not seem to have made the smallest difference to the even flow of College business. Elections followed the old lines and raised the old difficulties. In 1605, when there

certificate, which survives in the municipal records of Totnes, that a man who applied for admission to the almshouses there was not a leper (*Hist. MSS. Comm. 3rd Report* (1872), p. 348).

[1] The last meeting in the old house was on 25 June 1614, the first at Amen Corner on 23 August and the last on 26 July 1666.

[2] 25 June 1616.

[3] Goulston held the lease in 1623/4 and appears to have paid £200 for it. 14 February, 3 March.

[4] Lists of benefactors, Brit. Mus. MS. Sloane 55, fo. 4; 3914, fo. 62ᵛ; deputation to thank the countess of Shrewsbury (still in the Tower) 24 November 1615, the date on which Moundeford presented his accounts.   [5] 25 June 1617.

were two vacancies, three names were strongly supported from outside and some of the fellows thought that Dr. Heron, the senior among the candidates, ought also to be elected. The College extricated itself from this difficulty by electing all four and approving for the first time a change of statute by which the limit of twenty-four was to be interpreted as applying only to the ordinary fellows, royal physicians being additional to the number.[1] Two years later, a sign that selection was not easy, on the president's proposal a new statute was unanimously adopted that all elections of fellows were to be by ballot.[2] The wisdom of this was shown by the incident of the election of Dr. Crooke in 1613.[3] The question of numbers, however, was still unsettled. After the election of Dr. Baskerville to fill a vacancy created by the death of Dr. Selin, the treasurer wrote a letter proposing that by special grace Dr. Winston should be admitted in excess of the number of thirty (twenty-four ordinary fellows and six royal physicians): this was carried with a minority of two against. It was then decided to draft a statute to prevent any such action in the future, which seems not to have been done.[4] Another statute was carried immediately before the election of Mayerne: that the king's personal physicians were to be admitted whatever their nationality, but that the ordinary fellows must be British.[5] A point of precedence then arose; on the president's proposal it was decided that the king's ordinary physicians in receipt of salaries and holding letters patent should come first, with the elects next after them.[6] In anticipation of another awkward election the president proposed that in all elections of a president or a fellow, voting should be by ballot, the majority of those present deciding, and that if there were a tie a third man should be nominated. This was voted on three times. The number of fellows present was twenty on the first occasion, twenty-two on the second and thirty on the third; but the votes in favour were thirteen the first time (the president said fifteen), thirteen the second time, and fourteen the third. The number of negative votes and abstentions are not given, but these figures seem to reveal a steady majority and a futile whipping-up of opponents. But why should anyone have

[1] 22 December 1605. See above, p. 132.
[2] 22 December 1607. Balloting was prescribed for elections of fellows in the earliest statutes and the method described exactly in the revised statutes of 1647. Peas and beans were to be put into an urn, peas for ay, beans for no.
[3] See below, p. 205.   [4] 20 March 1614/15.
[5] 20, 25 June 1616. See below, p. 193.   [6] 3, 23 December 1616.

opposed such a harmless measure?[1] At last in 1618 the number of fellows was raised to thirty-four, including four royal physicians.[2]

The Annals of these years do indeed give the impression that when the fellows desired to alter their statutes, they did not always understand clearly what the existing statutes amounted to. The reading of the statutes at the solemn comitia was broken off on four occasions to consider points that might be amended, or simply because they were undergoing amendment.[3] There were two fairly long intervals during which the statutes were allowed to stay as they were, 1611–15 and 1619–21, but in the other years there were several changes, none of them amounting to very much. Some amendments gave effect to the recommendations of the judges in 1607[4]; there were changes in the regulations for admissions and elections, some of which have already been noticed. Their tendency was towards greater strictness. The most notable was the provision that new statutes must be agreed to by a majority of all the fellows.[5] A general revision, for which committees were appointed in 1623 and 1624, was still in progress in the following spring. No doubt it was delayed by the interruptions of the plague, and it was not completed until September 1626. No copy of the statutes as then revised is known, and it will be best to postpone observations on them until we reach the next revision, that of 1647.[6]

In enforcing discipline over its own members of all three grades the College discharged an invidious duty, so far as we can tell, judiciously and by so doing it not only made its own members more useful to the community but also set an example to the profession outside London. This work fell roughly into two parts, dealing respectively with malpractice and with professional etiquette. Of the former, no doubt the more important of the two, there is comparatively little to say. Only some exceptional circumstance could bring to notice the action of a physician in his solitary visits to patients. When Sir John Popham, a good friend to the College, died his friends and servants complained that he had been wrongly treated by Dr. Rawlins. After a discussion which occupied one full meeting of the comitia majora, the president and censors went into the matter thoroughly. They acquitted their colleague of both

---

[1] 3 July; 25, 30 September 1618.   [2] 18 April 1618.
[3] 26 June, 22 December 1609; 25 June 1610; 22 December 1617. On 22 December 1608 some recently approved statutes were sealed, probably the same as were submitted to Sir Christopher Yelverton for his opinion on 3 March 1608/9.
[4] 8 May 1607. See below, p. 210.   [5] 20, 21 April 1618.   [6] See below, p. 278.

malice and ignorance, but they reproved him for dealing single-handed with such a grave illness of so great a man, and for giving him so many medicines in his feeble condition when many people (presumably the friends and servants) were opposed to this treatment. Further they understood that Dr. Rawlins made up many medicines at home and sold them as secret remedies at unreasonable prices. In future he was to show them, if required, to the proper officers, and if he refused or offended in any of these particulars he was to pay a fine of £20. It cannot be said that, for the times, this showed either excessive regard for an eminent patient or excessive indulgence for the practitioner.[1]

This was the only case of adjudication on the practice of a fellow but there is no reason whatever to suppose that malpractices went on without coming to the notice of the College. The licentiate Dr. Domingo was accused of pushing an antidote to poison of unknown composition imported by an Italian. He said that he had seen it work successfully against four different poisons administered to dogs, but he was forbidden to administer anything unless he really knew about it.[2] Another licentiate Dr. John Brouart gave trouble on and off for more than twenty years. Arriving in England as a young Leiden graduate, he practised as Mayerne's assistant, and the College doubted whether that was worthy of a doctor. He wore his doctor's cap when he made his application, and produced a letter from the king out of his boot. Dr. Winston, quite unjustifiably, demanded that he should incorporate at an English university before being licensed; but several years later there were charges against him. No conviction ensured when an apothecary charged him with exacting a high price for a powder, the unintelligible recipe for which he refused to interpret. When Dr. Spicer declined to physic a patient because of his age and the time of year, the luckless Frenchman took over with a clyster and venesection; the patient died. The president settled this matter privately by exacting a fine of £5, but it was not Brouart's last offence, and as he was alleged to have accepted a fee of 2d. he seems to have sunk low.[3]

For the most part the matters of etiquette are scarcely worth our attention at this distance of time. Questions of manners in

---

[1] 24 June, 3 July 1607.　　　　　[2] 19 January 1610/11, /July 1607.
[3] 25 June, 13 August 1613; 11 July 1623; 3 March 1625/6; 4, 11 June, 10 December 1630; 23 May, 25 June 1635.

comitia and outside did not always arise from professional mis-
conduct. Dr. Ridgely, afterwards a fellow and well-provided with
recommendations from court, lost his temper when called on to pay
his licentiate's fee, 'stood much upon his gentry', and was rebuked.
Dr. Diodati, remembered for being the father of Milton's friend,
deserves sympathy as a religious exile, but it was very rude of him
to say, on the same provocation, that he was as good a man as the
president.[1] When Dr. de Laune twice persuaded a patient not to
take the medicine Diodati prescribed, the latter became abusive
in both French and Latin and had to be reprimanded.[2] The unfortunate Dr. Rawlins, in spite of various excuses, was fined 40s.
for giving medicine to one of Dr. Moundeford's patients.[3] There
was a squabble between Dr. Hering and Dr. Wright when they
both arrived to treat the same case.[4] Dr. Hamey and Dr. Wright
were, to us mysteriously, warned to behave better towards the
fellows.[5] Dr. Goulston was made to apologize in English words
prescribed by the censors for contradicting Dr. Hering and Dr.
Pattison in practice and speaking ill of them contrary to the statute.[6]
Even if they deserved what he said it may very well have been in
the public interest to muzzle him; just as the president was no
doubt right in refusing to break up the harmony of a convivial
occasion by going into allegations of slander between Sir William
Paddy and Dr. Hering.[7] At another dinner Dr. Hering got across
with Dr. Palmer.[8]

The College did not relax its vigilance in guarding its privileges.
In 1614 Sir William Paddy appeared before the lord mayor and a
full court of aldermen and secured a re-affirmation of the exemption
from bearing arms. This court asked for a full list of the fellows,
licentiates and candidates, which was duly handed in: the total
number was forty-one. The College was authorized to commit for
trial all other, unlicensed, physicians and surgeons who refused to
bear arms.[9] Nor would the College allow the hospitals to ignore its
existence. Dr. Palmer resigned his position as physician to St.
Thomas's and was charged with trying to introduce as his successor
a doctor unknown to the College and not a licentiate. He resented

---

[1] 9 November 1621.   [2] 17, 20, 23, 30 September 1622.
[3] 18 April 1602.   [4] October 1624.   [5] 12 August 1613.
[6] 23 May 1614.   [7] 23 August 1614.
[8] 25 June 1616. The licentiate Dr. Henry Smith uttered approbious words to the
president in the street, but threats sufficed to bring him to better behaviour: 4 June
1624.   [9] 30 September 1614.

this, but Sir William Paddy as president talked about the privileges and about legal proceedings; the comitia unanimously agreed that the matter gravely concerned the College and that Dr. Palmer had behaved wrongly. On further consideration, however, they decided to see whether the new man could pass the examination for a licence, which he did.[1]

As before the principal services done by the College to public authorities were connected with defence against the plague. The first royal order came from the lord treasurer direct and not through the City, in 1608/9: it was for four or more fellows to give counsel and help to sufferers in the City in return for a suitable salary. The president called for volunteers and six came forward.[2] At the president's request some of the fellows prepared notes on precautions and treatment for submission to the lord treasurer and the king, and these were digested by a committee.[3] The bad plague years restricted activity. There were no meetings between 17 June and 22 December 1603, and then none until 2 April 1604. No doubt for the same reason there were very thin comitia in 1610 and 1612/13.

One doleful task discharged by the College is remembered in general history. Sir Ralph Winwood, secretary of state, sent an order for three of their society to carry out a post-mortem examination, with her own physicians, on the body of their benefactor the Lady Arabella Stuart, who had died in the Tower. The report bears the signatures of six doctors, all of whom were fellows, though perhaps only three were there as representatives of the College.[4]

For a short time after the Gunpowder Plot it looked as if religion would give the College more anxiety than it had done for a good many years. In a new penal law it was enacted that no convicted recusant should at any time practise physic, nor use or exercise the trade or art of an apothecary, on pain of a fine of £100 of which half was to go to the king and half to the informer.[5] The law and the army were the only other professions that were treated so. The College obeyed this law in granting licences, and the question was once raised whether it ought not to go further and refuse even to examine papists.[6] A few years later parliament enacted that the

[1] 11 December 1609.
[2] 24 February 1608/9 Turner, Hering, Gwinn, Clement and, after them, Pope and Foxe.   [3] 3 March 1608/9: Paddy, Frear, Argeant, Palmer, Gwinne.
[4] 27 September 1615: Moundford (president), Paddy, Lister, Palmer, Argent, Gwinne.
[5] 3 Jac. I, c. 5, sec. 8.   [6] 23 December 1616.

oath of allegiance was to be taken by all the king's subjects. In the list of classes of people to whom it was to be tendered the last but one, after the universities and followed only by the aldermen, freemen etc. of corporate towns (the mayors being higher up) is 'all doctors of physick, and all other who practice physick, that now are or hereafter shall be admitted into the College of Physicians in London'. The fellows took the oath in two batches, on the second occasion with five licentiates also.[1] There were some Roman catholics who were able to reconcile the form of this oath with their consciences and the king had publicly defended it in print as unexceptionable, but in practice it operated as a religious test. The times, however, grew gentler and the College began to tolerate those whom it could not admit.[2] Neither the state nor the established church raised any objection. There was a fashionable practitioner, Dr. John Moore, whom everyone knew to be a Roman Catholic. The censors had their eye on him. He had been inhibited by Archbishop Abbot, or so it was said. He deposited £20 with the president, asking for a licence. The College prudently consulted the archbishop and he, going much beyond the law, advised them to admit neither papists nor puritans to practice. The president laid this letter before the comitia and asked whether Moore's practice should be connived at, if he passed the necessary examinations and until the king or the privy council prohibited him. Dr. Moore then handsomely offered his £20 as a free gift, and at some uncertain date some kind of promise was made him, for he settled down to paying an annual fee of £4.[3]

The most annoying of the Puritans the College had to do with was a demented citizen who had migrated from the Tallowchandlers to the Barber-Surgeons' Company and claimed to have learnt 'all his skill . . . of one Dr. Scull of Amsterdam, where he was sometyme a Brother'. He was several times in and out of the Counter in Wood Street; but he had supporters among the citizens, including a sheriff.[4] The turbulent Archbishop Williams of York took up his cause, and being also dean of Westminster as well as lord keeper, gave him a licence to practise in the liberties of Westminster. The College decided by a majority to send a deputation with its written

---

[1] 7 Jac. I, c. 6; 2 November 1610; 11 January 1610/11.   [2] See below, p. 233.
[3] 25 June 1612; 7 May, 4 June 1613; 22 December 1617; 3 July 1618; 1618/19; 3 March 1625/6.
[4] 3 May 1616; 5 December 1617; 9 January 1617/18; 8 May 1618, 12, 25 February 1618/19; 9, 15 June 1618; 9 April 1619.

protest which suggested that the archbishop's action was a try-on. The great man melted, admitted that he had only done it to please the wife of Sir Edwin Sandys, and politely gave in.[1]

In the City Puritan opposition to things as they were was becoming stronger and joining hands with other kinds of discontent. Among the fellows were some whose antecedents connected them with militant protestantism. Dr. Foxe's father wrote the classic Foxe's *Martyrs*, and Dr. Delaune came of Huguenot stock. We do not know whether they or others of the fellows sympathized with the growing opposition, and we cannot interpret the brief summary of a very elegant speech which Dr. Palmer made as president in 1621. He complained of too much talking and of mutterings, and of the opinions of many in the College not about medicine or science, but about public affairs.[2]

The reign of James I saw little or no change in the propensity of great men to commend their protégés to the College for one favour or another, but it brought a stiffening of the reactions of the College to it. To the king himself they showed all due deference. His Scottish physician Dr. Craig, after being admitted a fellow, incorporated at Oxford and a year later was co-opted as an elect.[3] When the time came to admit him some of the fellows raised the question whether this promotion was lawful since he was not an Englishman. After various arguments it was unanimously decided that the sole purpose of the statute was to exclude persons of foreign birth, and that as the Scots lived in the same island with the English and were governed by the same king the distinction between them had been abolished.[4] Legally it had not: three years later the judges decided that Scots born after the king's accession were naturalized but not those born before.[5] The king knew that the issue was still open, and he had strong feelings about it. The president produced a letter in which the monarch not very tactfully intimated his wish. In any event, he said, 'Wee purpose' to naturalize Craig 'out of hand'; but 'things are now betweene the two nations

---

[1] 15, 16 December 1623, 15 January, 5 November 1624. For other Puritan offenders see Burgess and Henoch Clapham, below, pp. 214, 216. John Pembrook, an advertiser, also had Puritan connexions: he admitted obtaining a remedy for gout from William Jacob, a Brownist: 3 May 1616.

[2] 'De doctrina non medica philosophica, sed pollitica.'

[3] For his admission as fellow see below, p. 197. [4] 3 January 1605/6.

[5] The case of the post-nati, also known as Calvin's case, from the name of the plaintiff Robert Calvin or Colville, afterwards second Lord Colville of Culross, in Cobbett's *State Trials*, ii (1809), 559.

in such termes, as no man of iudgment can accompt them two, but one'.[1] Craig was then admitted, and it was decided that *natione Britannus* should be substituted for *natione Anglicus* in the statute.[2] In this the College showed itself more liberal and more sensible than Oxford and Cambridge. When the king ventured to enquire about the possibility of finding places in those universities for students from Scotland, the heads of the colleges replied that their statutes made it impossible.[3] Very likely this was true and very likely the heads believed that they were irrevocably bound; but the lawyers could have come to the rescue.

Mystery surrounds a second intervention by the king. He wrote in support of Dr. Ridgley, whose election as a fellow had been held back in order that the candidates, of whom he was one, might be taken in order of seniority. In spite of much expostulation the president moved his election, but the elects and others asked to have it deferred until there should be a vacancy. A reply to the king was drafted, stating that the statutes forbade the election until that should come about. What followed, according to the registrar, the gods might know, but the College never heard.[4]

When King James's own last illness was coming upon him, he put Dr. Atkins, the president, in an awkward predicament by telling him about the treatment of an epileptic by one Savery.[5] The College knew that name. One of the candidates, in giving the censors a list of eight men and two women with bad records had added: 'But of all the Empericks about this Cittie it is not credible the practice that Savery hath.'[6] When the president reported what the king had said four of the senior fellows spoke up about Savery's impostures.[7] They were told to put it in writing for Atkins to show to the king. Later Atkins and Harvey brought a relation from the king's majesty. Savery had said that he was no physician but for the epilepsy only, and if he dealt with other patients the king would have him suppressed. Dr. Foxe advised that the king should be prayed to allow the College its right of summons and interrogation on oath, but that was not done.[8] Nothing more is heard of Savery.

---

[1] Copy in Annals after 31 January 1605/6.
[2] This was unanimously carried for the second time on 8 January.
[3] *Calendar of State Papers, Domestic, 1603–1610* (1857), pp. 569, 571; *1611–1618*, (1858), nos. 17–18.
[4] 1621. Dr. Ridgley became a fellow on 28 November 1622.   [5] 7 January 1624/5.
[6] 1623. He was one of the empirics consulted by the countess of Somerset in her career of crime.
[7] Moundeford, Fox, Meverell, and Wright.   [8] For this see below, pp. 231, 235.

Usually the College resisted undue pressure. The incorrigible Roger Jinkins once got off without even a reprimand mainly because he had been taken into the service of Lord Chancellor Ellesmere; but his master was very civil and promised that Jinkins should mend his ways.[1] Lord Sydney does not seem to have persisted in supporting one Saul, in the queen's service, who had been rejected for a licence in 1591, when he claimed to be a doctor of Leiden, but was so ignorant that the College wrote to Heurnius, the professor there, 'sharply reprehending him for committing such an error'.[2] Archbishop Bancroft was easily persuaded to withdraw his request for the release of the offending surgeon Lumken from prison: the man died at the house of his great patron Dr. Thomas Blaze, dean of Rochester.[3] Archbishop Abbot seems to have subsided quietly after being remonstrated with for telling Lady Wenman that an irritating woman, Mrs. Paine, did more good than all the physicians.[4] It was not so easy to dispose of the archbishop when he wanted a licence for John de Nicolas, a Spanish refugee who was a doctor of medicine but also a priest. Abbott suavely told the College deputation that the priestly character need not be held to be indelible. The College, instead of sticking only to the argument from its statutes, unwisely wrote that the number of medical men in London had already grown and the king had recently ordered all persons of quality to depart from London to their 'countries', so that fewer would be needed.[5] Abbott answered truly that this order would not stand in the way for long, but fortunately the College discovered that Nicolas was a flagitious rascal and that was the end of him.[6]

A third archbishop was the ill-fated dignitary Mark Anthony de Dominis, who wrote from his lodgings in the Savoy in favour of an Italian oculist, a protestant refugee from Ferrara, unqualified, but an honest man in his art. Dr. Foxe examined the honest man in Italian, and owning that he was ignorant of the anatomy of the eye, he answered that he only used one 'water' which, if it did no good

---

[1] 3 August 1604. Was it our old friend who was admonished on 6 February 1604/5 under the name of Jinkinson? See p. 155 above.

[2] See above, p. 135.

[3] 7 July 1606. See above, p. 152. Lumken's record of crime begins in 1589. Not long before his last imprisonment he was released at the request of the earl of Northumberland: 19, 20 July 1605, and *Historical Manuscripts Commission, Third Report* (1872), p. 53: the letter of the president and censors there printed is to Northumberland.

[4] 26 June 1615.

[5] Proclamation of 26 March 1622/3, Steele and Crawford, no. 1354.

[6] 28 October 1623.

likewise did no harm. The College refused its licence and wrote that it could do no more than tolerate him; it was for the surgeons to see whether he confined himself to his oculist's work, and the archbishop must be aware that in Venice, where he came from, even doctors were subject to similar local regulations.[1]

The prelates behaved reasonably well and so did such of the judges as backed their friends.[2] Once a concession was made to the countess of Richmond. She recommended Theodore Maileman of St. John's College, Oxford and Leiden. He was examined in English and made a hash of it; 'but for to give my Ladye content, let him be examined againe'.[3] Altogether there was too much of this sort of interference from outside. At an election of fellows one candidate was supported by the lord chancellor, a second by eight peers, and another by Archbishop Bancroft and Sir John Popham.[4] Leonard Po, of all people, mobilized his privy councillors first to gain him a general licence, which was grudgingly granted by a majority,[5] and then to help him to election as a fellow. Though the College affirmed the strictness of its statutes he was elected, again only be a majority, and politely welcomed by the president.[6] Some years later, although there had been no further mortifying occurrence like this, the College looked to its defences. Dr. Moundeford was one of the fellows who signed Po's general licence, but as president he proposed a new statute that any candidate who brought a letter of recommendation from any magnate was *ipso facto* to be rejected in the election to the fellowship.[7] At this time the proposal did not go through, but Dr. Atkins revived it when he had succeeded to the presidency, and so put an end to the abuse.[8]

The registrar did not record the death of Queen Elizabeth I in the College Annals. There was no reason why he should. No previous demise of the Crown was entered there, and the College had no happy private or personal memories of the great lady. She

[1] 17 September 1619.

[2] Popham himself, 15 October 1605; Sir David Williams, 10 April 1609. The latter's protégé John Malen was promised a licence 'quantum in nobis erit', but there the matter seems to have ended.

[3] 23 See E. Jameson, *Natural History of Quackery* (1961), pp. 25–7 Maileman is not in Innes-Smith.

[4] 22 December 1605.   [5] 11 December 1606. See above, p. 148.

[6] 25 June, 7 July 1609.

[7] 20 March 1614/5. The occasion of this seems to have been a letter from the earl of Suffolk supporting Winston against Baskerville.

[8] 21 April 1618, after the election of Ramsey who had the support of Viscount Haddington.

had indeed assented to the Charter granting anatomical subjects, but except for that official formality her name appeared in the College records only as a protector of John Banister and of certain unlicensed practitioners. When the new king had set out on his leisurely southward ride from Edinburgh the College did indeed consider whether it should greet him in a body on his arrival, with a suitable oration; but it decided not to do so unless ordered by his councillors.[1] No such order came. The change of sovereign only brought up one matter of business, and that was easily disposed of. As we have seen James I brought with him his first physician in Scotland, John Craig, who became physician in ordinary in England. It was advisable to find room for him in the College. Three days before the king arrived in London an applicant for admission replied 'satis apte' to the examiners; nevertheless his further examination was deferred and for the time being he was allowed to practise by connivance. Eleven months later Craig was examined and elected as a foreigner for the next vacancy; on the same day the Englishman was examined for the second time and in due course he passed his two other examinations and was sworn in as a candidate, having waited altogether seventeen months. The incident would scarcely be worth mentioning except that the name of the Englishman was William Harvey.[2]

Intellectually Craig was well worthy of his new position: he was a doctor of Basel, a friend and scientific correspondent of Tycho Brahe. His coming was in fact the first sign that King James, himself a scholar, an author, and an enemy to superstition, would pay attention to theoretical matters and to learned men, including physicians. Not long afterwards another and much more eminent foreign doctor appeared at court, Theodore Turquet de Mayerne, who finally settled in London in 1611 soon to become and long to remain a dominant figure in English medicine. Among other things he is famous for his notes of cases, many of which are still preserved in print and in manuscript, and it was probably through his example and influence that English medical men began to keep such notes, a notable improvement in their methods. But a year before Mayerne

[1] 21 April 1603.
[2] For the dates of the king's journey see S. Clarke, *Historian's Guide* (1690), pp. 1–2. Harvey was examined on 4 May 1603, 2 April, 11 May, 7 August and 5 October 1604, Craig on 2 April 1604. Munk, by one of his few lapses from accuracy, describes Craig as having attended King James in his last illness, when in fact this was his son and namesake.

paid his first visit to England an English writer known to the king had advocated the same reform, deploring 'the discontinuance of the ancient and serious diligence of Hippocrates, which used to set down a narrative of the special cases of his patients, and how they proceeded, and how they were judged by recovery or death'.[1] This author was Francis Bacon, and the book in which the criticism was thrown out, a survey of all knowledge and its prospects and the impediments to it, dedicated to James I, still stands as one of our classics. Bacon did not indeed write on medical matters as an expert, though he had the advantage of being a valetudinarian. He may have picked up the idea of case-notes from someone else, possibly even at second hand from Mayerne; but, however he collected his materials, the pages in which he reviewed medical science and practice were written with all his power. They criticized the current science with its 'much iteration but small addition' and the current practice, in which 'empirics and old women are more happy many times in their cures than learned physicians'. They are as pungent as Montaigne, and as irresistible as Euclid.

Sooner or later the movements of thought were bound to affect the daily work of the College of Physicians; it would be unreasonable to expect much direct evidence of this, but some we do find. Early in the new reign the College had an opportunity of showing where it stood in one of the crucial questions. The new bishop of London, Dr. Vaughan, asked its opinion on a girl who was held to be demoniac. Certain of their number were sent to see her and having used all proper means of investigation they found nothing but naked fictions and manifest simulations. Three fellows conveyed to the bishop the opinion of the College that this was a case of fraud.[2] After that there were only occasional flickerings from the practice or the suspicion of magic. John Bell, a minister of religion had written superstitious words on paper and used it to treat a woman suffering from a fever. He admitted it and promised not to repeat

---

[1] *Of the Proficience and Advancement of learning Divine and Human* (1605), pp. 38 ff. The substance of this whole passage is expanded in the Latin *De Augmentis Scientiarum* (1623), bk. iv, with some new thrusts, for instance on geriatrics, and on the eminence of physicians in studies other than their own.

[2] 4 March 1604/5. This was the case of Nan Gunter, which Harvey mentions in his *Praelectiones* fo. 11 v.: 'puto callum fecisse the mad woman pins in her arme', meaning that a callus was made fraudulently. For the rest of her story see R. A. Hunter and Ida MacAlpine in *Journal of the History of Medicine* xii (1957), 126. No decision is recorded in the case of 18 February 1613/4 when Mrs. Godfrey was accused of treating a child of 21 months who was said to be bewitched.

the offence; another man also promised on his behalf and he was dismissed unpunished.[1] Simon Forman was still about the great houses, setting up his *figura* and predicting before he prescribed.[2] His evil reputation grew worse year by year until his death in 1611. A wretched debtor who had been in the King's Bench Prison for seven years was fined 40s. for applying to his patients what appeared to be clean clouts, though he said there was the adamant on them which was both attractive and repellent: 'the North drawes and the South drives back'.[3] Another charlatan, one Robert Booker, anointed a patient from head to foot, recited a charm ('Three biters have bitt him, heart, tongue and eye', &c.), then gave him drink, making him believe that he was bewitched by someone whose identity the practitioner would disclose. This time the censors and the president wavered. In a report addressed to some unnamed authority they wrote: 'Of which witchcraft howbeit there may be some strangeness of the sick man's infirmity' and they thought that after his punishment for rash and evil practice he 'may be further ordered as your honour shall think fit'.[4] Even Booker was not the last magician who troubled the College.

Another crucial question was that between Galenic and chemical medicines. Mayerne had been unpleasantly involved in it in Paris. He had been attacked for lecturing in support of the use of chemical medicines; in reply he had maintained in a short treatise that they might safely be used without any breach of the rules of Hippocrates and Galen; the university physicians had condemned his treatise unanimously and had inflicted penalties on him. The English College was still faithful to Galen in its examinations. Theodore Goulston, who was elected a fellow in 1611, was a Greek scholar and busied himself with the text of Galen's minor works. A Cambridge doctor called Robert Allot, a fellow of St. John's, made his one appearance at the College and was examined, not severely: the result was without prejudice to any further examination, but he appeared too little versed in Galen and was therefore warned to study him more diligently. Whether he followed this advice does not appear, but six years later he was admitted a brother of the

---

[1] 7 November 1606.   [2] 4 December 1606; 13 March 1606/7.
[3] Christopher Beane, 6 February, 1617/18.
[4] 11 June 1623. His honour was some authority outside the College who had submitted the case to it. As he seems from these words to have had some jurisdiction, he may have been a judge, or the lord mayor or an ecclesiastic. The report was written afterwards by Dr. Clement who had attended with the president, Winston and Raven, the other censors.

Barber-Surgeons' Company.[1] Two other doctors, one from Cambridge and the other from Leiden were given the same advice when they passed, the latter being admonished also to attend to Hippocrates.[2] On another occasion, however, it may be held that the College's Galenism was now as moderate and tolerant as Mayerne's. This was before Mayerne came to England: when Robert Fludd of Oxford presented himself he was examined in both sorts of medicine, Galenic and chemical.[3]

This time Fludd failed in both; but three years later he became a fellow, to serve in due course four times as a censor. His entry to the College had been delayed more than once by his rudeness and by his disparaging remarks out of doors about the Galenists. Before very long he was an international celebrity, pouring out books under his own name and under pseudonyms to advocate Rosicrucianism, the contemporary hybrid of alchemy and theology. He practised successfully and lived in style, all of which made it embarrassing for the College that he was an incorrigible rebel, keeping an apothecary in his home. When matters of medical doctrine came before the College they always came as they did in Fludd's case, not as abstract questions of theory, but as elements in questions for practical decisions, and these necessarily turned on a mixture of personal and other factors as well. The record of the College in such deliberations is not unblemished, but it shows a consistent, if not always immovable, wish to choose the wiser alternatives.

There was a licentiate, admitted as such in 1594, called Stephen Bredwell, the son of a reputable licentiate of the College, and grandson of John Banister.[4] He was born in Oxford and studied medicine there, but had no doctor's degree. In 1607, when Dr. Hering and others of the fellows complained of his rudeness and pertinacity in consultations and elsewhere, he received a friendly warning that he should behave better.[5] Less than a month later there was a similar complaint against him from Dr. Forster[6] after which the College let him alone for three years, but then he appeared in full comitia and showed such insolence that the president sent him out and told him to come to the next meeting in a better frame of mind.[7] When he did reappear it turned out that he had offended in

[1] 5 July 1608; Young, *Annals*, p. 331.   [2] 5 June, 9 October 1618.
[3] 8 November 1608: 'in utraque medicina Galenica et Spagyrica.' Fludd had been a licentiate since 1606.   [4] See above, pp. 138–9.
[5] 7 August 1607.   [6] 4 September 1607.   [7] 2 April 1610.

three several ways. He had written in a 'libellus' that he would prepare medicines in his house and sell them and that he would 'retain' apothecaries. Secondly he had promulgated certain erroneous opinions of Sabucus Hispanus.[1] Thirdly he had claimed to be a fellow of the College by the same right as the others. Mr. Bredwell surrendered; he owned himself wrong in all three counts; but he did not sign the short form of apology and submission which was tendered to him. At a subsequent censors' day, after disregarding several summonses, he was charged with breaking his licentiate's oath and fined £4 for his contumacy and for the *libellus*. Month after month he kept up his resistance. The College, according to the registrar, thought very poorly of him, but in 1610/11 he took the oath of allegiance along with the other licentiates, and it looks as if in the end he lost nothing except honour.[2]

What are we to think of the College's attitude to him? In the point about his status there may be a trace of feeling that the licentiates had lost some of their rights since Linacre's time; or there may even be a crude anticipation of the licentiates' revolt of a century later. On the point about medicines and apothecaries the College had its statutes behind it. As to Sabucus and the paradox we should have Harvey against us unless we agreed, as Bredwell was made to do, that the *Galenici* had judged better of these matters, for Harvey was one of the fifteen inquisitors who made him recant. Whether he or any of the College knew the original work of 'Sabucus' may be doubted, for if they had seen the title-page they could hardly have failed to notice that the ostensible author was a woman, and if they had noticed it they could hardly have failed to say so, and they would not have invented a masculine Latin form for the name.

Much longer and much more tormenting was the episode of Francis Anthony. He answered his first summons in 1600, as a Cambridge M.A. of twenty-six years standing, and he made no

---

[1] 25 June 1610. The 'libellus', perhaps a broadsheet advertisement, does not seem to have survived. The charge 'quod παράδοξον Sabuci Hispani de chyli transitu, mesaricarum tractu umbilicalis usu, fibris, oesophagi omnigenis, nutritione per cutum, et aliis male promulgavit' evidently relates to the book, Oliva Sabuco de Nantes Barrera, *Nova Philosophia de Hominis Natura*, written by an apothecary of Alcaraz of which there were editions published in Madrid in 1587, 1588, 1622, and later. It professes to upset the physiology not only of Galen and Hippocrates but of others down to Fernel. For the imposture by which the authorship was ascribed to the author's daughter see F. M. Torner, *Doña Oliva Sabuco de Nantes (s.a. ?1935)*.

[2] 1 October, 9 November, 22 December 1610, 11 January 1610/11. For the oath see below, p. 192.

15

difficulty about admitting that he was practising in London. He was a chemical empiric with no medical qualifications; he administered a diaphoretic medicament prepared from gold and silver, and he mentioned the lord chamberlain (the younger Hunsdon), Sir (?John) Spenser and Sir Anthony Paulet as patients. He was examined, found to be very imperfect in all the parts of medicine and wholly unlearned, and forbidden to practise. He carried his practice on, and was packed off to the Counter in Wood Street. The lord chief justice let him out, and the College sent the usual deputation, whereupon Anthony submitted and the College contented itself with a fine of £5.[1] Three months later he was at it again, and, refusing to pay another fine of £5 he was fined the maximum of £20 and again committed to prison.[2] Less than another year and he confessed to two other cases, one of which had ended fatally. He was imprisoned; his wife begged for mercy with tears but in vain. The whole assembled College was amazed when a combative person of the name of Tippar appeared on his behalf, loudly demanding the return of £20 which he had paid to the president for Anthony's release, 'calling some of the companie beggarly Jackes; and geeving the lye in the throat to other soome; and to the whole assembly saieng, that he cared not a fart for them'. But it was mainly at Tippar's instance that the College relented again. By this time Anthony was in poverty[3] and for several years his story is almost a blank,[4] but they must have been years of recuperation. In 1609 there was much about him in the now lost Book of Examinations.[5]

In 1610 Anthony wrote a letter to the president and censors with a copy of his book on drinkable gold.[6] Thus began a public controversy in which Matthew Gwinne, professor of medicine at Gresham College, wrote against Anthony as the champion of the College of Physicians. He maintained the positions that metallic medicines were not superior to vegetable and animal medicines, that Anthony's method did not dissolve gold and that there was no such thing as a panacea. Commendatory verses were included in the book in the

---

[1] 5 July, 7 November, 5, 22 December 1600, 6 February 1600/1.
[2] 8 May 1601.   [3] 5, 19 February 1601/2, 11 June, 3, 6 August 1602.
[4] A serious charge on 7 November 1606 was not followed up.
[5] 10 April 1609.
[6] *Medicinae Chymicae et Veri Potabilis Auri Assertio* (Cambridge, 1610). The idea and the name of potable gold were not new: they go back to the sixteenth century, and Shakespeare's Prince Harry says 'Other less fine in carat is more precious, Preserving life in medicine potable'. In the catalogue of the College library in 1660 there appears Quatriami, *Dichiaratione di tutte le metaphore e dell oro potabile* (Rome, 1587).

manner of the time, and their writers were among the most solid members of the College: Paddy, Craig, Forster, Fryer, and Hammond. Paddy, as president certified his approbation at the end, and the dedication was to the king. It is only from this book and not from its own records that we know of a trial of Anthony's method which had been conducted by the College in 1609, in the presence of Lord Knyvet, the warden of the Mint and several experts, with a negative result.[1] Anthony replied to Gwinne, and in the year of his death, 1623, he was again assailed by a less considerable opponent, Dr. John Cotta, a practitioner in Northampton who wrote several books but did not write very well. So far as the learned world was concerned the general question about metals was not yet closed; but the greater knowledge of the present time as good as confirms Gwinne's conclusions, though not all his arguments.

It was, however, as a practitioner that Anthony concerned the College directly, and in this capacity there were decisions to prosecute him in 1612 and in 1616,[2] but apparently nothing came of them. In 1614, according to Dr. Goulston, a dying theologian, Dr. Sanderson, put the blame on the *aurum potabile*, for which he had paid first £1 and then 40s. for essence of gold.[3] The chemical empiric seems to have gone on his way unmolested, perhaps because he had powerful friends; but it is probable that he came to appreciate the advantages of conformity. His two sons both became physicians. One of them, John Anthony, became a dutiful fellow of the College, though he is said to have gained a handsome income from selling his father's remedy, and there were one or two occasions when he gave trouble to the censors. It is curious to notice that he first came to the notice of the College through a letter of introduction written soon after his father's death by the duke of Richmond.[4]

The whole of the routine work of the president and censors in examining amounted, of course, to steadily insisting on respect for the art as they understood it, and occasionally it bore on some particular point of science. In 1611 they gave a certificate condemning as dangerous to life a medicine which had antimony as one of its

---

[1] *Aurum non Aurum* (1611), p. 169. The actual title is very long: *In Amatorem Chymiae Assertorem . . . Fra. Anthonium, Matthaei Gwynn . . . Adversaria*. For some inscrutable reason Gwinne, who wrote the Annals at this time, said (p. 169) that it came 'ex Actis sive Annalibus Collegii'.

[2] 16 October. [3] 18 April 1614; 13 September 1616.

[4] 22 December 1623; 23 January 1623/4; 3 February 1625/6; 8 June, 7 December 1632; 11 October, 6 December 1650.

ingredients.[1] At a later time Dr. Ramsey complained of Dr. Diodati, of whom we have heard before,[2] that he had maintained paradoxes, one as coming from Fernel, that the heat of the urine was mitigated by fasting: Diodati denied the charge as malicious.[3] There were questions about Dr. Helkiah Crooke's book on anatomy. Dr. Crooke's name was already connected with several scarcely creditable incidents. Before scraping in as a candidate by ten votes out of fifteen he was under censure for indiscipline, and afterwards he had to apologize to the president for disrespect in the course of defending himself against overcharging for bad treatment.[4] In 1614 the bishop of London, John King, who had the duty, under the star chamber ordinance then in force, of licensing medical books, submitted for the advice of the College a copy of a book on human anatomy written for the surgeons by Crooke and half-printed. Some of the fellows held that nothing of the sort should be printed in English. Others thought that the more obscene *quaestiones* and diagrams should be cut out and the rest corrected; a large majority (*plurimi*) thought that book iv, on the parts of generation, should be deleted and that Crooke should be enjoined to admit that the work was a translation, as it was largely derived from Laurentius and Bauhinus. The comitia decided to send Sir William Paddy and Dr. Lister to the bishop to arrange that the whole work should be suppressed and the printer paid or, failing that, that book iv should be deleted.[5] Crooke was in arrears with his fees to the College, and does not seem to have behaved in a conciliatory manner.[6] Several months later the president told the wife of Jaggard, the printer, that the whole book was disapproved, but if book iv as it then stood was printed he would have it burned wherever he found it. At last Dr. Gifford and Dr. Clement were deputed to correct book iv and book v (the latter allied in subject to the former); they each undertook to read twenty-four sheets. The whole book *Mikrokosmographia, a Description of the Body of Man*, with a dedication to the king, was published in 1615, as corrected by two doctors, or so it is said, for some observers cannot see any sign that it was corrected at all. In 1631 the author presented a copy of the second edition to the College library, where it still is, but he

---

[1] 6 December 1611: the certificate is described in the margin as 'contra Morris Williams'. For antimony, see above, p. 153.

[2] See above, p. 190.   [3] 4 April 1623.

[4] 1612; 7 May, 25 June, 29 November, 22 December 1613.

[5] 11 November 1614.   [6] 22 December 1614.

still had trouble in that quarter. He came up for election as a fellow. Sir William Paddy objected that Crooke, in a letter to the king, had accused the College of indecencies in public anatomical dissections, He said that he had accused not the College but Paddy and Gwinn as demonstrators at Barber-Surgeons' Hall 'against whom his spleen was'.[1] On a ballot he was rejected, but then he submitted, though still denying the words alleged against him; the president proposed his name, and he was elected for the next vacancy by 17 votes out of 20.[2] When the final vote came on he had another altercation with Paddy, but he was elected by twelve votes out of 23, whereas Dr. Bowne, who was also elected, obtained 19.[3]

We shall come back later to his book,[4] but there is no need to spend many words on the attitude of the College to it. From the first they were perhaps unfavourable to the author; it was not an original work and they were no doubt justified, if severe, in stipulating that its character as a compilation should be acknowledged; but on the main point about propriety they resisted the diffusion of knowledge and they seem to have been surprisingly squeamish. On the other hand they did recognize merit when they saw it. Under Dr. Moundeford's presidency they gave a certificate of approval for the work of the eminent botanist, the apothecary Matthieu de l'Obel.[5]

The surgeons and occasionally their apprentices and their wives continued to commit the same offences that they had always committed. During the reign of James I a small number were imprisoned and a small number gave bonds in substantial sums of money to refrain from practising medicine. Seven or more were fined and ten or more admonished; others were charged but not convicted. Some of the hardened offenders were essentially empirics who practised a good deal of medicine under cover of surgery.[6] The cover was sometimes tenuous. In at least one instance the Annals do not mention that the offender was a surgeon.[7] One man was a surgeon

[1] 21 April 1618. [2] 3 July 1618. [3] 10 April 1620. [4] See below, p. 297.
[5] 10 September 1613. See Raven, p. 237, where the date is given conjecturally as 1614.
[6] Such as Lumken (see above, p. 135 and below, p. 195) or Edward Owen, who appeared in 1590, 1596, and 1605/6.
[7] Arthur Doughton 19 February 1607/8, 8 September 1615: he may however, not be the same man as the Arthur Doughton who appears as a signatory of two surgeons' certificates in 1633: J. H. Bloom and R. R. James, *Medical Practitioners in the Diocese of London, 1529–1725* (1935), pp. 23, 25. His first offence was in a case of lunacy.

but not free of the Company nor,apparently, licensed by the bishop.[1] Most of them, however, were straightforward surgeons with no sense of their limitations. There was nothing distinctive in their offences, administering medicines, advertising them, administering the wrong medicines, taking excessive fees. What distinguished them was the variety of defences open to them. Several took shelter under the alleged instructions of physicians who were in attendance on the same patients. One, perhaps even more ingeniously, invoked the name of the College's *bête noire*, Dr. Bonham.[2] It was so difficult to catch them out that even when Harvey said he would prove the illicit practice that one of them denied, nothing seems to have come of it.[3] Some maintained that they had licences which justified what they had done, whether from a university[4] or from other authorities. George Butler made a great display of his licence from the archbishop of Canterbury, confirmed under the Great Seal, to practise surgery and also medicine so far as it was necessary to surgery. He mentioned the names of two gentlemen of the Temple who were his legal advisers. The president and Sir William Paddy worked on the archbishop, the lord chancellor, the master of the rolls and the attorney general to such purpose that the licence was revoked; but that was only the beginning of Butler's career of misdoing.[5] Nor was he the only person to revive the tiresome sophistry about the medicine that was necessary to the office of a surgeon.[6] The surgeons as a body had never assented to the restrictive official definition of their art.

The old-established system of assigning monopoly rights by charter to organized crafts had never prevented rivalries between them. The few high officers through whose hands the petitions and the resulting charters passed had no appropriate machinery for estimating how a new grant would affect those already in existence. The more complicated the whole structure of interlocking monopolies became, the more inconsistencies were bound to result, and this was made worse by the secrecy to which the members of the various corporations were sworn. An interested third party might easily not hear of, let alone see the petition or the drafts which preceded the granting of a charter. Thus it was possible for one corporation to steal a march on another, and the Barber-Surgeons

---

[1] Thomas Greenwood, 6 December 1616.   [2] See below, p. 208.
[3] William Kellett, 11 February 1613/14.   [4] Stephen Hobbs, B.A., 2 July 1613.
[5] 5, 12 May, 2 June, 1 September 1620. See below, p. 263.
[6] Mr. Allen of Southwark also raised it, 9 October 1607.

were well aware of it. Early in James's reign they applied for a new charter, and only after they had drafted it could the College procure a copy, compare it with the old charter of Henry VIII, pick out the exceptionable points and take legal advice about how to act. A deputation went to Viscount Cranborne, formerly Sir Robert Cecil and now lord treasurer, to explain how the charter injured the College and the public.[1] It seems that the College objected to several of the provisions, and they may have disliked the strengthening of the Barber-Surgeons' powers by several clauses relating to search, imprisonment and licensing; but the main dispute seems to have been over the demarcation between medicine and surgery. The surgeons believed that the physicians had taken upon themselves the arts of the surgeon and the apothecary as well as their own, and for themselves they desired to be permitted, as they claimed to have been before, to use in London and in the army and navy such wound-drinks, potions and other inward remedies, as they knew by experience to be necessary for their patients. They promoted a private bill in parliament for this purpose with the king's permission. It followed the lines of a Bill preferred when Mr. Barker was master (1597–8).[2] The Bill was thrown out, and the surgeons suspected that this was due mainly to the opposition of the College.[3]

Leonard Po, who once inside was very zealous for the College privileges, came of his own accord to unmask a plot against them. In conversation a surgeon had told him that they would try again on more equal terms, and if they failed, at whatever risk to themselves they would put in a petition which should affix an indelible stigma to the College. The guileless surgeon, Richard Mapes, whom the registrar referred to as 'Mops', imparted the names of six of his fellow-conspirators.[4] A fortnight later the surgeons approached the College, wishing, or so they said, to remove differences and promote friendship. They admitted that their Bill had been very unfair and

[1] Text in South, pp. 361 ff., undated, there described as a draft bill but apparently a draft charter; Annals, 6 February 1604/5, 3 May 1605; Young, p. 326 for the decision of the Barber-Surgeons' Company on 28 February 1604/5 to invite the College to a conference which seems not to have taken place.

[2] South, pp. 197–8. The counsel who advised the Company were the recorder and Mr. Wilbraham.

[3] Text of the Barber-Surgeons' Petition to the House of Commons in Goodall, pp. 359 ff., printed also in *Commons' Journals*.

[4] 13 March 1606/7. It is not clear how this incident is related to the Barber-Surgeons' resolution, for which no date is given, to show the physicians that part of a new Bill which concerned the practice of physic (South, p. 200).

unreasonable, but they said this was the fault of the lawyers, who had tried to appear too clever and perverted the sense of the Bill. It was not meant to infringe the privileges of the College. The president replied that it would have been more prudent to consult the College beforehand and follow its advice. The surgeons then denied with many words that they had furtively tried to get all they wanted, to the great prejudice of the College. At last the president agreed to their submitting a proposal in writing, but said the College would have no dealings with the offensive Mops. Mops, however, voluntarily came to the president and acknowledged his offence; the special comitia accepted the apology and the whole incident was over.[1]

As a body the College stayed well on the right side of authority; and it relied on authority for help in the interminable struggle with the opposing forces. For the first three years of James I the procession of offenders passed through on censor's days and there was no important change for the better. There were old acquaintances, Paul Buck, David Ward,[2] Thomasina Scarlet[3] and Catherine Clark.[4] Altogether forty-nine men and five women were convicted, three men and six women were accused but went free, which does not prove they were innocent. Two men confessed that they had been illegally in practice for ten years.[5] Two made their inauspicious first appearances of whom much more was to be heard in the future. One was Dr. Jacob Domingo, an extra-licentiate who was granted a London licence[6]; the other, Arthur Dee son of the Elizabethan magician, had hung up a sign.[7] All of it, however, was humdrum routine until Dr. Bonham appeared.

Thomas Bonham was probably in his forties when his troubles began. He had worked his way up from being a sizar at St. John's College, Cambridge; had incorporated as a B.A. at Oxford soon after taking that degree and in 1595 became a Cambridge doctor of medicine. In 1605 he was examined by the censors for a licence,

---

[1] As only five fellows attended the special comitia it appears that the College was not much concerned. It is surprising that in 1624, after the fellows had been asked to give the names of malpractising surgeons and of witnesses against them, a committee reported that it had found something against apothecaries but nothing against surgeons: 2, 25 June 1624. The absence of witnesses does not, however, prove that there were no breaches of the rules. See below, p. 242.
[2] 4 April 1606.   [3] 6 June 1603.   [4] 17 June 1603.
[5] Stifolds Gean, 8 June 1604; James Blackburne, 6 February 1604/5.
[6] 4 March 1604/5; 6 December 1605.   [7] 4 April 1604/5.

but failed to satisfy them; they told him to devote himself to his studies more diligently and to come to the next general comitia.[1] His second examination followed after four months, but by this time he had engaged in practice. He was ordered to desist and to pay a fine of £5 or go to prison.[2] By October 1606 he had disregarded repeated summonses: the censors fined him £10 and ordered his arrest.[3] He paid no attention, according to the registrar, either to the authority of the College or to the statutes of the realm; but more than a year after this sentence he did obey a summons. The president asked him whether he had come to give satisfaction or to be examined. Putting on his hat Dr. Bonham insolently and scornfully replied that he had practised medicine without any leave from the College and would go on doing so. He would obey the president and censors in nothing: they had no authority over university doctors. Then up spoke Mr. Smith, a barrister of the Inner Temple, whom Bonham had brought with him, trying to twist the Acts of Parliament to that sense. The president and censors considered the case in all its aspects and committed Dr. Bonham to prison.[4] To the Counter in the Poultry he went.

In less than a week he was out again. His case had been tried in the court of king's bench and he was released by order of the judges. There is no report of this trial and so we do not know the grounds of the decision. They may have been merely technical. The court may only have considered matters of law which did not affect the authority of the College in any general way; but possibly the College already knew that the challenge came from something more formidable than Dr. Bonham's impudence and Mr. Smith's ingenuity. One of the weak points in its strategic position was that the universities had never fully accepted its claims and had never co-operated cordially with it. During the interval between Dr. Bonham's second fine and his imprisonment the College had occasion to revise its statute about university degrees. The admitting

---

[1] 6 December 1605 'parum apte respondit'. The next general comitia was on 22 December, so this seems to mean that he was to come as a prospective licentiate, to hear the statutes read and so forth.

[2] 14 April 1606.   [3] 3 October.

[4] 7 November 1606. From this point onwards the original authorities from the legal side are R. Brownlow and J. Goldsbrough *Reports* (1651), pp. 255 ff. and Sir Edward Coke, *Reports*, pt. viii (1738), pp. 107 ff. These reports are well reproduced by Goodall. I have not given detailed references to them. An excellent account of the constitutional aspect of Bonham's case is given by J. W. Gough, *Fundamental Law in English Constitutional History* (1955), especially pp. 31–38. It is discussed in passages distributed through no less than five volumes of Sir William Holdsworth's *History of English Law*.

of Dr. Craig had re-opened the questions of the maximum number of fellows and the rights of candidates.[1] In straightening them out the comitia decided that in future (saving the expectations of those who were already candidates) no one was to be admitted as a fellow unless, after becoming a master of arts, he had spent seven continuous years either wholly in 'our' universities[2] or partly in them and partly in foreign universities. It was held unjust that any foreign university, perhaps obscure and ignoble, should claim a right to confer the degree on those whom our own judged not to have made sufficient progress in their studies.[3]

Whether this propitiatory language had anything to do with Dr. Bonham or not, his release compelled the College to make sure how its authority over English doctors stood in the law. In those days there was a practice, easily open to abuse, by which the Crown could consult the judges extra-judicially and so discover beforehand what they thought about a legal issue which might arise in court. The College, no doubt at the instance of counsel, drew up nine questions and the king passed them on to the lord chancellor, Ellesmere, and Sir John Popham, chief justice of the king's bench. By virtue of the king's order these two summoned Sir Thomas Fleming, chief baron of the exchequer and two judges from each of the two courts of the king's bench and the common pleas. On 1 May 1607 all seven met at the lord chancellor's house, York House, near Charing Cross, and after considering the charters and statutes delivered their answers.

First they said that graduates of Oxford and Cambridge might not practice medicine in London or within seven miles of it without the College licence; secondly that such graduates, but in physic only, might practise in all other places of England without further examination[4]; thirdly that the College had the right to correct and govern the practice of all persons in the City, &c., whether licensed or not; and fourthly that all who practised physic in the City &c., must submit themselves to examination by the president and College if they were required thereunto, 'notwithstanding any licence, allowance or privilege given them in Oxford or Cambridge either by their degree or otherwise.'

[1] See above, p. 134.
[2] This appears to mean English and not British.
[3] 1 August 1606: see above, p. 134 for the former statute.
[4] As Sir Thomas Walmsley, one of the judges then present, said in the subsequent proceedings this was common law before 3 Henry VIII.

These were the main questions and, so far as London was concerned, the answers were entirely favourable to the College.[1] Five subsidiary questions followed, which dealt with the punishment of offenders. The first of the answers to these may have seemed oracular. It said that the power of committing to prison under the Act of 1 May 'could not be interpreted otherwise than the express words of the Statute are'. This meant that the College could imprison only for malpractice, and that illicit practice must be punished by fines. The next two were clear enough: the president and censors might commit for offences against any lawful order of the College and might impose reasonable fines and detain the parties until they were paid. They might, like other corporations, take a reasonable entrance fee for their general expenses. After these came two which required action by the College itself. The question was whether those only were to be committed who were guilty of malpractice, as in the charter; unlicensed practitioners being liable only to a fine of £5 for each month. The judges resolved that if the president and College made an ordinance against unlicensed practice, then, for breach and contempt of it they might not only fine but commit. In the same way if they made an ordinance for the president and censors to commit and fine those who refused to be examined on charges of malpractice, it would be good and lawful.

Even this was not all. The lord chancellor put two more questions. Might the party committed for unskilful or temerarious practice have an action for false imprisonment against the College and thereby draw in issue (that is, make it the business of the court to decide) the goodness or badness of the physic? All resolved that he was 'concluded' by the sentence and judgement of the censors. If an unlicensed man practised physic in London no more than once, twice or thrice in one month was he an offender against the charter and statutes? All resolved that he was.[2]

The president lost no time in announcing the good news, and asked for a deputation to carry the thanks of the College for so much labour in its business and such a 'candid interpretation' of the queries moved.[3] New statutes were promptly drafted, passed and

---

[1] No answer was given to the second part of the first question, on the extent of the exception at the end of the statute of 3 Henry VIII, but in view of the other answers this was of no importance.

[2] Texts in Goodall, pp. 276–81. There is no evidence that anyone outside the College had access to these answers.   [3] 3 May 1607.

sealed to give effect to the judges' recommendations, covering the whole ground of censorial jurisdiction, unlicensed practice, summons, refusal to submit to examination and failure to satisfy the examiners.[1]

The College enjoyed its triumph unsuspectingly for two years. In and after June 1607 it seems indeed to have failed to collect the evidence it wanted against Bonham[2] but in the winter of 1608/9 it struck at him again and struck home. The court of king's bench did all it desired and five of the fellows were detailed with the president to convey its gratitude to the lord chancellor, the other judges, and the attorney and solicitor general.[3] But one thing had been overlooked. The principal actor in the drama had not yet taken the stage. Sir Edward Coke had not been summoned to the meeting of judges. He was not only the most learned of all authorities on the common law, but its fearless and combative champion against all comers including when necessary the king himself. He was the great personal and professional rival of Bacon, and his sharp, restricted mind was utterly unlike Bacon's mind. As it happened he was a Cambridge man and he was chief justice of the court of common pleas. The common pleas, had never before given a judgement on the College charter and statutes, but it was there and not in the king's bench, which ordinarily dealt with the affairs of corporations, that Dr. Bonham brought an action for his alleged wrongful imprisonment as long ago as 1606. Sir John Doddridge, appearing for the plaintiff picked holes in the College's view of the statutes, and in the following term the case was argued for two days by all the judges of the common pleas. Coke held forth from the bench. He lauded the universities and his own Cambridge. He said the College of Physicians could imprison for malpractice but not for practising without a licence: the only punishment for that was a fine of £5 for each month. They could not bring such an action before themselves but ought to exhibit an information in a court of law. They could not punish by fine and also by imprisonment because no man ought to be punished twice for the same offence. They had sued Dr. Bonham for their whole fine of £5 when half of it belonged to the king. When he wrote his judgement down Coke gave seven directions for the

---

[1] The sealing was on 7 July 1607. The text is given in MS. Sloane 3914 fos. 113–17 and is incorporated in the code of 1647 as cap. xv 'De Permissis sive Licentiatis as Praxin': see below, p. 408.

[2] 5 June 1607; 5 February 1607/8; 1 July 1608.   [3] 3 February 1608/9.

College, tying them strictly. There was to be no forfeit for unlicensed practice of less than a month; commitals must be immediate; no fine or imprisonment could be imposed without a record of it; the cause for which a man was fined or imprisoned must be certain, for it was traversable in an action for false imprisonment in a court of law. In these last two grounds judgement was for Bonham, and he was awarded damages of £40.[1]

In the course of his judgement Coke said that when an Act of Parliament was against right and reason the common law would adjudge it to be void. Lawyers and historians have argued ever since about why he said this, and what he meant, and whether he was right. These problems may not have interested the beaten defendants, the College, though their confidence in their Acts of Parliament, to say nothing of charters, may well have been shaken for the moment. Their confidence in the rightness of their cause was not shaken. Bonham was in prison. A letter came from Archbishop Bancroft, also a Cambridge man, asking for his release and intimating plainly 'otherwise I shall be driven . . . to move the lordes' (of the council) 'in his behalf'. A deputation went to explain and the archbishop took it in very good part; yet the stubborn doctor would not give in and persisted in his suit.[2] The College was equally unyielding. The president and elects met at the president's house with the registrar and unanimously decided to proceed against the judgement by writ of error. They also decided to petition the king to give them power in the future to summon all practitioners, to administer an oath to witnesses, to take bonds of those who were fined and whatever else was necessary for their task. 'God grant that we may obtain this', the registrar wrote in his Latin, 'lest Medicine perish and the Empirics triumph'.[3]

The College undertook to pay all the costs of the litigation, so that no expense should fall on the officers in whose names it was conducted. The judgement was reversed by writ of error in the king's bench. But this did not mean that the principles laid down by Coke were annulled. Dr. Bonham seems to have continued in London practice, perhaps as a Barber-Surgeon. We know little of his later life. In university and in legal circles he certainly had

---

[1] Coke, *Reports*, pt. viii.   [2] 6 October 1609.
[3] 1 March 1608/10. The reason for asking power to administer an oath presumably was that if the proceedings were subsequently called in question in a court of law a witness who had been sworn would be less likely to go back on the evidence he had given to the censors.

friends: in 1611 he incorporated M.D. in Oxford and in 1614 he was admitted to Gray's Inn, the Inn of which Bacon was a bencher. In 1621 he was active again in professional matters as a signatory to the Barber-Surgeons' petition against the king's new charter to the College.[1] By 1630 he had died, and his 'servant' Edward Poeton put together from his papers a book called *The Chyrurgians Closet or Antidotarie Chyrurgicall*.[2]

The ups and downs of the Bonham affair had some effect on the course of the censors' work. In its earliest stages they were unusually active. In the twelve months after Dr. Bonham's first fine several persons refused to appear when summoned, but seven men and two women were fined or imprisoned or both. There were old offenders, Simon Forman,[3] James Forrester,[4] and Robert Swaine,[5] all accused on the same day. Three licences were granted to practitioners who were competent to hold them, but had not come in by the front door.[6] Two undeserving characters who had been tolerated for years were deprived of this favour, and one of them needed to show a letter from the earl of Shrewsbury to escape punishment.[7] In the summer of 1607 the veterans Paul Buck and Robert Swaine were fined after patients of theirs had died,[8] but little else is recorded. Henoch Clapham was dealt with. He was a Puritan theologian of some note, and he had also published writings about the plague, having stayed in London in one of the plague years and observed it. Now he admitted that he had displayed many notices in the City promising to treat many diseases; but he said he was ignorant of the privileges of the College and the admonition he received was not unkind.[9] At the end of November the registrar looked back on five folio pages of his own handwriting and wrote

[1] See below, p. 231.
[2] William Cole, the Cambridge antiquary, conjectured that Thomas Bonham may have been the father of his namesake, a fellow of King's. The son was born at the Queen's Head Tavern in Paternoster Row (Brit. Mus. Add. MS. 5816, fo. 93). Cole also owned Add. MS. 5863 in which there is a note on Bonham's book, correctly reported in *Dict. of Nat. Biog.*, *s. n.* Bonham. I have not seen any copy of the book: there are at least two in America.
[3] 4 December 1606, 9 January, 13 March 1606/7.
[4] 4 December 1606, 13 March 1606/7, 22 December 1607.
[5] 4 December 1606, 9 January 1606/7, 4 December 1607.
[6] Jacob Domingo (who was accused of malpractice on 19 January 1610/11), Thomas Percival (who tried on 4 and 6 April to pass off a provincial licence as entitling him to practise in London), and Dr. William Conway. Munk says that he finds no mention of Conway before his summons for practising in London, 7 July 1606: but on 5 July 1599 a letter on his behalf from the earl of Nottingham was read and consideration of it deferred until he should be examined.
[7] 14 April, 2 May 1606.   [8] 7 August 1606.   [9] 4 September 1607.

'And all these things were done in the months of October and November now ended'; but there had been only ten accusations and not a single sentence. One of the accused, the odious Mrs. Paine, tried to shelter behind the name of Dr. Bonham.[1] Two names that would be heard of again, were those of a Paris doctor, Thomas Tenant, perhaps a Frenchman,[2] and William Eyre or Eier, a doctor of Leiden,[3] The hunt was losing its vigour. In January 1607/8 Swaine was fined £5 and sent to prison, but released when he paid 40s. and complained that he was hardly treated because a suit brought by informers was pending against him in the court of the exchequer.[4] Nothing was decided about an aged impostor from Gelderland called Putnam or Putmans because the earl of Exeter wrote on his behalf,[5] and bad-tempered Mrs. Plumley of Rother-hithe came off very lightly principally because her husband was one of the musicians of the Chapel Royal.[6] In the summer Dr. Tenant admitted giving a patient, deceased, one pill, the size of a pea, but the only crime that led to punishment was that of some Italians who had imported 1,000 or 2,000 doses of an archicathartic medicine: their leader was fined £20 and imprisoned till he paid.[7]

Unfortunately a fortnight before Dr. Bonham's conviction in the king's bench, the registrar decided not to record the business of the censors' days in the new volume of the Annals which begins at that point, but to content himself with entering references to the Book of Examinations, which no longer exists. From January 1608/9 therefore our record is defective until the summer of 1614, when Dr. Gwinne reverted to his former habit. It tells us nothing, for instance, about the successful suit against Edmund Gardiner in the king's bench in 1609/10.[8] There seems, however, no room for doubting that once Bonham was convicted the College showed new energy. Between that February day and Christmas 1609 it was decided to bring Lawrence Browne, doctor of Leiden, before the

---

[1] 27 November, 22 December 1607, 8 January 1607/8.
[2] 7 February 1605/6, 4 December 1606, to be summoned; 4 September and 8 January 1607/8 accused of malpractice and charging excessive fees.
[3] These are two of the five or six versions of his name, some of which begin with the letter A. He was accused of unlicensed practice on 7 February 1605/6, produced his Leiden diploma (of 1596, Innes-Smith) on 4 December 1607, incorporated at Oxford in 1608 and was left in peace until 1609, possibly because of the difficulties over Bonham.
[4] 8 January 1607/8.   [5] 5, 19 February 1607/8; 12 January 1609/10.
[6] 19 February 1607/8.   [7] 25 July, 5 August 1608.
[8] Goodall, pp. 147–60. This may be the Gardiner who was imprisoned in 1602/3, or the Gardiner who, along with his wife, was bound over on 12 August 1608 to pay up to £30. Katherine Gardiner, a Dutchwoman, was examined on 3 February 1608/9.

courts, and also Dr. Eyre. Four men were forbidden to practise:
John Craford, a Scot; Denys O' Roughan, an Irish priest, one
Nicholas Rowland and Thomas Lewis. Dr. Tenant was arrested
and escaped from prison by a ruse. Two other men and Mrs. Paine
and another woman went to gaol. The two Peter Chamberlens,
were each fined 40s. for bad and illicit practice.[1] The censors indeed
went too far; at any rate they swooped on one truly respectable
alien who had been practising quietly since 1598. He was a Leiden
doctor, born of a good merchant family in Bruges, and for six
years he had been physician to the tsar Fedor Ivanovitch. He was
fined £5 and so the name of Baldwin Hamey first appeared in
the College books.[2] Perhaps that was the only mistake in the
round-up.

There was a definite check in January 1609/10. About a score
of offenders were summoned in that and the following two months,
of whom not a single one appeared.[3] In June the College was to
collect evidence against Forman, Forrester, and Tenant, and again
in October when the president had to make a speech against
empirics. In 1611 Richard Powell had to pay £4 and go to prison;
but that is the only sign of rigour. In 1612 at the Michaelmas
comitia the licentiates were warned not to consult with empirics
and told to bring their names to the College. The new president,
Dr. Moundeford, made an emphatic speech about coercing them.[4]
John Nott or Note, who admitted that he practised surgery, was
fined £14 and sent to prison for malpractice in a case of 'the new
disease'.[5] But the machinery of coercion was out of gear. At the next
comitia the president produced a list of ten doctors of medicine
who were engaged in illicit practice in the City. It was decided that
legal proceedings should be taken against two graduates of English
universities, Dr. Anthony and Dr. Barker, and two foreign, Dr.
Eyre and Dr. Dee. The president had forbidden Dr. John Burgess
to practise. Dr. Burgess, once a famous Puritan divine, who had
been sent to the Tower for a sermon preached before the king, was
a Cambridge doctor of medicine. It was suspected that Dr. Rawlins

[1] See below, p. 236.
[2] See the biography of J. J. Keevil, *Hamey the Stranger* (1952).
[3] On 19 January there was an obscure wrangle between Dr. Rawlins and William
Forester, who claimed to have a Cambridge licence and whom the attorney general
asked the College to treat with indulgence (*mitius*).
[4] 16 October 1612.
[5] 13 November 1612. Nott is called 'Dr.' in the Annals, but seems not to have deserved it.

had consorted with him.[1] He withdrew as far as Isleworth, a good eight miles from the City, where his practice became large and lucrative. Dr. Barker was an old man and in the queen's service; his son, like the father an Oxonian, appeared for him and actually said 'he thinks the university hath given him sufficient authority to practise anywhere. If not he will acquaint them with it, knowe their answear, and make further answeare.' The College seems to have failed to obtain a judgement against him.[2] Dr. Bennet alleged the privileges of Cambridge University as a justification for practising in London, but, after an admonition from the censors and a talk with the president, he seems to have struck his colours.[3] The rest, papists and protestants, were tolerated.

None of this did the least harm to the empirics. Nor were the more prominent of them weakened when the College set about Mrs. Phoenix (who blamed her husband, long since gone to Flushing), Mother Flatt, Mrs. Fletcher, the Venetian naval carpenter Giovanni Antonio, or the 'generosus adolescens' John Bartlett, who admitted giving pills but 'thought ther had been no lawe against it'. There was one good day, 19 October 1613, when two smart sentences were imposed: as Dr. Andrews said in one of the cases, something must be done *in terrorem*.[4] But the terror did not spread extensively. Even Paul Buck was still unsubdued.[5] Whether Dr. Bonham had anything to do with it or not, the situation was out of hand.

[1] 22 December 1612. For Dr. Burgess's plague-water see *A Book of Simples*, ed. H. W. Lewer (1908), p. 68.
[2] 6 November 1612. As usual the Annals tell us nothing about the legal proceedings.
[3] 6 May 1615. This is probably Roger Bennet, who practised in Herefordshire.
[4] On 25 June 1614 'Alphonso medicaster' was fined £6 and committed, and on 7 October 1614 a braggart called Isaac Franke was reduced to tears and fined £5. No sentence is recorded on Dr. Baldwin, who owned to two years practice in London: 17 September 1622; 4 April 1623.
[5] So Dr. Hering indicated on 4 June 1613.

XII: JACOBEAN PLANS, 1614–20

WHEN the College had carried on its work for nearly a hundred years it was confronted with a proposal for changes in the organization of the apothecaries which were bound to affect physicians.[1] As London grew in population and in wealth the business of the apothecaries expanded and some of them, like many men of other crafts in similar situations, became dissatisfied with their position as a subordinate element in a large, composite company. Gideon de Laune, the Huguenot apothecary to the queen, though he was not a member of the Grocers' Company, became the leader of a movement for secession from it. With eleven apothecaries who were freemen he promoted a Bill in the commons in 1610 for the establishment of an apothecaries' company with a monopoly of the trade, which would thus be closed to the main body of grocers. Most of the apothecaries preferred the safety and the tangible advantages of membership in one of the twelve 'great companies'. The Grocers' Company opposed the Bill and it got no further than a first reading[2]; most of the rebels deserted their leader; but in 1614 he was strong enough to make a second effort, this time by an application for a royal charter.

At the solemn comitia of the College on 18 April 1614, the morrow of Palm Sunday, Francis Anthony's behaviour came up for discussion,[3] and this led on to a general canvassing of methods for dealing firmly with the empirics. Should the College approach the king or the highest persons of the realm, the privy council, the judges or the parliament then sitting?[4] The evil was agreed to be growing worse, and a strong committee was appointed to consider it.[5] A month later one of the elects, Dr. Atkins, reported what had

---

[1] From this point the relations of the College with the apothecaries are traced in C. Wall and H. C. Cameron, *History of the Worshipful Society of Apothecaries*, revised, annotated and edited by E. A. Underwood, vol. i (1963). The second and more important part of this volume, 'Notes and Sources', is wholly the work of Dr. Underwood and prints many important texts and excerpts from the records of the College and the Society. In subsequent footnotes this volume is referred to as 'Underwood'.

[2] *Commons Journals*, 12 June 1610.   [3] See above, p. 201.

[4] This was the Addled Parliament, which was dissolved on 7 June, so we hear no more of it.

[5] Paddy, Atkins, Lister, Argent, Harvey, Clement, Goulston, with Moundeford, the president.

passed between the king and himself. He said much about physicians, surgeons, and apothecaries, but—we may think excusably—he refused to put it in writing even in summary for the Annals. At last one and another of the fellows began to ask whether it would be a good plan for the apothecaries to be separated from the spicers, that is from the Grocers' Company. The majority agreed that from the point of view of the College it would. Three of the former committee were appointed to deal with the proposal, and a deputation was sent to the king, carrying a letter of thanks which depicted the present ills and said nothing specifically about any remedy other than correcting the misdoings of the apothecaries.[1]

Perhaps no one at the time understood how momentous this decision was. On the face of it, it meant that the apothecaries were to be detached from the powerful allies who made it difficult to confine them to their proper subsidiary functions. That could not be done without affronting the Grocers and the City, and the physicians no doubt went into that conflict with their eyes open, relying on their friends in high places. They probably did not foresee that a specialized body of apothecaries would tend to be more united in the ambition to gain the right to practise. Worse still no one seems to have given any thought to the main underlying issue. In the long run it would be impossible to exclude the apothecaries from medical practice unless, on the one hand, they had ample opportunities for making a satisfying livelihood in their own allotted sphere, and, unless on the other hand, the inhabitants of London were so well provided with qualified medical attendants that they would cease to prefer the cheaper and more approachable apothecary to the physician. As part of a comprehensive plan the proposal might have succeeded; but it stopped short of providing for any additions to the two score fellows and licentiates who monopolized legitimate practice in a city with much more now than a quarter of a million inhabitants. It chalked out the ground on which the contest with the apothecaries was to be decided under the rules of the law and the constitution, but no one foresaw on either side that after nearly ninety years the apothecaries would be declared the winners and that, in the division of the stakes, the physicians would carry away enough to keep them as happy as ever.

---

[1] 23 May 1614. The new committee were Lister, Palmer and Argent. Palmer was not present on 18 April.

The problem was not only new for the College; it had never arisen before in any part of Europe. William Harvey, giving evidence against the apothecaries in 1634 or 1635 deposed that in all the places where he had travelled, such as Cologne, Frankfurt, Nuremberg, Vienna, Prague, Siena, Florence, Rome, and Naples, the apothecaries were 'in reference and dependency' upon the physicians, and for the most part tied by oaths to certain orders. Their numbers were limited, the prices of their medicines were fixed for them, and they were allowed to make for common sale only such medicines as were appointed by the dispensatory of each place. Everywhere their medicines were searched and corrected by the physicians. When he mentioned the oaths, Harvey referred to the French dispensatory of Renodeus.[1] In France there were many universities, and there were complaints that in some provinces the physicians were too many and often ill-taught. England depended largely on the instruction of continental universities, and no one suggested either that London should have a medical faculty of its own or that there should be some other institution in which apothecaries might qualify themselves for practice by learning anatomy, physiology, and therapeutics. If society had been differently constituted the City might have used Gresham College and the Barber Surgeons' Hall for some such purpose, but as it was there was no chance whatever of such a plan. The apothecaries did not ask for any widening of their education; nor did they express, even if they felt, the distinctive ideas of professional men. Throughout the period of dispute they never imposed or even formulated rules for the ethics and etiquette of practice. Once the contest was joined each side inevitably hardened in its existing principles; nor was any voice effectively raised on behalf of society as a whole or the general body of patients as a whole.

It would be unfair to conclude that the decision of the College in 1614 was hasty. It was not unanimous, though we do not know exactly why some of the fellows opposed it. Almost from the start it was accompanied by a revival of the laudable project which had been asleep for twenty years for a pharmacopoeia or *antidotarium generale*, to bring science to bear by standardizing and improving the dispensing of medicines. Dr. Moundeford, the president, along with Sir William Paddy, Dr. Lister, and Dr. Atkins himself, could remember the failure of the former attempt, and it is to the

[1] Underwood, p. 304.

credit of the College that it set to work again to compare the pharmacopoeias of Bergamo, Nuremberg, and others 'together with our
own'.[1] They wanted the apothecaries' shops to be worthy of their
place in a well-ordered medical system.

The president may have had in mind divisions of opinion quite
unrelated to the question of the apothecaries when he made a speech
soon after this against fellows who absented themselves from the
dinners which were intended to promote peace among them, and
complained of the ill manners of some whom he did not name in
relation to himself and Drs. Forster and Argent. This was at the
first meeting in the new building, the day before Dr. Foxe's dinner
there.[2] The first undoubted signs of trouble came in the following
winter. The president propounded to eight fellows, apparently in
an informal meeting, the question whether any fellow who dis-
sented from a resolution passed by the College might speak or do
anything against it if it were called in question in a higher court.
'The proposition was accepted generally, and determined nega-
tively' which must mean that it was understood as general and
not referring only to a particular case, and that it was rejected.[3] Next
day in a meeting at which nineteen fellows were present, the president read part of the oath of admission, drawing the inference from it
that they were all sworn not to contravene the resolution on the
separation of the apothecaries and the spicers. Thereupon Dr.
Atkins explained at length that he had privately settled it with the
king that the apothecaries were to be separated and so to become
honest men (*viros probos*). Then there had been a discussion (*causa
disputata*) for two days between the spicers and the apothecaries
in the presence of the attorney general, the solicitor general and two
of the king's physicians, Mayerne and himself.[4] This is Mayerne's
first appearance in this matter. His sister was the wife of an apothecary, the botanist Matthieu de Lobel's son. No doubt he knew that
in Paris the apothecaries had been separated from the *épiciers*

[1] 25 June 1614. 'Una cum nostris' may refer to the pharmacopoeias in current use in
London but more probably refers to papers which survived from 1594: see above, p.
161.   [2] 25 June 1614.
[3] 13 February 1614/5. The fellows present were Atkins, Ridley, Lister, Palmer,
Argent, Harvey, Foxe, Goulston. The registrar was not summoned and Foxe wrote the
minute.
[4] This was in consequence of an order from the privy council on 29 May 1614 to the
lord chief justice of England and Sir Thomas Lake, made after the receipt of a petition
of the lord mayor and alderman against the proposed separation. The two referees
were to hear representatives of the College and apothecaries nominated by the Grocers'
Company: *Acts of the Privy Council, 1613–1614* (1921), p. 451.

exactly a century earlier,[1] and it is conceivable that he may have supported the plan for general reasons independent of the London situation.

On the basis of a report of the discussion, Dr. Atkins went on, a charter was granted to the apothecaries under the privy seal and it was being made ready to pass the Great Seal, but at this stage the Grocers and the aldermen of London came into action. Some of them went to the king and said that the grant 'imminished' the ancient liberties of the City; that the order of the City companies would be upset if the apothecaries took rank next after the Grocers, and that the government (*imperium*) of London would suffer if they were exempted from watch and ward. The last two points refer to favours which it was intended to confer on the apothecaries in order to commend the plan to them but which were afterwards dropped. The king referred all three points to the privy council, but on condition that the good work with which he had formerly been satisfied should not be impaired.[2] The comitia were either already aware or learnt from Dr. Atkins that the apothecaries were to be bound by their freemen's oath not to give advice to patients or to offer them service except in emergencies and not to make up prescriptions other than those of physicians recognized by the College. He ended his speech by holding out the prospect that the College would hold the apothecaries in subjection (*in servitute*) as never before, and he earnestly begged the fellows to stand by their resolution.

This was the signal for Sir William Paddy to protest that the scheme had originated neither with the king nor with the College but had been promoted by Atkins alone; that the oath regarded College matters while this was the affair neither of the College nor of the fellows, but a question between the apothecaries, the Grocers and the City. If anything was decided by a majority in comitia about other people's affairs it should be entered as a resolution but

---

[1] There were two rival bodies of apothecaries: see E. H. Guitard, 'Les apothicaires privilégiés dans l'ancienne France' in *XVIIth International Congress of Medicine, Sec. xxiii History of Medicine* (1914), pp. 411 ff.

[2] This agrees with the privy council minute of 27 January 1614/15: *Acts of the Privy Council 1615–1616* (1925) p. 32, from which we also learn that the two sides were to be represented by counsel and that the hearing was to be on 15 February, the day after the comitia. When Dr. Atkins mentioned the privy seal, he should have said the signet. For the headings agreed on 23 May 1614 between Mayerne, Atkins and 76 apothecaries see Underwood, pp. 13–14, 217–18. One trifling point which seems to require further substantiation is the statement that these headings were submitted to the comitia.

each fellow should retain the right to his own opinion.[1] Some years earlier some of the apothecaries had sought the same separation from parliament and had approached him about it, but in vain.[2] On went Sir William, but the president cut him short and nominated Drs. Ridley, Lister, Argent and Fox to inform Dr. Atkins, who presumably had departed, that the majority had decided in favour of the separation of apothecaries and Grocers.

After this the business moved uncertainly forward through the necessary stages, in spite of reluctant elements in all the three bodies concerned. On 18 April 1615 the king signified his pleasure that there should be no discussion of the principle of separation, but only of matters of form and convenience. We may pause over the events on one September day in 1616.[3] In the morning the president, censors and registrar with the wardens of the apothecaries (still in the Grocers' Company) carried out the solemn inspection of the apothecaries, and Dr. Argent was also among the physicians. Now Dr. Argent married the sister of a fellow of the College, Dr. Paul Delaune,[4] and this doctor, very likely a relative of the Huguenot refugee physician of the same name,[5] was certainly the brother of an apothecary. Gideon Delaune was not indeed an ordinary apothecary; he was a rich and influential citizen around whom legends grew; but, even if his case is exceptional, it was not unique. There were two others in the higher strata: Mayerne's and that of the registrar, Dr. Gwinne who was brother-in-law to the lord admiral's apothecary.[6] No doubt it was the same at a less distinguished level. At any rate there was no complete social gulf between the two 'faculties'. After the inspection Dr. Fludd gave a dinner at the College for the fellows who had taken part in it, and also for other fellows and their wives. This is the first time we hear of ladies dining in the dedicated building. After dinner two apothecaries were interrogated about some unpleasing drugs found on their premises in the morning and were duly admonished. We may hope that the College had been polite enough to invite the wardens and Gideon Delaune and their wives to the dinner.

[1] suum animum cuique relinquendum.
[2] This no doubt refers to the Bill of 1610: see above p. 218.
[3] 6 September 1616; *Acts of the Privy Council, 1615–1616*, pp. 32, 125.
[4] Annals, 4 October 1622.   [5] See above, p. 142.
[6] This fact is stated in Dr. Lancelot Browne's letter to Cecil soliciting the place of physician to the Tower, vacated on the previous day by the death of Marbeck, for his son-in-law William Harvey. The letter is dated 'From an apothecary's shop in Fanchurch Street': *Historical Manuscripts Commission, Salisbury Papers*, xv (1930), 206.

In April 1617 the president appointed a new committee to serve with him on the negotiation (*causa*) between the Grocers and the apothecaries.[1] By that time to all appearance the charter was almost through in a draft which bears the date 30 May.[2] The preamble describes it as granted on the petition of the apothecaries and of the king's physicians Mayerne and Atkins, for the putting down of empirics and unskilful and ignorant men who make and compound medicines. It incorporates 115 named apothecaries and 'all other' who have been brought up and are skilful in the said faculty and are freemen of the Grocers' or any other company, giving them a monopoly in the City and for seven miles about it to the exclusion of the Grocers. The corporate name is 'the Master, Wardens and Society of the Art and Mystery of Apothecaries'; the text, which is in English, uses the words 'art', 'mystery' and 'society' in various combinations but never either 'company' or 'college'. The new body was reckoned from the beginning as one of the City companies, but after 1684 it came to use, as it does now, the distinctive name of 'society'.[3] Its subordination to the College of Physicians was defined in two clauses. First there was to be a seven years apprenticeship, at the end of which the master and wardens were to call 'unto them the president of the College or Commonalty of the faculty of physicians of London . . . or any physician or physicians by the said president to be nominated'. With their advice the apprentice was to be examined before he should presume to keep shop or to prepare, make, mingle, work, compound, utter, sell (and so forth) any medicines. Secondly, although the master and wardens were to have the right, as often as should seem expedient to them, to examine those exercising the mystery, to remove or prohibit the unskilful, to burn offending medicines and drugs before the offenders' doors and to impose fines at their discretion (not, like the College and the Grocers to imprison), still nothing in this was to be to the prejudice of the College nor to take away its jurisdiction, authority, oversight or correction. The fellows of the College and the physicians to the king and the prince[4] might exercise the art of the physician in all its parts and enjoy 'all other powers, privileges and liberties as . . . in pharmacy they used to enjoy'.

---

[1] Moundeford, Ridley, Palmer, Argent, Clifford.

[2] In Goodall, pp. 119 ff., Goodall mistakenly thought that this was the charter which ultimately passed the Great Seal.

[3] Underwood, pp. 19, 101, n. 1.   [4] The future King Charles I.

JACOBEAN PLANS, 1614–20 225

This was not all that the College wanted, and a further revision followed. The old lord chancellor Viscount Brackley, better known by his earlier title of Lord Ellesmere, seems to have been unwilling to let the new charter pass the Great Seal until there was full agreement among the interested parties. Perhaps he thought there were legal impediments to the new grant. In March 1616/17, however, he resigned and died. His successor, with the rank of lord keeper, was none other than Francis Bacon. It was no doubt due to Bacon that the final step was taken in 6 December 1617, and that the charter was less favourable to the physicians than they had expected it to be in 1615.[1] The College was to be consulted on all proposed by-laws of the Society which concerned medicines or compositions or the uses of the same; but no oath was prescribed to restrain the freemen from practising medicine and to confine their dispensing to making up prescriptions from physicians recognized by the College. Nor were any rules laid down for the supply of poisons. That there was no allusion to the compulsory use of the proposed antidotary seems only to mean that, as we shall see, this matter was to be dealt with in a document of another kind. From the very beginning the College regarded the Society as imperfectly constituted.

It was easy to foresee that trouble might arise from the customary clause saving the rights of the City of London, since the Grocers were still umbrageous, but there was never any question of the College's ranging itself with the City against the court. It may have had good hopes of the new venture, and at any rate it did nothing to prevent a fair experiment. The physicians did not take exception to two passages in the Charter which opened a gap through which sheep might someday stray. In the long list of things which the apothecary was not to do until he was admitted a freeman after examination, he was forbidden to apply or minister medicines. When he was admitted he might not only keep shop but he might 'give, apply or administer' medicines. The legal draughtsmen used so many words that the saving clause about the rights of the College may well have appeared to blot these out.

We need not follow the fortunes of the Society of Apothecaries once its charter was granted; how the Grocers petitioned to have it annulled and obstructed the transference of freemen; how the

[1] Text in C. R. B. Barrett, *History of the Society of Apothecaries of London* (1905), pp. ccxxx ff.

apothecaries were reluctant to pay their entrance fees and take their oaths; or how the Society obtained its grant of arms. It was not until 1620 that the king announced in a proclamation that the Apothecaries were separated from the Grocers, and put under the direction of the Physicians. Even this was accompanied by the announcement that the king had appointed commissioners to settle the differences between the two companies.[1] What concerns us here is the co-operation, such as it was, between the Apothecaries and the College, and the best approach to that important question is to judge, from a comparison of the years before and after the incorporation whether it made any substantial change in the policing of the apothecaries' shops.

In the eleven years before the incorporation, the censors seem to have convicted only about eight apothecaries of actual offences, such as prescribing, or selling medicines without a prescription, which was much the same thing. Most of them were either cautioned or lightly fined. Only one went to prison, and that was for failing to answer summonses: when he asked pardon his offences were condoned on account of his poverty. The trouble was, however, that convictions were so hard to obtain. There were several cases in which apothecaries or their servants[2] had pretty certainly prescribed by word of mouth, but adequate evidence was wanting. In 1613 the privy council issued a warrant to all apothecaries in the City and suburbs, ordering that on the coming of the president and censors (presumably on their annual inspection) they should without delay deliver all 'bills and receipts' (prescriptions) of any practitioners not licensed by the College.[3] This shows that at least some apothecaries were suspected of working with the empirics; it may have had some effect beyond reminding them to destroy or mislay the incriminating papers. No one could watch them continuously: it must have been by a rare stroke of luck that James Fothergill was caught showing a customer Dr. Frear's prescription for worms.[4] There were many loopholes for undesirable practices. Mr. Smith admitted that he had antimony tablets (*tabulas stibiatas*) on sale 'as (he saith) all apothecaryes use', and that he often sent

---

[1] Steele and Crawford, no. 1289, 4 August 1620. The commissioners reported their decisions in 1621/2: for their proceedings see Underwood, pp. 222 ff. The same work gives on pp. 225 ff. a full account of a star chamber action brought by the Society in 1622 against certain grocers who infringed its monopoly.

[2] I wish we knew more about Lawrence Willington 'apothecario famulus, ludi magister' (19 February 1612/13).

[3] 22 April 1613: copy in Annals.   [4] 14 January 1615/16.

them to Mr. Noble, a practitioner in the country.[1] Some of the offending apothecaries were among the dregs of the craft,[2] but some were respectable and some of the apothecaries gave evidence against empirics. The president and censors had sufficient confidence in their standards to submit medicines to them for analysis.[3] None of them was ever defiant.

For more than three years after the incorporation no new factors intervened to complicate the physicians' supervision of the sellers of medicines, and we have no knowledge of any charges brought against apothecaries and adjudicated on by the censors. It seems that the new court of assistants was taking its duties seriously,[4] and it may have relieved the College of some of the police-work. There is one indication that relations were satisfactory. After the visitation in 1619 the College discussed jointly with the master and wardens whether the vitiated medicines then detected should be burnt publicly, and if so whether at the offenders' doors or in the public hall.[5] This promising state of things, however, was not to continue, and to show how it broke up we must return to another train of events.

King James's proclamation on the Apothecaries' charter included a reference to another proclamation which had preceded it by two years. This announced that a book entitled *Pharmacopoeia Londinensis* had been compiled by the College of Physicians at the king's command and was ready for the press. No one throughout the whole of England was to compound any medicine, or to distil any oil or waters or extractions named in it except by the manner therein prescribed, unless specially ordered by some learned physician. No one not a member of the Apothecaries' Company was to sell any composition named in the book or any medicine within London or seven miles about it, on pain of contempt.[6] So the second limb of the physicians' programme of 1614 was completed.[7]

The work, all done gratuitously and behind the scenes had been considerable. The committee of nine were at it for more than two

---

[1] 20 November 1612.
[2] I fear John Ely may have been one of these, though he was humane: he administered a red powder with rose-hip and sloe jam: 9 October 1607.
[3] See the certificate signed by six apothecaries condemning three sorts of powder of alkermes: 7 March 1616/17.
[4] In 1620 it refused to recognize the monopoly of John Wolf Rumbler, the king's apothecary, for the sale of mercury sublimate, Barrett, p. 7.
[5] 12 November 1619.
[6] Steele and Crawford, no. 1209, 26 April 1618.   [7] See above, p. 220.

years before they brought their papers in to be examined by the registrar and four of the elects.[1] When they met to survey their materials these five discovered that much was missing from what had been brought together by the former committee, presumably that of 1594.[2] They broke up with nothing accomplished and sent off the beadle with their report to the president, Dr. Atkins, throwing the blame on one of his predecessors.[3] There was nothing to be done but to appoint a new committee, this time again of nine.[4] Names were added and subtracted twice more in the following winter.[5] The fellows were to impart any suitable scientific secrets (*magistralia*) known to them which were not yet in commercial production (*nondum in officinis usurpata*) but might be of special use. Another year went by, and when yet another committee was appointed,[6] it was arranged that Dr. Clement and Dr. Fox should correct the proofs, and four prominent apothecaries were required to give daily attendance, which they assiduously did.[7] The last committee of all was nominated by the president at the solemn spring comitia of 1618 to consider matters of the highest moment, though we know not what.[8] Mayerne was a member for the first time, and he was to write a dedicatory letter to the king. Various fellows, Drs. Palmer, Hering and Baskerville to start with, were to write the preface. Then the king's Proclamation appeared, and the printer published the book on his own responsibility. The president had not finished his work on it and he was away from London. He found the book full of errors. Nothing would do but a new printing.[9] Before the time of the autumn comitia the copy for the new impression was in the registrar's hands and the printer, attending in person, undertook to print it if the fellows would make a contribution to the cost.[10] There was a long discussion in January on the epilogue for the volume. The registrar read a draft made by the president, Sir

[1] Ridley, Lister, Argent, Foxe, Ridley and Argent were members of the committee of 1614.
[2] 'Qui prius consuluerant', see above, p. 161.   [3] 13, 14 September 1616.
[4] 30 September 1616.   Argent, Hering, Harvey, Foxe, Andrews, Goulston (who, according to the minute, had served before) with the addition of Clement, Baskerville and Winston.
[5] 6 December, Frear, Palmer, Andrews, Rogers; 24 January 1616/17, Moundeford, Lister, Palmer, Argent, Clement, Foxe.
[6] Argent, Clifford, Gwinne, Clement, 20 February 1617/18.
[7] Their names were Philips, Higgins, Fownes, Darnelly, Parkinson, and Sheriff, named in the charter as the master, wardens and three of the assistants.
[8] Palm Monday 1618, Mayerne, Palmer, Argent, Gifford, Gwinne, Baskerville, Meverell, Ridgley, and Mr. Matthias, whom I have not identified.
[9] Epilogue to 'second' edition.   [10] 25 September 1618.

William Paddy, but then Dr. Atkins read another. On 7 December 1618 this official edition appeared, seven months after the king had made it compulsory. The epilogue was a Latin invective against the printer.

Only those few who have laboured in co-operative enterprises of learning will divine what emotions and stresses may be veiled by these bald entries of the College annalist. A comparison of the suppressed, and consequently very scarce, first issue with the authorized text was never made until the first issue was republished in facsimile in America in 1944. It showed immediately that the differences between the two were far more numerous and more substantial than had been supposed on the authority of the Annals. The editor provided a large mass of explanatory and illustrative learning in his introduction and footnotes, and sought to explain the differences as amounting to a change from a mere catalogue to a catalogue amply *raisonné*, and as connected with a contest between a more progressive element in the College and the older, more classically-minded, generation. These inferences are, however, drawn entirely from printed materials, and in various respects they are not compatible with the account which the Annals give of the genesis of the *Pharmacopoeia*. They rest on a free use of uncontrolled hypotheses, and must be regarded as unproven.[1]

It is, however, legitimate to ask in a general way whether the exertions and emotions of the College were justified by the result. The answer to this deceptively simple question involves a judgement on the relation between the scientific knowledge of the time and its application to pharmacy. A full answer would require much research. There had recently been great additions to the known *materia medica* from two sources. New vegetable products had been brought from beyond the oceans, and some of them, such as tobacco were already popular for various appropriate and inappropriate purposes. Chemical medicines, or some of them, were accepted as respectable. The inevitable conservatism obstructed the way. In the sixteen-thirties Dr. Othowell Meverall, one of the more old-fashioned physicians, assured an enquiring junior that chemical

---

[1] *Pharmacopoeia Londinensis of 1618, with a historical Introduction by G. Urdang* (State Historical Society of Wisconsin, 1944). Dr. Urdang's editorial work will be of much assistance to students of this phase of the history of pharmacy, but those who use it should beware of mistranslations from the Latin. There is no mention of the manuscript in English which appears to be a draft or translation of part of the earlier issue, Brit. Mus. MS. Sloane 2768.

medicines were beneficial enough for young patients but only for them.[1] He was applying his own impressions to what he had read in the old books, and this was all that the compilers could do when they put together their *Pharmacopoeia*. Not until the late seventeenth century was the task of scientific revision clearly envisaged; not until the eighteenth did medical writers on the Continent and in England lay down clear lines for it to follow; not until 1788, in its sixth edition, was the London *Pharmacopoeia* cleared of the rubbish of the old polypharmacy. The earlier revisions apparently all lagged behind the advance of knowledge, and it seems difficult to praise them except in so far as they were the products of good intentions.

Two limbs of the programme of 1614 had been completed but there was also a third, not mentioned so early as the other two, but finished almost simultaneously and integrated with them. At the peak of Dr. Bonham's fortunes the registrar foresaw that unless three more privileges could be obtained from the king, medicine would perish and the empirics would triumph. These three desiderata were the powers to summon all practitioners, to administer an oath to witnesses and to take bonds of those who were fined. No doubt they were all mentioned at the comitia of 18 April 1614 which resulted in Dr. Atkins's approach to the king. The fellows must have been surprised when Dr. Atkins said nothing about any of them but only started the new offensive against the apothecaries, and this may explain Sir William Paddy's outburst against him.[2] It was some time before the question was revived. In 1616 Dr. Atkins became president and before the end of that year the discussion had proceeded so far that seven fellows were appointed to confer with the lawyers about a petition to the king for larger privileges.[3] After the first contact with the lawyers the president ordered that three of the fellows should continue the interviews, and approach the lord chief justice (presumably Coke, who had been moved from the common pleas to the king's bench). Dr. Atkins also produced a list of points which were to be included in the new charter and asked the fellows to let him have **any** further suggestions on the following day.[4] At the Christmas comitia he spoke about the king's singular favour to the College, and four of the fellows were nominated to accompany him to the lord chief justice. The business

---

[1] The younger man was Hamey, then a candidate, which was his position from 1630 to 1633/4. He reports this interesting conversation at length in the life of Meverall, written in 1648, in 'Bustorum Aliquot Reliquiae'.

[2] See above. p. 222.   [3] 3 December 1616.   [4] 6 December 1616.

went through reasonably quickly. At the June comitia Dr. Moundeford and Dr. Ridley were appointed to read the charter through. On 8 October it was dated and ten days later it was shown to the College, Great Seal and all.[1]

The new charter was all that the College wished. With much expenditure of words it named Drs. Atkins, Mayerne and Lister as the petitioners; confirmed the existing powers of the College; gave it the right to sue for all penalties inflicted by it and to retain the king's share for its own use without rendering any account; and gave the president and censors the right to examine, survey, govern, correct and punish all physicians, practitioners of physic, apothecaries, druggists, distillers and so forth in London. We may pause to remark that this is the first we have heard of distillers: we shall hear of them again. The charter went on to confer on the censors (without the president) or any three of them the right to summon and examine all London physicians and practisers of physic, and to fine them up to 40s. for disobeying the summons, for unlicensed practice up to £3 and seven days imprisonment or longer if a fine was unpaid; for administering unfit medicine up to £10 and fourteen days, or longer as before. These provisions seem to embody an important result of the conferences with Coke. In Bonham's case he had ruled that the College must prove a month's illicit practice: now he concurred in the liberating grant of the new power to convict without proving that the practice had continued for any minimum time.

Apothecaries, surgeons, druggists, persons employed to attend patients (whom we should call nurses) and servants of patients might be served with a summons under the common seal of the College to give evidence before the president and censors on oath. If they refused to testify they might be fined £1. The power to search and destroy apothecaries' and such-like wares was supplemented with a right to summon the owners and examine them on oath concerning their composition, to fine them £1 for non-appearance, and for defective medicines to fine them £3 and imprison them until they should pay. The maintenance of a common hall, the making of ordinances, the office of 'register' and other officers, the taking of recognizances up to £100, the purchase of land up to the annual value of 100 marks (£66. 13s. 4d.), and the freedom from bearing arms in the City and within seven miles of it were all conceded.

[1] 25 June, 16 October 1617; text of Charter in Goodall, pp. 37 ff.

Finally the king promised that he or his heirs or successors would give their assent to any Bill of the next parliament for confirming all these powers to the College. For all this the College was to pay a yearly rent of £6.

We shall see in due course how it came about that no confirmatory Bill was ever presented for the royal assent. There had been no parliament since 1614, and there was none until January 1621/2, but there was no legal challenge of the new powers in the interval and so the experience of these four years provides a good test of their efficacy for their purpose. So far as the surgeons and the apothecaries are concerned we have already covered the ground.[1] We have now to see what happened to the miscellaneous crowd of empirics and dabblers. In 1614, about the time of his emotional entry in the Annals, Dr. Gwinne resumed his practice of reporting their examinations in that record.[2] There seems to have been a round-up in the winter of 1614–15. A Cambridge master of arts, Simon Bowde of Norwich, admitted two years of practice and said he did not know the law: he was prohibited for the future.[3] William Shepherd claimed to be *insanorum medicaster*: he had manacled and miserably misused a woman patient, charging a fee of £10. He was imprisoned and then knelt to ask forgiveness.[4] Dr. Arthur Dee owned up to three years and maintained that he had the right; he too was forbidden, but as he was burdened with a family he was only threatened with the penalties of the law. An astrologer, William Hart, was forbidden. A highly suspect Portuguese Roman catholic called Emmanuel Gomel, who had come over from Antwerp, refused to be examined, but he was let off as a transient alien and also, alas, to please Sir Peregrine Bertie who came to the censors' day with him.[5] Another Cambridge master Richard Hanger said he was awaiting his doctorate and had merely delayed asking for his examination; he was dismissed *clementer*, which clearly means connivance.[6] That concluded the winter drive. Jane Waterworth was let off merely because she was a poor little thing (*paupercula*); on the same day the £3 bond of another woman old in years and

---

[1] See above, pp. 214–7.
[2] The last place where the Annals merely refer the reader to the Book of Examinations is on 4 March 1613/14.
[3] 4 November 1614.
[4] The part of the entry of 13 January 1614/15 relating to Shepherd is printed in R. Hunter and Ida Macalpine, *Three Hundred Years of Psychiatry* (1963), p. 91. He named Leonellus Farentinus as an author whom he had read.
[5] 13 January 1614/15.   [6] 3 February 1614/15.

offences was declared forfeit.[1] One man paid 10s.; another promised to leave town[2]; the warrant for committing another woman was prepared but the censors had pity on her.[3] On 3 December 1616 the president complained that no one had responded to his appeal for the names of empirics. Unless our information is deficient, in the preceding two years £5 10s. had been inflicted in penalties and one short term of imprisonment.

About this time we hear of three men with medical qualifications who were not licensed. Two of them seem to deserve sympathy. John Hawkins was a doctor of Padua, but not of an English university. He was advised to incorporate, but two years later it was arranged that he should practise without a licence, paying £4 a year like a licentiate but nominally as a penalty (*nomine poenae*). He was probably a papist, and this device for conniving at their practice had not been invented when he first appeared. In the meantime he may simply have been tolerated without paying.[4] Mr. Henslowe of Suffolk was an M.A. who had practised there for eight years with a bishop's licence. He said he had studied philosophy at the Sorbonne and in Seville, but he was advised to study medicine at Oxford or Cambridge, which he said was difficult because he was married, and he was forbidden to practise in London.[5] John Draper was less excusable. He was warned in 1610 and went on treating patients thereafter by his own judgement and out of authors. He said he was not a papist and did not know whether his wife was one or not. He was alleged to have been associated with Dr. Bonham. He said that he had not applied to the College because he 'hoped not for favour'—not unnaturally—and he said he had been told 'that he cannot have license without so much money in his purse to satisfye'. This presumably refers only to the lawful fees and does not hint at further exactions. At any rate he changed his mind and asked to be examined; he was told he must first visit the fellows, and that is all we know of him.[6] In the twelve months before the receipt of the charter only one complete impostor was inhibited, a woman, and that without penalty. But two determined empirics were summoned and, on one excuse or another, did not come: Paul Buck,[7] and one Willis. Nor did a surgeon who was to rise high in the scale of notoriety, George Butler.[8]

---

[1] 8 September 1615.   [2] 1, 15 December 1615.   [3] 3 May, 7 June 1616.
[4] 14 January 1615/16; 14 April 1626.   [5] 13 September 1616.
[6] 10 January, 7 March 1616/17.   [7] 7 February 1616/17.   [8] 4 July 1617.

17

There does not seem to have been any marked improvement after the charter. In two years there was one pretty severe sentence. Henry Smith, a priest who had forsaken his vocation, treated a woman patient who died. On the evidence of the widower, the apothecary, and Drs. Atkins and Baskerville he was fined £10, imprisoned, and ordered to give his bond of £100 not to practise. A deputation had to make sure that the archbishop of Canterbury had no objection and Dr. Atkins even had to play the king; but after much wriggling (*multum luctatus*) Smith paid.[1] But there was no other case in which the censors were strict. Simon Bowde was up again and said that there was judicial opinion that anyone was free to treat certain diseases: serious as this was, it earned nothing but an admonition.[2] No harm seems to have befallen the empirics Lambe, Bartholomew Jaquinto, and Vanlo (*Germanus*, probably a Netherlander).[3] Dr. Duval, accused of illicit and evil practice failed to appear though the French ambassador undertook that he would.[4] Dr. Eyre appeared no less than ten times. On the third occasion he was fined £20 for all his past offences, paid within three days and continued to practise. He remarked 'It is the practice of the College not to admit any man of worth', whereupon he was examined for the first time and approved. Again he was fined £10 for malpractice, but the prison sentence which he incurred at the same time was remitted when he apologized to the comitia for what he had said. He failed at the second examination but he was given another chance with easy questions. Although his answers gave no satisfaction, he was allowed to continue in practice on condition that he called in one of the fellows in the more serious cases.[5] The new charter did not make the lot of the intruders any harder than it had been before. The only possible explanation of this anticlimax must be that the College did not venture to act under the Charter by administering an oath to witnesses or by taking recognizances. It is indeed clear from the parliamentary proceedings of 1621 that they thought the authority of the Charter would be open to challenge unless it were confirmed

[1] 4, 11 May; 25, 29 June 1621. This is not the licentiate Dr. Henry Smith, admitted in 1613, a bad-tempered old gentleman who was fined on 22 November and 15 December 1622 for rudeness to the president and Sir William Paddy.

[2] 4 December 1618: see above, p. 232.

[3] 7 May, 22 December 1619, 4 February 1619/20. The lord mayor referred to the College a quarrel between Jaquinto and one Bonscio over a case which Vanlo had treated. The censors decided it was not their business, but the president settled it: 4 February 1619/20. For the dreadful fate of William Lambe see below, p. 259.

[4] 24, 27 January 1619/20.   [5] 6 February 1617/18-1 September 1620.

by parliament, and this lends substantial support to the view, adopted in later times, that the College never accepted the Charter of James I.[1]

It was not only the constituted authorities who invented plans and schemes, but the medical sphere was remarkably free from the officious projectors who pestered every government in Europe. The College had no difficulty in frustrating the design of a Scotsman named Morris or Morrison, which had been shown to the king. He proposed that, in exchange for an annual payment of £5, he should levy fines on all those who practised without licences beyond the seven-mile limit of the College, keeping the king's share of the fines for himelf and receiving half a crown for registering every licence granted by a bishop.[2]

When Robert Paulet and Raphe Kewe petitioned the king for a patent to practise in person or by deputy their rare secret for curing ruptures by outward applications and inward cordials, the king referred their petition direct to the College, and the College sent a prudent answer which seems to have been effective. They did not commit themselves to any opinion on the likelihood of treating ruptures successfully by these means, but they wrote that they suspected all secret practices, which were mostly colours and shadowers for ignorance and falsehood. Since there were many sorts of ruptures, not all curable by one medicine, they prayed that the petitioners might prove the value of their remedies 'by reason and experience', that is experiment, in which event they would report to His Majesty.[3]

On another occasion, however, they opposed a petition which was no doubt objectionable but which dealt with a real need. Midwives, as we have seen, were subject to some kind of examination as to character and skill, but the standard was low.[4] In France there had been reforms in the later sixteenth century, and in Paris at least the surgeons exercised a real supervision with beneficial results. In England history knows little about the thousands of women who carried the daily responsibility of this essential work. Historians for the most part regard Charles Dickens as the only authority on seventeenth- and eighteenth-century midwifery. A great deal is known, however, about one extraordinary family of men-midwives, the Chamberlens, who were, we may say, the

---

[1] See below, p. 374.
[2] 3, May, 10 June 1605.
[3] 20 March 1617/18.
[4] Above, p. 66.

undisputed heads of this special line of practice for about a century. Of Huguenot extraction they grew great partly by the invention, their family secret, of the short forceps for delivery in childbirth: but for three generations they also possessed the gifts of pushing their fortunes and disregarding ordinary ideas of decorum.[1] Two of them were flourishing at this time, two brothers both called Peter.[2] They were freemen of the Barber-Surgeons' Company and they were often in trouble with the College. From 1607 to 1620 the elder was found guilty four times of practising medicine or practising badly or both; on one charge both brothers were convicted, and the younger was twice accused, though without sufficient evidence. They were not easy to cope with: they had influence both at court and in the City. The elder brother was accoucheur to the queen and son-in-law to William de Laune.[3] The younger could rely in the hour of need on the support of the earl of Pembroke.[4]

The College is therefore unlikely to have been favourably disposed to the Chamberlen family. A few days after the College took the first steps towards applying for its new charter the king remitted another petition for a charter to his attorney general, who at this time was Sir Francis Bacon himself.[5] It came from the midwives in and about the City of London. It declared that many women and their children perished through want of skill in midwives, and that the skill of the most skilful should be bettered, and none allowed except those who were meet, which was impossible unless they were incorporated and made a society.[6] They therefore petitioned for this and for lectures on anatomy, for regulations and for better education. Their petition deserves a place in the history of feminism. It expressed the disconcerting doctrine that what was sauce for the gander was sauce for the goose. In transmitting it to Bacon the king wrote that he had liked well of it, and directed the attorney general to signify the royal approval 'by a word or two to be subscribed

---

[1] J. H. Aveling, *The Chamberlens and the Midwifery Forceps* (1882) is a very good book and gives, often in full, all the references to members of the family in the College Annals. Hugh Chamberlen the younger (1664-1728), in the fourth generation, was an irreproachable fellow of the College.

[2] In some other instances it is known that a younger brother was given the same Christian name as an elder brother in order to preserve it in the family if the elder should die. It was still rare in England to give a child two Christian names.

[3] 6 November 1607.   [4] 2 June, 7 July 1620.

[5] The texts of the king's letter to Bacon, 27 December 1616, and other documents are in the Annals after 30 June 1617. The petition is undated.

[6] For the word 'society' see above, p. 224. Here it seems to be used simply as a very general name for a body or association, without any specific implications.

under this petition'. Bacon complied: he had also understood from Mayerne that it was full of piety and appearance of saving life. If the king would declare his pleasure Bacon would consult those physicians and others who understood it best and draft a charter ('draw the book') accordingly. The next step came promptly: the privy council referred the petition to the College of Physicians.[1] We do not know whether it was also sent, as Bacon seems to have intended, to any others besides the physicians.

The College sprang to arms. The president (Dr. Atkins) and four others were to consider the opinions of the fellows and these were to be sent in writing as soon as possible.[2] But before this was done there was a debate in the comitia. The president brought forward some suggestions made to him by Sir William Paddy and the registrar which amounted to an alternative scheme. It was opposed by Peter Chamberlen the younger, who was heard in support of the midwives. His presence as an advocate, in conjunction with later events, makes it seem likely that the midwives had not acted on their own initiative but that they had the ambition of the Chamberlens as well as feminism behind them. Chamberlen argued boldly. He asked whether any fellow of the College could deal with a difficult problem about parturition better than an obstetric surgeon, and he boasted that he and his brother were the only two experts in these matters. He did not persuade his hearers.[3]

The College recognized that many abuses arose from the unskilfulness of ignorant midwives; but it thought the plan of making them into an incorporated society to govern themselves new, unheard of and without example in any commonwealth. A better way would be that before a midwife was admitted by a bishop or his chancellor, she should be examined by the president and two or three of the gravest of the College[4] nominated by him. They offered 'to depute such grave and learned men as shall alwaies be ready to resolve all their doubtes and instruct them in what they desire conceringe midwiferye' and once or twice a year to make private dissections and anatomies to the use of their whole company. They also proposed that malpractice in midwifery should be brought under the jurisdiction of the censors.[5]

[1] 10 January 1616/17.
[2] 24 January 1616/17: the four were Drs. Moundeford, Lister, Palmer, and Argent, strong men.
[3] 21 February 1616/17: see also below, p. 253.   [4] Here referred to as 'that society'.
[5] 21 February 116/17 and undated reply to the privy council.

These counter-proposals served their immediate purpose of thwarting the midwives' movement. Whether the College had any positive desire to give them effect we cannot know; nor what impression they made on Bacon and Mayerne, or on the king if he heard of them, or on the midwives. We can only say that there is no trace of any intention of pressing for them, and that the College would have found them at least as difficult to administer as its existing functions. We cannot indeed assume that the midwives, with or without the Chamberlens, would have succeeded any better. Perhaps no effective remedy was possible then; but everyone agreed on the need and no one openly denied that there was an opportunity. It is inevitable that personal incompatibilities should sometimes checkmate beneficent plans, but in this case it seems that both sides were to blame.

Although it arose from no new conception of the College's functions in a changing world, and although its results fell short of the hopes of those who framed it, we should not judge the programme of 1614 altogether adversely. The incidents of the surgeons' charter and the Bonham case showed exactly how far the law allowed the College to go in exercising its statutory powers. Dr. Atkins, who seems to have been a very able president, and to have been well supported especially by Mayerne and Dr. Moundeford, formed a coherent plan and carried it out by means of the one resource open to the College, the support of ministers and the king himself. No more could be done. Within two months of the comitia of 1614 which began the period of action, parliament was dissolved and for the next six years it was impossible to seek any authority less vulnerable than that of royal charters and proclamations. The scene changed completely in January 1620/1 when a new parliament assembled.

XIII : THE COLLEGE HOLDS
ITS OWN, 1621-40

IN January 1620/1 King James's third parliament met. It came into existence because of the king's financial needs and his relations with foreign powers. On a far lower plane it also afforded an opportunity for his subjects, including corporations, to state their needs and to seek parliamentary sanction for their plans. Before the session began the College appointed a committee of the president and five fellows to discuss the means of getting the Act confirming their new Charter, to which the king had promised his assent.[1] The Apothecaries took similar steps and the College raised no objection. Besides a confirmation of their own charter they opposed that of the Distillers.[2] In February, when the College committee was re-appointed with one small personal change, the president raised a new question, the menace from the surgeons, who were applying to parliament for freedom to practise medicine. Harvey and Clement were to consult Mayerne; there was much deliberating and combining.[3] All the fellows were asked to approach their friends in parliament, in the first place the university members, and to report the results. Two fellows were appointed to deal with each of the university members; there was much discussion in private about one of the junior fellows, Dr. Lawrence Wright, and in the end the president designated four fellows to interview Dr. Wright's brother in Gray's Inn, their father's Inn, about the surgeons.[4]

It was evident already that there were rocks ahead. The discussions about Dr. Wright may perhaps bear some relation to his subsequent career as an adherent of the Puritan opposition, which was vocal in the house of commons. Harvey reported on the attitude of the Cambridge university burgesses, and his report was disquieting. They were perfectly sound on the pretentions of the surgeons, but they reserved their opinion on the exclusion of

---

[1] 12 December 1620.   [2] Underwood, p. 242.
[3] 1 February 1620/21. Both the surgeons and the apothecaries submitted printed 'briefs' to this parliament; but the College does not appear to have done so, in which perhaps it was negligent.   [4] 17 February.

clergymen from practice. They said they could not act jointly (*convenire*) with the College because of their privileges. They accused the College of licensing *rustici*, ignorant persons, and of licensing foreign rather than English graduates. They took exception to the form of the examination as beneath the dignity of doctors. The president proposed that the deputed fellows should deny the charges, carrying with them a copy of the charter and appropriate excerpts from it, and should do what could be done to mollify the critics. Various points could be explained, such as the statute about admissions and the option allowed to the applicant at his second examination to be examined in subjects prepared beforehand. But the coolness of Cambridge was ominous. The shadow of Dr. Bonham lay over the proceedings, and, what was worse, Cambridge had put the College in the positions of denying, in the matter of admissions, that it was exercising a monopoly. 'Monopoly' was a hateful word. Of all the rankling grievances brought up in the commons, monopolies were exciting the greatest odium, not, of course, the innumerable old-established monopolies of corporations, but those recently granted by the Crown, as it was asserted, to gratify private interests at the expense of the public. The investigation of these monopolies had not gone very far when it took a turn which had two lessons for the College, first that its own collegiate affairs might become involved in the great national controversies, and secondly that in Jacobean England legal procedure and statesmanlike planning had a sordid underside.

The most conspicuous of those who had certified that the impugned monopolies were lawful and beneficial was the lord chancellor Francis Bacon. He was impeached by the house of commons for taking bribes. The commons set about collecting evidence against him. Two of the Grocers' Company, Sir Thomas Myddleton and Alderman Johnson came forward with others to testify. They declared that when the king referred the matter between the Grocers and the Apothecaries to Bacon he received £200 from their Company; that he also received a taster of gold worth between £40 and £50 and a present of ambergris from 'the apothecaries that stood with the Grocers'. Two of the apothecaries in the other camp who are named in their charter added that he accepted £100 from 'the new Company of Apothecaries that stood against the Grocers'. Bacon admitted it all. He could only plead that this was no iudicial business but a concord or composition between the parties, all three of which had 'received good' and had common purses, so that he had not taken a corrupt bribe.[1] After his fall he wrote in a letter that the charter was a fair business both for law and convenience, but he added: 'You may perhaps think me partial to Potycaries, that have been ever puddering in physic all my life.'[2] Indeed partiality to the apothecaries had been alleged as a charge against him. The Grocers and the apothecaries who went with them wrote that Lord Chancellor Egerton never affixed the Great Seal to the Apothecaries' charter, but that after his death Bacon, then lord keeper, did it, and that the commissioners, of whom he was one, made their order without any report to the king.[3] Bacon wrote truly enough that the king made the charter his own and took it much to heart. This City quarrel, and the prospects of the College with it were close to the whirlpool of national politics.

The parliament of 1621 satisfied no one's hopes. It lasted on and off for nearly a year, but it was a year of friction and ill-feeling: neither the physicians nor the surgeons nor the apothecaries put any of their business through. There followed two clear years in which public business was back on the old footing. The king issued new open warrants to the lord mayor and all judges and justices charging them to support the College in its action against empirics.[4] But this action yielded nothing better than the old indecisive results. Helen Rix, indeed, when in prison failed in her application for a Habeas Corpus and seems to have been altogether defeated.[5] William Blanke was fined and gave his bond, but that was by no means the end of him.[6] Very few of the small craft were sunk. The only newcomer of note, Tobias Simpson, whose sister was accused with him, was supported by the earl of Holderness and the bishop of London: though fined and imprisoned, he was impenitent.[7] When the impostors were so bold, it was no wonder that the surgeons

---

[1] 'Confession and Humble Submission' of Bacon in J. Spedding, *Letters and Life of Bacon*, vii (1874), 514; A. B. Beaven, *Aldermen of the City of London* (1908); articles 24–26 of the Impeachment. A taster is a cup for tasting wine; the value of this is mis-stated by Spedding, whose error is corrected by Underwood, p. 220, n. 29.

[2] To Sir Humphrey May, in 1624 when he feared the matter might be taken up again in parliament (Spedding, vii. 514).

[3] Petition of 1621 in House of Lords Papers, *Historical MSS. Commission, Third Report* (1872), p. 27.

[4] Dated 2 July 1622; text in Annals, vol. iii, fo. B; referred to 20 July. For a similar order of 26 November 1617 see *Acts of the Privy Council 1616–1617* (1927), p. 387.

[5] 8, 20 July 1622.

[6] 17 September 1622. He had a licence from the archbishop of Canterbury, and on another occasion was imprisoned but released on *habeas corpus*: C. Merret, *Collections* (1660), p. 124.   [7] 5, 11 July, 1 August 1623.

misbehaved. The obstinate George Butler was sent by the lord chief justice to the College for examination, with the inevitable result; whereupon he suffered severe penalties and continued on his way as before.[1] The national warlike preparations of the time led to a new quarrel with the surgeons collectively. Dr. Clement and Dr. Winston proceeded to Barber-Surgeons' Hall for the examination of naval surgeons. They were not admitted. Mr. Fenton was summoned to answer for this affront; but no satisfaction was given.[2] Equally regrettable was the demeanour of the apothecaries. There was a misunderstanding or worse about the orders of the College that apothecaries were not to work for the irregulars.[3] The president of the College accompanied the apothecaries on their annual search,[4] and their wardens submitted a questionable specimen of confection of alkermes for comparison with the *Pharmacopoeia*[5]; but there were half a dozen cases of illicit practice by their freemen. Some of the offenders were bad men like Abraham Hugobert, who had been fined by the Society itself,[6] but some appear to have been of good standing. The College appointed a committee on surgeons and apothecaries practising medicine, which reported something against the apothecaries, but nothing against surgeons.[7]

On 19 February 1623/4 King James opened his fourth and last parliament, and the conflicting corporations braced themselves for renewed hostilities. Six weeks later the committee of grievances reported to the house of commons on the case of the Grocers and the Apothecaries of London. The whirligig of time had brought in one of its revenges, for the reporter was Sir Edward Coke. Much had happened to him since Bonham's case. He had been dismissed from the bench and imprisoned in the Tower, but now as a member of parliament he was one of the leaders of opposition to the king. He reported that the Apothecaries could not prove any consent of the Grocers to their separation, so that on that ground their charter 'fell'. Besides that it was full of many great inconveniences. It granted the monopoly of drugs and distilling, a great wrong to merchants who could thus sell their commodities only to a few buyers and, as it were, by retail, which was a cause of the decay of trade. There were novel claims in it: as that any Grocer engaging in this trade should be sued in the star chamber. The Grocers

---

[1] 7, 16 May, 13 June 1623.   [2] 30 January 1622/3.   [3] 29 November 1622.
[4] Barrett, p. 19, says that this is noted in their records for the first time on 18 February 1622/3.   [5] 9, 16 May 1623.
[6] 11 April, 16 May 1623; Barrett, p. 10.   [7] 25 June 1623.

maintained that apothecaries should deal only in those confections which required their art. The committee held that the charter was a grievance in creation and execution; but they thought fit that the Apothecaries should submit a Bill giving them the sole right to make such medicines and potions as required skill. The house of commons passed a resolution in the sense of the report. The Bill was read for the first time on 19 April, and it was sent to a committee with Coke as chairman, and some able members, such as Sir Hugh Myddleton, Sir Thomas's brother.[1]

The king stood staunchly by his word. When the City seconded the Grocers' case, he told the lord mayor that he had granted the charter from his own judgement for the health of his people, knowing that grocers were not competent judges of the practice of medicine. The speaker of the house of commons was to be told this.[2] And within a few days the king told the whole house himself. In a speech proroguing the parliament he said: 'I myself did devise that corporation and do allow it.'[3]

During the prorogation the Apothecaries' Charter was re-affirmed by a royal warrant, but their court of assistants drafted a paper to the effect that they would not exercise any of their powers, except binding and freeing apprentices and electing officers, until they had obtained their further powers from parliament at the next session.[4] The College also was busy with preparations for the re-assembling of parliament. During the previous session it had, of course, been indirectly concerned in the apothecaries' business; and it seems that the question of a Bill to confirm its own charter had taken a serious turn. The president and nine of the fellows had taken their charter to Westminster, no doubt at a summons from the committee on the Apothecaries' Bill. It was restored to them by the king a day or two after the end of the session, when the Apothecaries also received their charter back. Coke's committee appears to have heard evidence from the College and to have called in question the validity of some provisions of its Jacobean charter. The College had to devise a policy in relation to this and several connected matters. At a private meeting one morning it was agreed that Dr. Atkins should speak before the *commissionarii* (which must

---

[1] *Journals of the House of Commons*, i (1742), 756, 770, 772, 798.
[2] Barrett, p. 23 from a letter of Sir Edward Conway, secretary of state, to Sir Robert Heath, solicitor-general, 25 May 1624.
[3] Cobbett, *Parliamentary History*, i (1806), 1491, 1503.
[4] Barrett, p. 23.

mean the committee of the commons) on the charter and the necessity of the power there granted of administering an oath. Sir William Paddy was to open the case and oppose the petition of the surgeons. A few days later in another small meeting heads for a Bill were mentioned: reasons for the oath, exemption from bearing arms, the right to have a house, increased powers of citation. Mr. Serjeant Bramston, who seems to have been present, explained the difference between a Bill and a petition and suggested that the Bill should be presented in the house of lords. This eminent lawyer was the son-in-law of the president, Dr. Moundeford, and he was a good friend to the College, but there is a note of discontent in the registrar's note of this meeting, for he had not been invited and knew only what the president chose to tell him.[1] In June the president orated about the privileges and said he would tender the oath —as authorized by the charter—if the College agreed; but Dr. Atkins wanted first to have the opinion of the lawyers; Dr. Argent doubted whether the date had not expired[2]; Dr. Herring thought the oath might be tendered, and nothing was settled. On the same day Dr. Foxe and the other fellows deputed with him brought forward six questions. The comitia decided to refer to counsel the first two queries, whether the king should be petitioned about the objections which had been raised against the power of taking evidence and whether the censors should proceed to take bonds by virtue of the charter. The third query was whether the names of all unlawful practitioners should be brought into the College in order to show the bad results of its inability to restrain them. It was decided the names should be given in to the president. Fourthly, since parliament had made no demonstration of declaring the charter a grievance, it was asked whether proceedings should be taken to recover the expense incurred and damages from some member or members who had cast on them the false (and we may add inappropriate) imputation that they were 'grievers of the soule'. This foolish suggestion was negatived. Next came a point about the surgeons. Should the College claim the right to search surgical chests for the navy?[3] This does not seem to have been answered, and it seems to have been thought prudent not to take any action about the last query, on abusive remarks by a surgeon, though he

[1] 24 April, 3 May, (undated) May 1624.
[2] I do not understand what time-limit is referred to, unless it be that for taking the oath of allegiance: there cannot have been a time-limit for the oaths of witnesses.
[3] See below, p. 265.

called the physicians knaves, and another of his craft said 'Scurvy physicians and knave pothecaries'.[1]

The attorney general and the solicitor general had perhaps learnt caution from Bacon's disaster: they promised to do what they could for the College but declined to take fees. A junior was joined to Bramston, who was very busy in this year, his first as a serjeant-at-law; a committee of eight was to prepare the case against the surgeons.[2] In October Sir William Paddy, Dr. Meverell and the much-discussed Dr. Wright were charged with the defence of the College before parliament, and another committee was to consider reforming the apothecaries.[3] After that the Annals run dry: the registrar recorded acidly in February that he had entered nothing about what was done in the meantime about the surgeons and apothecaries because it was kept secret.[4]

Whatever was done, when it came to fruition the College had lost its most powerful friend: the old king died in March. Parliament was dissolved by the demise of the Crown; a new house of commons was elected, and it presented the Apothecaries' charter as a grievance. The king replied that this was to be left to a Bill to be passed in both houses.[5] In the press of business over war with Spain, it was not until February 1625/6 that a Bill was presented for 'avoiding deceits and abuses in making and compounding of physical receipts and medicines and for suppressing empirics' in London and for seven miles about. It proposed to give the apothecaries the sole right to compound medicines: no wonder the College promptly declared against it and sent off a deputation to the commons. The Bill went to a committee on the following day, a strong committee with some of those who had served the last time and also with a physician, Samuel Turner, a new member for Shaftesbury.[6] He was a Padua doctor, the son of Peter Turner, formerly a fellow of the College and in several parliaments member for Bridport. Whether or where he ever practised we do not know, nor what he thought of the Bill. He suddenly made himself famous that week by telling the house that the duke of Buckingham was the cause of all their grievances.[7] Once more the ill-will betweeen the King and

[1] 2 June 1624.   [2] (undated) June 1624.   [3] 9 October 1624.
[4] 15 February 1624/5: *quia celatum.*
[5] King Charles I, *Bibliotheca Regia* (1659), p. 276.
[6] *Journals of the House of Commons*, i (1742), 823, 830, 851.
[7] Buckingham's name only appears twice in the Annals: in 1618/19 he wrote in favour of Dr. Lawrence Bowne; in 1626/7, along with three other peers he wrote to ask the College to connive at the practice of Mr. George Hill. Perhaps it was because

the opposition put a stop to all parliamentary business: the houses were dissolved on 18 June. Other parliaments met and contended with King Charles, but none of them attempted to tinker up the Jacobean medical planning, and after 1629 there was no parliament at all for eleven years. The relations of the College and its enemies with the state were once again relations with the Crown.

The one subject about which the parliament of 1626 communicated with the College was religion. When it met there was widespread anxiety, genuine or factitious, about the danger of popery. Knowing this, King Charles had already issued a commission to provide for the execution of the penal laws[1] but the commons wanted to make sure. A letter from one of their committees was read to the College asking for the names of those practising physic and pharmacy in London who were suspected of being papists. The fellows who were present mentioned such names as they could think of, thirteen physicians and five or six apothecaries. Five of the thirteen were known catholics whom the College tolerated.[2] The two Friers, Thomas and John, sons of the Thomas who had been a fellow and died in 1623, were presumably in the same position except that they did not pay fees disguised as fines. There were two whose position had never been regularized, although the College knew all about them, the fashionable Dr. Moore and Dr. Cadyman, who had court connexions.[3] Two, Thomas Fludd and Simon Baskerville were fellows of the College. A few days later, Webb, a Padua doctor was brought in and allowed to practise on paying the usual £4 a year *nomine poenae*.[4] It appears that the College was not alarmed either for itself or for the catholic law-breakers, and nothing unpleasant happened to any of them.

The rule against practice by ministers of religion was enforced,

King James died in the country that the College was not consulted about the charge in Buckingham's impeachment that he brought in a physician, Remington of Dunmow, without leave of the king's doctors: see *Historical Manuscripts Commission, 8th Report* (1881), p. 5.

[1] 3 November 1625.

[2] 29 March 1626: Price, Eggleshem, Jaquinto, John Bartlet, Berry. Of Gifford nothing seems to be mentioned elsewhere in the Annals, unless he is the fellow admitted in 1598. For Price, a Bologna doctor, see 7 December 1627; 4 January, 1 February 1627/8: on the last occasion he was turned out of the building after an unseemly tirade against Henry VIII and Queen Elizabeth.

[3] He was fined £20 for malpractice on 20 June 1625 and was first charged on 4 April 1623 after practising for two years. In December 1630 he first took the oaths of allegiance and obedience to the College and was licensed; and was then admitted a fellow as the queen's physician.

[4] 7 April 1626.

though not consistently.[1] One Puritan minister, who was destined
to become a celebrity, troubled the College now for a second time.
Alexander Leighton was M.A. of St. Andrews and had studied
medicine at Leiden. In 1619 he was practising in London. He told
the College that he was in priest's orders, but could not exercise
his priesthood because of his scruples against ceremonies. He said
that he had read the whole of Galen, but his answers were poor.
He promised not to practise again. The College inhibited him, not
because it distrusted his promise but because his perversity in
church matters made it seem unlikely that he could make a livelihood
in any other way.[2] Sure enough, in 1626 he was up again and
admitted that he had practised for eleven years. The College,
refusing to license him until he should satisfy it on the statutory
point about his orders, inhibited him again.[3] Six months later he
was under arrest. The College tried to bargain for a payment
nomine poenae, but Leighton made a derisory offer, and it is not
clear what became of his practice.[4] Not long afterwards he spent
some years in Holland, where he wrote a militant book against
bishops. When he came back to London the court of high commission pounced on him; he was degraded from his orders and
barbarously punished by the star chamber. After a considerable
interval the College took notice of this sentence. He was no longer
in orders and, being in the Fleet prison, he was not in a good way
of practice but 'They . . . censured Mr. Leighton (called Dr.
Leighton) whoe was censured in the starr chamber and lost his
eares, to be *infamis*.'[5] No doubt they had been reminded of his
existence because on the same day they revoked the licence of Dr.
Bastwicke, the son-in-law of Leonard Po, for no other reason than
that he too had been sentenced by the high commission. They were
to hear of these two Puritans again.

   One other minister of the gospel, a Cambridge man and a doctor
of Padua, was admonished not to practise, and, for all we know,
bowed to the admonition,[6] but it is hard to resist the suspicion that
the College was biased on the episcopal side. Mr. Langham was
perpetual curate of Thurlby in Lincolnshire, but for 40s. *nomine
poenae* he was allowed to practise in London.[7] Mr. Pordage,

---

[1] Dr. Abbot *theologus*, who was complained of as an unlicensed practitioner presumably did not claim any qualification: 21 April 1625.
[2] 24 September 1619.   [3] 7 July 1626.   [4] 5 January 1626/7.
[5] 18 February 1634/5: the star chamber sentence was in 1630.
[6] Philip Vincent of Peterhouse, 6 September 1639.   [7] 10 June 1627.

however, was denied a licence, although he only owned to being a deacon.[1] It is not clear whether the College refused to tolerate John Hofman, a religious refugee from Germany who was strongly supported both from the court and from the medical world, nor whether he deserved to be tolerated.[2] Another refugee William Fortin, a Paris doctor, failed on examination.[3]

It may be that the College gained on the whole by keeping clear of the religious divisions of the nation, and this might have been impossible if it had opened its doors to the clergy, some at least of whom might have compromised it on one side or the other. Holy Orders were not, however, in themselves inimical to efficiency in medicine. In the provinces there was no rule on either side against combining the two professions. There is more evidence about clerical doctors and medical clergymen from the seventeenth century than from the sixteenth, possibly because our records become better as time moves forward, but more likely because they were more numerous. For this there are several possible reasons. The one most commonly alleged is economic, and it is supposed to have worked in both directions. Robert Burton, whose authority should be taken seriously, wrote that he knew many physicians who had taken orders in the hope of a benefice, and that many poor country vicars for want of other means were driven 'to turn mountebanks, quacksalvers, empirics'.[4] But he gave the argument too cynical a turn. Some of the clergymen in question, such as John Favour, the prosperous and well-known vicar of Halifax, were not in need of money. Burton's younger contemporary George Herbert, in a book which expressed the ideals of the pastoral clergy, treats medical service as part of the devotion of the country parson to his flock. He may render it himself or his wife may do it, and we may note that Archbishop Abbott licensed a clergyman's wife to practise medicine.[5] If neither the parson nor his wife has the skill, Herbert continues, and if he can afford it, he will keep some young practitioner in his house; if all else fails he will retain some neighbour physician to serve his parish. 'Yet it is easy for any Scholar to attaine to such a measure of Phisick as may be of much use to him both for himself and others.' This could be done by seeing one

[1] 9 June 1637, 26 January 1637/8.
[2] 19 January 1626/7. 25 June 1627.   [3] 10 June 1627.
[4] *The Anatomy of Melancholy* (1622): 'to the Reader'.
[5] Catherine Greene, wife of the vicar of Royston, in 1620: R. R. James in *Janus*, xli (1936), 97 ff.

dissection, by reading Fernel, by keeping a herbal by him and studying the home-bred simples, not the apothecaries' imported drugs.[1]
This all calls to mind another aspect of clerical life: the number of
educated clergymen was increasing. Amateur physicians were still
plentiful in all walks of life, and the best of them were allies, not
rivals, of the qualified physicians. George Herbert's brother, Lord
Herbert of Cherbury, recommended medicine and botany as
studies for gentlemen, not with a view to practice but to keep a
check on apothecaries, who frequently put in substitutes for the
materials they ought to have used.[2] Many people still collected
medical recipes and passed them on to their friends. Those who
had studied at the universities, as many of the clergy had, could
at least understand why it was that medicine required serious study,
and what distinguished the physicians from empirics. Herbert
wrote that 'it is a justice and debt to the Common-wealth he lives
in, not to incroach on other Professions, but to live on his own'.

In the English society of those days it was still an advantage for
the physicians, and not only in helping to maintain their status,
that their studies were not yet fully professionalized but to some
extent formed part of the common stock of culture, as they had
done in the days of Linacre and Sir Thomas More. A gifted amateur,
William Vaughan, the poet and colonial traveller, wrote reputably
not only from his experience of the illnesses incident to travel in
Newfoundland but also on general medical matters.[3] No intellectual
barrier separated his world from that of the doctors whose names
are remembered in literary history. Perhaps few of their modern
readers know that Thomas Campion was a physician, or Thomas
Lodge, or the translator Philemon Holland. Even our friend Dr.
Matthew Gwinne, the registrar of the College, published poems
and two Latin plays. It is only in the time of Charles I that we
begin to find scraps of direct information about the social intercourse of the fellows but we may be sure that their intellectual
comradeship ranged over many other things besides their statutes
and comitia and censors' days.

One incident of the year 1626 may be mentioned here because
it seems to imply that the College, taken all round and not only as

---

[1] *A Priest to the Temple* (1652), c. xxiii. The preface is dated 1632. This preference for
home-grown remedies was not Herbert's own invention but had considerable support
among medical authors.   [2] *Autobiography*, ed. Sir Sidney Lee (1907), p. 28.
[3] *The Newlanders Cure* (1630); *Natural and Artificiall Directions for Health* (1600):
Bacon accepted the dedication of the fifth edition of this book in 1617.

a piece of machinery for specified functions, had a good name among physicians. Paul de Laune, a fellow since 1618, had gone to Ireland as physician to the lord deputy, Lord Falkland. He was one of five doctors who signed a letter to the College announcing that in answer to a petition of theirs the king had been pleased to found (*instituere*) a college in Dublin for the repression of unqualified practitioners of medicine.[1] It was still only a college to be, but it was to be modelled on Henry VIII's London foundation, and they therefore asked the College to communicate to them its statutes, charters and so forth. To this the College replied in its politest Latin, expressing not so much gratification as approval; but instead of dispatching a bundle of muniments, it invited the five to send over a carefully selected representative. He should see everything that could be to the purpose; he would be able to make sure of getting exactly the right advice and information. Also he would be able to explain what the king had granted, and what its extent was. The vagueness of the Irish letter on this point had suggested caution; it may even have led to suspicions and enquiries at court. Whether that was so or not, there came a disappointed reply from Dublin, saying that none of the five could spare the time for such a long absence from his affairs. Not until after forty years, during which terrible things happened in Ireland, did the College of Physicians of Dublin obtain its royal charter; but, even if it was premature and disingenuous the attempt of 1627 was the first step towards the imitation of the London College in many lands.

It was in 1628 that William Harvey, who had been Lumleian lecturer since 1615, published his book *De Motu Cordis*. We shall discuss the great man and his great book in a later chapter, but here is the place to notice some facts about the College to which we shall then return. They seem to show that in matters of study and teaching the College was doing more than holding its own. The Lumleian lectures and the annual cold-weather dissections provided a first-rate regular course of education in anatomy; but in 1624 it was supplemented with special instruction in morbid anatomy. It is not surprising that there was some difficulty over finding fellows

---

[1] 4 August 1626; 3 February 1626/7. The other signatories of the letters were James Metcalfe, Dermott Meara, Christopher Talbot and John Verdon. Meara, the only one of these mentioned in the *Dictionary of National Biography*, had studied in Oxford and on the Continent was was a poet and medical author. Dr. de Laune seems still to have been talking in the following year about founding a college: Bedell to Usher, 1 April 1628.

who were willing to undertake the unsavoury task. The first proposal was that it should be done by the junior fellows. When they
modestly declined, five of the seniors put themselves at the disposal
of the College.[1] In the winter of 1628-9 the president, Dr. Foxe,
wanted to hold comitia for the admission of some candidates and
chose one of the days of this extraordinary prelection. There was a
pretty good attendance and it may be inferred that the fellows
were known to be interested.[2] Next winter Dr. Crooke, whom we
remember as a refractory author and a regular anatomical lecturer
to the surgeons, gave the three-days lecture in the anatomical
theatre.[3] Two years later a committee was appointed to consider a
letter from the unnamed donor of the lecture. He seems to have
paid for it year by year and to have asked for it to be established on
a permanent footing.[4]

No more is heard until after the death of Dr. Goulston, a member
of the committee, in 1632. He seems to have been the anonymous
donor. In his will he left a rent-charge of £12 a year for the maintenance of an annual lecture within the College, to be given by one
of the four youngest fellows. A dead body was if possible to be procured and two or more diseases treated of on the forenoons and
afternoons of three successive days. When in due course the money
became available, the four junior fellows were all amenable, and
the first appointment went to the senior of them, Dr. William
Goddard. With an eye to the future the president proposed that the
duty of giving the lecture should be inserted into the fellows' oath,
and this was carried.[5] The subject for the year, chosen by the
censors and the committee, was the diseases of the nether belly.[6]
Whether this enjoyable function took place is not recorded. The
first Gulstonian lecture which is known to have been delivered was
given by William Rant in 1639 and highly thought of.[7] Whether
it was given in Latin we do not know; by 1648 when the younger

---

[1] 30 October 1624.
[2] 10 December 1628: president and fifteen fellows present.
[3] 11-14 December 1629. For the next appointment see 22 December 1630.
[4] 2 November 1631: the committee was the president and Drs. Gifford, Harvey,
Goulston, Baskerville, Winston, Hawley, Alston, and Foxe. In the winter of 1629-30 it
was decided to suspend the lecture and devote the money to the redemption of
Goulston's lease (22 December 1629), so that the benefactor perhaps only began to pay
after that.   [5] 23 December 1633; 23 July 1635.   [6] 14 August 1635.
[7] 10 October 1639. Rant, according to J. Venn, *Biographical History of Caius College*
(1897) was the son of a medical practitioner of Norwich, also of Caius, not, as Munk
has it, of a notary public. His younger brother went to the bar, sat in parliament and
was knighted.

Baldwin Hamey took his turn he lectured in English. One other detail about dissections may be mentioned. Dr. Foxe, when he was president, desired, and the College agreed, that the College should apply themselves to dissection of bodies with their own hands, so that no assistant from outside need be employed. No reason is stated.[1]

There are not many other traces of new intellectual activity, but such as they are they do amount to something. The library showed signs of life. Dr. Matthew Holbosch, a German who had practised physic in England for many years bequeathed 680 volumes,[2] and Mr. Matthias, whose executor was Sir George Hastings, left a bequest of books.[3] Regulations were made about access and borrowing.[4] The abortive proposal for a garden which we shall mention below[5] may have had a secondary motive of hostility to the apothecaries, but in itself it was meritorious, and it fitted the scientific mood of the time: it was in 1622–33 that the earl of Danby founded the Oxford University Botanical Garden. Another project with the same perhaps ambiguous motives and the same merits was put forward by Dr. Foxe as president. He proposed that a properly preserved collection of medicaments and simples should be made, and that one of the fellows should give a short exposition of them, lasting one term. This was unanimously accepted, and a large committee was appointed to choose the lecturer, define his subjects and decide how he was to be paid.[6] The onset of national emergencies probably prevented any further progress.

In questions regarding medical publications the College was at least vigilant. It refused to approve a Latin tractate written against the Spaniard Petrus Severinus by the Frenchman Henricus Borgesius, to whom it also refused a licence to practise.[7] It expressed distaste when Mr. Thomas Bryan or Brian presented his book on urines.[8] It ordered that no fellow, candidate or licentiate should sign a testimonial or write any commendatory epistle or verses for any medical or surgical book unless the president and the censors, acting together, had first approved it. That was in consequence of some unsatisfactory occurrence, perhaps in connexion with Bryan.[9] It made no comment when Dr. Fludd presented

---

[1] 27 April 1638. [2] 25 June 1629 and Munk, iii. 365. [3] 25 June 1631.
[4] 2 November 1631; 26 March 1632; 3 July 1635. [5] See below, p. 256.
[6] 23 December 1639. [7] 2 August, 6 September 1639.
[8] 23 March 1634/5. *The Pisse-Prophet or certain Pisse-Pot Lectures* (1637), presumably the book in question, was reprinted in 1679. [9] 28 March, 12 June 1634/5.

his works to the College, which he proposed to have clasped, fit for the library. Alas that they have perished.[1]

There were a few cases of malpractice or breaches of etiquette by physicians, half of them raised by complaints from patients of standing, but the only one that deserves mention was one concerning Peter Chamberlen. A month after his election as a fellow a letter was read in which he justified himself to the president for keeping an apothecary in his house.[2] Unfortunately that is all that we know about his case. The traditional advice to study Galen was tendered three times.[3] Few points arose of which we can say that they have any intellectual interest. We cannot say this of the antidote submitted by Jean Puncteau or Ponteus, who proposed as a test that he should take twenty grains of arsenic with sublimate, and presented letters from the universities of Paris and Montpellier. The College, apparently regarding this as a matter of worldly business rather than of science, referred it to Mayerne, and when the man of genius procured the king's mandate to the College to make an investigation, it replied that it would not hinder him from obtaining the king's favour.[4] Another scientific issue was evaded when a tailor called Thomas Winch, whose modest fee was a shilling, appeared. He gave no medicines: he treated agues by reading in a book and taking the parings of the patients' nails. The president and censors decided to take counsel, but they only recorded the problem: 'It is an ill practise: and it is thought he doth abuse our arte: but notwithstanding it is doubted whether it fall in the compass of *mala praxis* of phisicke or no: it is granted to be charming but whether it be phisicke, that is doubted.'[5]

In 1634 two midwives petitioned the College against Dr. Chamberlen, who, it appeared, had himself petitioned the king to make the midwives a corporation with himself as governor. It was alleged, and consistently with his known character, that he was trying, quite apart from his project for the future, to set up a monopoly by obliging midwives to consult no one but him in their cases 'being a young man to the disparagement of all other phisitions and the inslavinge of your petitioners'. The king referred the petition to the archbishop of Canterbury and the bishop of London, the licensing authorities who, after due enquiry, decided sternly

---

[1] 25 June 1635.   [2] 27 April 1628.
[3] To Bastwick, 1626/7; to Salmon 1633/4; to Lawrence 1639.
[4] 2 October 1629; 7 April 1630.   [5] 16 March 1627/8.

against Dr. Chamberlen. They ordered him to take out an episcopal licence for midwifery as his father had done, to attend the rich and the poor without distinction, and to desist from his attempts to acquire control over the midwives.[1] The midwives petitioned the College. Although he was a fellow Peter Chamberlen refused either to hand in a copy of his proposals or to submit his case to the censors. The College, with a reference to his father's similar proposal in the previous reign, advised against him. It accused him of often refusing his services to the poor and of making hard bargains with the rich, contrary to its statutes. Its objections to him and his proposals were stated forcibly and at great length. The College held that the Chamberlens' method of delivery by the use of iron instruments belonged more to surgery than to medicine, and had little to do with normal midwifery. This time it made no offer to instruct midwives, but maintained that they had English books of anatomy which gave all they needed to know. The new proposals were rejected even more ignominiously than those of the elder Chamberlen.[2] There was, however, a sign that the family pre-dominance would not last for ever, and that there would soon be more men-midwives of consideration. Dr. John Hinton was willingly given leave to practise that art until he should have fulfilled the four years required before he could be examined for admission to the College.[3]

The shadow of the plague hung heavily over these years. It interfered with the activities of the College in 1625; in 1630 there was no meeting between 3 July and 5 November except at Michael-mas; in the next year the ordinary dissection was postponed because the plague was near Amen Corner, and for some weeks the College met at the president's house in Warwick Court, a few hundred yards away. There was no meeting between 25 June 1636 and 13 January 1636/7, on which date five fellows assembled. In 1625 some of the fellows had to follow the court to Oxford; in all of these years there were valid reasons why some should evacuate the City as their patients did. It may be that the scarcity of physicians left openings for the irregulars. Stephen Bredwell, in a sensible tract on the plague remarked that 'Mountebanks goe quack in the Country among the contemners of learning' and mentioned with

---

[1] The decision is given in full in J. H. Aveling, *The Chamberlens* (1882), pp. 43 ff.
[2] 28 August; 1, 8 September 1634.
[3] 6 February 1634/5: this entry is given in full by Munk. Hinton afterwards became a royal physician, a knight and a fellow of the College.

contempt a Spaniard who practised.[1] But the College as a body did what was asked of it. In 1625 it advised the lord mayor.[2] In 1629-30 it prepared regulations which the privy council issued officially. It did similar service in the following year[3] and in 1637.

The privy council sought the advice of the College on other matters besides the plague. When the aldermen of the neighbouring wards petitioned against the fumes from the alum-works at St. Katherine's by the Tower, the College reported and convinced the privy council that the vapours endangered health by their putrid quality.[4] To answer another question it resorted to an elaborate procedure. By this the elects and groups of six fellows each indited separate opinions, of which the upshot was that English and Irish tobacco as it was usually taken could not but be very unwholesome and hurtful.[5] Warlike preparations, as a matter of course, included calls to the College for volunteers to act as physicians to the military and naval sick and wounded.[6] The king acted through other channels in referring to the College the question whether Mr. Lane had died by poison, and after a thorough investigation the College decided this question in the affirmative.[7] Other public authorities followed these examples. At the request of the coroner of London the censors supplies a certificate for use in a court of justice that a man had died from the effects of a potion administered by an apothecary's apprentice.[8] The king's footman drew attention to an abuse in the preparing of a medical substance: buck's horn was being passed off as hartshorn. The College first instructed the apothecaries to have the hartshorn rasped in their own houses, and promised later to give the righteous raspers certificates against the raspers of bucks' horns.[9] Even private merchants and shopkeepers appealed to the wisdom of the College against clumsy officials. The

[1] *Physicke for the Sicknesse commonly called the Plague* (1636), to the Reader.

[2] 19, 21 April 1625.

[3] 15 March 1629/30-30 April 1630: 4 March 1630/1-26 March 1631. *Acts of the Privy Council, May 1629-May 1630* (1960, nos. 992, 1000).

[4] 10 June-24 July 1627. The report printed in *Acts of the Privy Council, January-August 1627* (1938), pp. 444-5, with petition on p. 434; *September 1627-June 1628* (1940), p. 20.

[5] 13 October 1628 and *Acts July 1628-April 1629* (1948), no. 483. It is clear from the proclamation of 30 December 1619 (Steele and Crawford, no. 1268) that the College merely supplied a medical reason for a measure of economic protection for the colonial growers.

[6] 18 December 1627; 12 June 1635; 1 May, 22 June 1640, and *Acts June 1627-September 1628* (1940), p. 182.

[7] 30-31 May 1632. See below, p. 268.

[8] 9 May 1635.   [9] 26 October 1637, 2 August 1639.

garbler was alleged to let the damp in when he examined senna; but the College seems to have preferred not to intervene against him.[1]

Perhaps it was chiefly because the government was short of money that it conferred no tangible favours in return. Dr. Atkins had the idea of petitioning the king for help in providing the College with an adequate garden. Whether there was anything worth calling a physic garden at Amen Corner is more than doubtful, and the College could not afford either to stock a garden or to pay gardeners' wages. This weakness probably grew more irksome as relations with the apothecaries, who were well provided with gardens of their own, became less friendly. The king referred the petition to the privy council; the council addressed itself to the College, which appointed a committee. At this point Dr. Atkins fell ill, and nothing further seems to have happened.[2]

King Charles I did once take up a proposal for improving medical education. Sir James Fullerton, a Scot, on an occasion when Dr. Atkins was present, put it pressingly to the king that Dr. James Primrose, another Scot, should be allowed to lecture publicly on medicine in London. The king referred the matter to Dr. Atkins, who very humbly, and we may add both properly and circumspectly, asked leave to consult the College.[3] Dr. Primrose was a man of merit with experience of provincial practice; he had recently become a licentiate, because he was born in France and so was ineligible for a fellowship. At his first examination the censors (Harvey, Andrewes, Hodson, and Crooke) declared themselves abundantly satisfied.[4] The present intention no doubt was that he should take fees for lecturing, and there seems to have been a demand at this time for private medical teaching.[5] Dr. Atkins, however, scented mischief. He summoned a special comitia, to which he complained that the president and censors had admitted Dr. Primrose without the assent of the whole College. They defended themselves rather feebly, and then Dr. Atkins propounded three questions as from the king. Since the king desired this lecture, should one of the fellows give it, or should it be left to Dr. Primrose; should it be in

---

[1] 16 February 1635/6.

[2] 12–15 December 1631. The list of benefactors in Brit. Mus. MS. Sloane 55, fo. 4 manages to include King Charles for his good-will to the garden and the building of the anatomical theatre.

[3] 9 January 1629/30.

[4] 3 December 1629. The 'natione Britannus' of the statute may have been taken to mean 'born in Britain' or less probably Primrose may have been a French subject.

[5] See the reference to Dr. Edmund Smith's private dissection, below, p. 264.

the College building or elsewhere; and who should be the audience. The fellows one by one answered these questions, and the College replied to the king. It began by saying that such a lecture could not be useful because one of the same nature was already given in Gresham College, and although the professor was very diligent therein he complained much of want of hearers. At this date the professor was the active Dr. Winston: he was not present at the comitia, but he must have made the complaint, and the College seems to have believed that he was not merely a diligent but a good lecturer. Then the College entreated that its own house might be spared: besides the frequent meetings, they had the Lumleian lectures there twice a week, and their tenant, whose rent was their only revenue, would have to give up his lease if anything were added to the 'encumbrances' of which he had complained already. The tenant, Dr. Goulston, was present. As to the audience the fellows desired to be excused from joining it because they were all practitioners of physic and as such were all fit rather to be professors than auditors. If, however, the king ordered that the lecture should be read, one or other of the fellows would readily undertake it, and the College humbly informed the king that by his licence Dr. Primrose, like all other young men, was bound to attend the College lectures for some years.

This reply was barely civil, It had the desired effect, but the reader may well wonder whether it was not unduly arrogant. The College, of course, had to stand up for itself, and it had held its own for more than a century by insisting on its privileges. This it continued to do even when the threat came from the Crown. The king's ill-fated demand for ship money touched the sensitive point of the College's exemption from contributing to taxation for armaments.[1] Even where it may seem to us to have made excessive claims, it sometimes acted in the public interest. The death of Dr. Clements created a vacancy in the place of physician to Christ's Hospital. It was justly feared that the governors, a City committee, would appoint some irregular practitioner, perhaps the egregious Buggs.[2] It was decided to tell the lord mayor that it would be illegal to appoint anyone without a licence, and to enquire whether the founder had not reserved the post, after the first holder Mr.

---

[1] 12 February, 19 March 1626/7; 16 January 1634, when arms were also in question. On 5 June 1635 Dr. Alston complained that he personally 'was troubled for arms'.
[2] For whom see below, pp. 260-1, 266-7.

Bredwell, to members of the College.[1] There was no such restriction and when the appointment was made it was not open to any complaint.

The finances of the College throw some light on its condition at this time. There is nothing interesting about the routine arrangements: fees and fines financed the officers and incidental expenses; the dinners were paid for, sometimes after attempts at evasion, by fellows; the Lumleian lectures had their earmarked endowment. But the two houses raised new questions. The Stone House was let on lease, and there was a danger, or so Dr. Atkins thought, that Merton College, the owners of the other part of the house, might establish a title to it.[2] The new house in Amen Corner was leased from the dean and canons. Dr. Goulston, by lending £200 on mortgage, had enabled the College to buy the lease, apparently for seven years. Without any urgency he showed signs of wanting his money back, and the lease itself had to be renewed. The only way of meeting these charges was the way which the College had always followed for expenditure on buildings, a levy on the members. From 1628 to 1639 the College pressed the fellows, candidates and licentiates hard, and sometimes with disappointing results: in 1638 there was still a debt of £300.[3] The wealthier fellows, however, came forward generously, and it is a good sign when an institution attracts this kind of support from its own members. Atkins and Harvey each gave £20; Atkins left £100 in his will, and Sir William Paddy £20,[4] and there was Goulston's legacy for a special purpose. On the whole the fellows seem to have been prosperous, though one, Dr. Read, was excused from half the £20 for his dinner on the ground of poverty,[5] and perhaps if he had been well off Dr. Crooke's admission fee of £5 would not have been returned when he resigned from his fellowship to retire into the country.[6]

[1] 20 May 1636.   [2] 1 October 1632.   [3] 25 June 1638.
[4] 6 March 1634/5.   [5] 25 June 1634.   [6] 23 May 1635.

XIV : DOUBTFUL PROSPECTS,
1621–40

URING the reign of Charles I the harmony of the College was not unruffled, but when there was discord it seems to have been comparatively mild and short-lived. Dr. Argent complained vehemently in his speech on retiring from the presidency that the junior fellows, which seems to mean all except the elects, had been negligent in their attendances and had not given him the support they owed. On behalf of them all Dr. Spicer in becoming terms apologized and promised amendment.[1] There may have been something worse behind Dr. Foxe's anger when, on a similar occasion, he denounced the disloyalty of some of the fellows, but, whatever it was, it is forgotten.[2] The College had its share in the contentment on which many people afterwards looked back regretfully, but now and again it was reminded of the darkening underside of English life. Archbishop Laud's friend Richard Neile, bishop of Durham, an able if unlearned man and a privy councillor, asked for a report on a prisoner called John Lambe. When the College first heard of this repulsive charlatan eight years before, he was making money by crystal-gazing and other frauds mainly among City ladies, but now, in spite of a bad record of convictions for sorcery, he enjoyed the protection of the king's favourite the duke of Buckingham, and the world of fashion believed in him. He represented himself as a persecuted physician. The College examined him in English, and reported his answers. He was grotesquely ignorant of the simplest elements of medicine and surgery and of another science, astrology, which appears here for the last time in the College records. In the end he begged for mercy.[3] The London populace feared him as an astrologer and hated him as a creature of the duke. Six months after the examination Lambe was set upon as he left the Fortune Theatre and battered to death. The City was heavily fined for the outrage, but none of the perpetrators was brought to justice.

More serious doubts about the soundness of its position arise if we remember that in wide areas the College was barely holding its

[1] 30 September 1628.   [2] 1 October 1638.   [3] 7 May 1619; 18 December 1627.

own. In 1634 the old problem of relations with the universities cropped up again. The regius professor of physic at Cambridge, John Collins, unlike his seven predecessors from 1554 to 1626, was a fellow of the College. The registrar wrote to remind him that in the past Cambridge had by some ill fate given doctorates and licences to persons who had not received a liberal education, and among them Buggs, an apothecary who had served his apprenticeship and become a master-man, but had obtained a Leiden degree after a month or two of residence there. If there were any power in reserve by which the university could undo this, it would strengthen the College in keeping Buggs off; in any case it would be well if such undeserving persons did not receive Cambridge honours in the future.[1] The indignant Collins poured out to his dearly-loved colleague Dr. Clement a moving profession of helplessness. This evil was not new; it went back to the heroic age. In all colleges and learned societies (*societates literariae*) the ignorant lorded it over the lettered. Experience had taught him that he must acquiesce in the decisions of the university; he explained the statutory procedure; he protested that he was blameless in the matter of Buggs, who, in point of fact, was not a Cambridge doctor.[2]

Three months after writing this letter Collins died. His successor Ralph Winterton was not a fellow of the College, but he had opposed the candidature of Buggs and also two or three unsuitable applications for Cambridge licences. He was a classical doctor of the old school; indeed he was the protagonist of ornamental Greek and Latin studies among his medical contemporaries. It was, however, in English that he wrote a very long letter to associate himself with the point of view of the College. He added ministers of religion to the list of the unworthy holders of licences. He admitted that, whereas the Cambridge medical course took twelve years, foreign doctors could incorporate in an instant for a small sum of money. He summed up the deplorable state of affairs in words that might well have been turned against him: 'Chirurgians and apothecaryes are sought unto, and physicians seldome but in a desperate case are consulted with, when the patient is ready to dye, and in this kind wee have too many examples.' He intended to stand firm,

---

[1] 12 September 1634. The incorporation of doctors from foreign universities was regulated by a grace of 24 January 1624/5, which required the testing of the candidate by a disputation.

[2] 16 September 1634. He did, however, receive in that year a Cambridge licence to practice.

and he had the necessary support in Cambridge; but it would be useless unless the College could persuade the Oxford regius professor and faculty to do the same. Even that would not suffice. The only remedy must come from the archbishop of Canterbury.[1] Archbishop Laud was at the height of his power in church and state, he was chancellor of Oxford; he was friendly to Winterton. His new code of statutes for Oxford came into force not very long after this, but it left this problem untouched and he never seems to have taken up the cudgels for the physicians against their enemies. The Laudian revival in the Church of England may even have strengthened the system of episcopal licensing and encouraged the practice of medicine by ministers of religion.[2] This archbishop was not the man to restrict the scope of clerical activities; he seems to have had less contact with the College than his predecessors, and, for whatever reason, it never appealed to him as Winterton hoped it would.[3] Would such an appeal have averted the dreadful event of 1635 when Dr. Buggs of Leiden incorporated at Oxford?[4]

The struggle against illicit practice went on steadily, and with redoubled energy on the side of the College. It does not seem possible to judge whether the empirics became bolder and more numerous, as has sometimes been said, or whether on the other hand they were more successfully kept within bounds. They fell into the familiar classes. From 1624 to 1640 we hear of more than thirty women, most of them apparently in a small way of business and, when caught, submissive. Only one is said to have treated a lady of title[5]; two were midwives[6]; one widow hung out bills.[7] One was a clergyman's wife.[8] We should like to know more about a woman named Rutland 'pueris praefecta in Nosocomio Londinensi', which seems to mean that she was one of the two matrons at Christ's Hospital.[9] She treated tonsils and severe headaches with only limited and temporary success; she said she had learnt her art from her deceased predecessor, and she was punished very mildly. Only two or three women seem to have gone to prison.

[1] 25 August 1635: printed with alterations of spelling, &c., in Goodall, pp. 443–5.
[2] This must remain uncertain until episcopal and other registers have been further explored.
[3] On 11 January 1638 Marbury, who had no degree, asked for a licence on the strength of a certificate from the Oxford regius professor 'and other of that faculty' but it does not appear to have been granted.
[4] J. Foster, *Alumni Oxonienses*, vol. i (1891), where Buggs is mistakenly described as of Padua.   [5] Lady Harrington, June 1624.   [6] 3 June, 9 July 1631.
[7] 3 June 1631.   [8] 'Uxor Domini Goodcole ministri', 10 June 1627.
[9] There were also 42 women keepers, but *praefecta* seems too big a word for them.

As of old the foreigners were troublesome and very mixed.[1] Bartholomew Vanderlasse, a German who had no medical degree and could not speak Latin impromptu, admitted that he had practised in London for eleven years. He was conditionally tolerated but continued to offend for several years more.[2] The Neapolitan Dr. Bartholomew Jaquinto moved in higher circles: the earl of Manchester was his patient and the Venetian ambassador harboured him and spoke up for him in his hour of need; but, although admitted to toleration after three years as a mere intruder, he was clearly guilty of malpractice.[3] Gaspar Tomand or Tooman of Zürich, who claimed to be a doctor, pleaded that he was ignorant of the law about licences and treated only his own countrymen; but prescriptions of his were found which he had written for divers persons of quality, and he lay under suspicion of being a clergyman.[4] Most exasperating of all were two Dutchmen, the brothers Gerard and Arnold Boet. Each in his way achieved distinction as a learned author and they both had interesting careers; but as medical men they had an extraordinary record of contempt for the rules and the College. It was not only that malpractice was brought home to both of them and that they were insolent. Gerard employed his brother as an assistant in his practice, and also a young man whom he undertook to train for three years as a physician; he paid both of them in cash and clothing. He committed the unique outrage of employing a woman as his apothecary. She was Dutch by birth and the College forbade her to keep shop.[5]

Among the fellows Dr. Winston was the doughtiest opponent of all impostors, and he was given charge of various special operations against them.[6] One of his proposals was for suppressing the foreigners, and to this we owe not only legal proceedings against

---

[1] Dr. Henry Hughes of St. John's College, Oxford, and Padua (3 May 1639) may be mentioned here because he was physician to Charles Lewis, elector palatine. He had been *medicus ad familiam* to Sir Isaac Wake. He seems to have desisted from illicit practice in London.

[2] 4 March 1624/5; 16 March, 9 April 1630; 9 July 1631. His birthplace was Lippa in Saxony, probably the *Grafschaft* Lippe in Lower Saxony.

[3] 2 June 1626; 1 February 1627/8; 9 April, 7 May 1630.

[4] 28 June 1627; 19 November 1630; 4 November, 22 December 1631.

[5] Both the brothers are in the *Dictionary of National Biography* under the name of Boote, de Boot, Bootius or Botius; but the accounts given there should be corrected from *Nieuw Nederlandsch Biografisch Woordenboek*. The many relevant entries in the Annals run from 4 March 1630/1 to 6 November 1646. The points mentioned in the last two sentences will be found on 16, 17 February 1631/2; 11 June 1632.

[6] 25 June 1632; 13 February 1636/7.

Vanderlasse and Gerard Boet, but also a list of foreigners practising in London, ten members of the College and twelve without licences.[1] Within a few years, however, fresh names appeared. A Frenchman called Brushye sued a widow-woman in the king's bench for calling him a mountebank, and the College gave her a certificate that he was not a member.[2] There were two new Italian empirics, Clarvetto and Matteo Lucatello, and Peter Francis of Amsterdam, a specialist for gout.[3] The College made a charitable grant to a German physician named Rhenmus, who complained of poverty: the amount was 6s.[4]

It is perhaps worth mentioning that there was something like common action by the more settled of the irregulars. One Day presented himself at the College in the capacity of advocate or solicitor for the empirics, wishing to put up arguments for them.[5] He cannot have represented the whole of the motley crowd. There were specialists such as Shepheard who dealt with phrenetics, and another curer of mad folks who lodged with a surgeon in Moorfields[6]; there was a chemist who was sent before a court of justice[7]; there were a handful who had some pretentions to education; but their behaviour followed the old patterns. Two new devices appeared. The more alarming was the antimonial cup, which was openly put on sale for a shilling at the sign of the Magpie.[8] Purging ale, which had a run of several years, could also be deadly.[9] Among the individual malefactors we need linger over none, passing by even William Trigge the shoemaker or lastmaker, although he gave the College much occupation. There was nothing to distinguish him beyond his persistence, and his good luck in once securing an acquittal in a court of law. The College could not bring evidence of what medicine he had given because he had prepared it in private.[10]

Among the surgeons, however, George Butler played the lead in a case which figures in the Law Reports. Before prosecuting him

[1] 17 February 1631/2. The twelve were Tomand, Vanderlasse, the two Boets, Jaquinto, the Frenchmen Ecklin, du Val, Punctaeus and two whose names were unknown; the German Dr. Moulter or Muleter and the Italian Despotin.
[2] 4 September 1635, 4 October 1639.
[3] 6 November 1635; 5 July 1640; 4 October 1639.
[4] 4 September 1635.   [5] 19 January 1626/7.
[6] 16 February 1626/7; 25 June, 16 December 1631; 6 June 1634.
[7] 5 July 1633.   [8] 5, 12 June 1635; 3 April 1637.
[9] 28 April, 27 May, 17, 21 June 1631; morrow of Palm Sunday 1634. There is no mention of the antimonial wine which was much used in France.
[10] From 3 June 1631 to 26 January 1637/8. For the acquittal see C. Merret, *Collections* (1660), p. 124.

it was necessary to obtain the lord chamberlain's written assurance that his position as extraordinary surgeon to the king did not entitle him to protection. He moved among reputable people, and Dr. Smith was admonished by the president of the College for admitting Butler's apothecary to his private dissection. It has been thought that Butler was a herbalist, but this is an unjustified inference from his line of defence. His defence is of no medical significance; it rested on the Quack's Charter of 34 Henry VIII, and it failed as Gardiner's attempt to use that Act against the College had failed.[1] The judgement was that the Act did not give liberty to any person who practised for lucre or profit, whether or no the statute of 1 Mary had again set all on the foot of 14 Henry VIII. Counsel for the College stated the Common Law as it existed before these statutes,[2] and counsel for the defendant talked some engaging nonsense: 'for the Stone and Strangury and Ague there needs no great skill to discover them, and then the cure of them is more by experience and practice than learning. And I have heard of a physician, that went 100 miles to know a Medicine for those diseases of an old Woman, who had long time experience thereof.' When it was all over Sir John Heath, the chief justice of the common pleas persuaded the College to be content with less than it might have exacted and it does appear that Butler's professional career came to an end, at least in London. We may note that the College considered printing its case against him, but did not do it.[3]

During these years other surgeons were convicted of the usual offences, but in small numbers seldom exceeding one or two in each year, and there is little or nothing of interest in the details. For their profession it was a favourable period. The College had not previously given licences of any kind to surgeons except to two exceptionally well-qualified men of high position, Balthasar Guersie and John Banister; but it now gave conditional licences in identical terms to Mr. Fenton, to James Moulins, Mullins or Moleynes, who was a lithotomist to both St. Bartholomew's and to St. Thomas's Hospitals, and to the Frenchman Maurice Aubert,

---

[1] See above, p. 215.   [2] See above, p. 31.
[3] Goodall, pp. 221 ff. reproduces the reports. On 31 August 1626 the privy council issued an open warrant for Butler to be brought before it: *Acts, June–December 1626* (1938), p. 233. The entries in the Annals are from 1 September 1626 to 5 July 1633, those referred to above being on 22 March 1629, 28 January, 4 February 1630/1, 3 July 1633.

surgeon to Queen Henrietta Maria. Even in instances like these there might be dangers in softening the distinction between the two branches: a certain Thomas Cooke, who seems to have done serious damage, said that he had learnt his medicine from his master Moulins.[1]

The ending of the Jacobean peace gave an impetus to the demand for sea-surgeons which was already growing with the rise of oceanic trade.[2] The physicians were no more than spectators of the consequent re-organization of recruitment, service-conditions and pay; but they had never relinquished their claim to supervise surgery as a part of medicine.[3] They had one opportunity of asserting it. In the course of their dispute with the apothecaries they persuaded the attorney general to insert in an information for the star chamber the proposal that trepanning and major operations should never be done without the advice of a physician, but the surgeons suggested to the king that surgeons would not serve in the navy on these terms, and that it was necessary for them to be licensed to practise physic. The president of the College countered this by calling for volunteers among the fellows to serve in the navy if required. Four fellows and one doctor not yet a fellow came forward, but they were never called upon, and the privy council took the side of the surgeons.[4] The only other naval business in which the College tried to get a footing was the examination of the surgeons' sea-chests, in which both the Barber-Surgeons and the Apothecaries were more directly concerned. As against the surgeons the College made no headway.

Relations with the apothecaries went from bad to worse. In 1624/5 Dr. Foxe suggested that such of them and of the surgeons as practised medicine should be publicly denounced and that any member of the College who dealt with them after that should be subjected to a statutory penalty.[5] This proposal seems to have been unwise: any attempt to take such action against a fellow might well have provoked disputes within the College, and the idea was dropped. The boycotting of apothecaries does not seem to have been an

---

[1] 4 February 1630/1; 27 May, 9 July, 7 December 1632.
[2] This subject is treated in all its aspects in J. J. Keevil, *Medicine and the Navy* i (1957), 149 ff.
[3] In 1626/7 the Barber-Surgeons had a new charter in hand, but at the prompting of the College, which scented encroachment, Lord Keeper Coventry refused to affix the Great Seal to it: 19 March 1626/7; 28 August 1627.
[4] 25 June 1632, 12 June 1635: the fellows were Hawly, Hamey, Goddard and Dawson, the other Hinton. [5] Morrow of Palm Sunday 1624/5.

effective weapon. Mr. Thomas, who was accused of being George Butler's apothecary and assistant said that he doubted not he should make physic notwithstanding the College's interdiction; indeed he went so far as to tell the beadle that the privy council's warrant for the attachment of empirics[1] was not worth three skips of a louse. From 1626 to 1640 more than a score of apothecaries were accused of practising physic or other serious offences. Among them were several of the leading members of the Society. One of these found guilty belonged to the family of the distinguished and now aged botanist Matthieu de Lobel[2]; another brought commendatory letters from three bishops.[3] Two or three were punished severely, and one put up a tough resistance for nine long years.

This was Mr. Buggs, once a stage-player, who was shameless enough to carry on his business within a stonesthrow of the College (*hic prope*) in Warwick Lane. In 1630 evidence accumulated against him; in 1631 more cases were alleged and the censors searched his shop; in 1632 incriminating objects were found there at the visitation and he went to prison in the Fleet. Sir Robert Heath, chief justice of the common pleas, made the humane suggestion that for the long vacation he might be let out on a Habeas Corpus. The College would not relent; on the contrary the president and censors decided to examine him in prison about another fatal case—at least the third—that they had heard of. That interrogation, however, did not take place. The clerk of the Apothecaries' Company came to negotiate for the payment of Buggs's fine in two instalments. He paid in October, and before Christmas he was convicted again, his bond declared forfeit, and a new action begun against him. But facts of a different order interrupt the monotonous succession of his summonses, arrests and convictions. In 1634 he arrived from overseas an indubitable doctor of Leiden. He incorporated at Oxford. In 1635/6 he confessed that he had practised medicine in London during the intervening two years. He admitted that he had never been an academic or brought up in any university, but he had been bred in an apothecary's shop, 'which he held sufficient to make a Physitian'.[4] It has been claimed for him that he was probably an expert physician. He was the first apothe-

---

[1] See above, p. 241.   [2] 3 February 1626/7, 25 June 1627.   [3] Gwyne, 28 June 1627.
[4] The facts of Buggs's career are given with full references to the authorities, including the Annals and valuable extracts from them, in Underwood, especially pp. 245 ff. and 304 ff. While appreciating Dr. Underwood's discoveries and his critical treatment of the material I feel bound to accept in the main the College's estimate of Buggs's skill.

cary who took a medical degree but remained a freeman of the
Society of Apothecaries. In this sense he was the forerunner of the
general practitioners of a later age.

Although there was all this to complain of, besides the usual
irreverence,[1] the two governing bodies carried on their common
business satisfactorily for several years. The court of assistants
fined apothecaries who kept more than the permitted number of
apprentices, and maintained discipline among their brethren, but
in 1630 friction arose over two matters. One of them was settled
for good but the other started a long train of disputes. The easier
matter was that of Brookes's powder. This apothecary had invented
the powder and the censors decided that it did not come under the
definition of Mithridate, in which case it would have contravened
the rule about following the *Pharmacopoeia*; but Brookes had a
grievance against the master and wardens for seizing his stock, and
they in their turn were aggrieved when the censors, not content
with a specimen, insisted on having the whole stock sent to them
and even kept two boxes when all was over.[2] While this was going
on the president, Dr. Argent took occasion to point out to the
apothecaries that the oath which they took on admission to their
craft was defective and could not do anything to improve the practice
of medicine. He suggested some new points that should be inserted
in the interests of the medical art and of the commonwealth.[3] These
were (i) that the apothecaries should make up their medicines
truly according to the physicians' prescriptions, (ii) that they should
not put in any corrupt ingredients, and (iii) that they should not
sell goods which were falsified or had lost their virtue. For the
time being nothing untoward happened, but we may suspect a
diplomatic motive in their hospitality when the apothecaries invited the physicians for the first time to dine with them after the
next search.[4] They dined at the Mitre in Bread Street; but some
months later the College decided to summon the master and wardens
to have the three new clauses for the oath presented to them by the
president.[5] The meeting is not recorded, nor are we told exactly
what steps the president proposed for following it up[6]; but a few
months later fortune put into the hands of the College a golden
opportunity for pressing its cause.

[1] 6 June, 1 September 1626.
[2] 12, 19, 26 November 1630; 28 January 1630/1; Barrett, p. 35.
[3] 19 November 1630.   [4] Barrett, p. 37; this was on 11 August 1631.
[5] 2 November 1631.   [6] 22 December 1631.

It was on 27 May 1632 that the king referred to the College the case of Mr. Lane's mysterious death.[1] Three days later the College reported that the cause of death was poison, and they ended their report by asking first that eight named substances should not be sold except to persons who gave their names and stated their purposes in buying, secondly that no apothecary should be allowed to compound or adminster any medicine, especially emetics, purgatives, soporifics and medicines containing mercury or antimony, except on the prescription of a living doctor which they were to produce on demand. According to their own Annals they complained that the apothecaries intruded into the practice of medicine, and they proposed remedies 'but such only as had regard to the publick good, more than to the advancement of their own profession.' After the first hearing[2] they added some new proposals. Harvey intimated that the lords of the council were willing to prohibit the selling of poison without safeguards, and in its final form this regulation provided that there must be a prescription and it must be filed and so on. There was an odd provision about prescriptions by deceased physicians: the apothecaries were not to make them up, and if anybody brought one the person who took the physic was to sign his name to it. The Apothecaries' Company should fix prices for the compound medicines in the *Pharmacopoeia*. In addition to the president's three clauses they should be sworn to make all their medicines according to that book.[3] Dr. Atkins reminded the College on the same occasion that there was a clause in the apothecaries' charter that their apprentices should be examined by the College.[4] The apothecaries never paid much attention to this rule except when they wanted to placate the physicians, but, no doubt in consequence of a message from the College, the Company from this summer invited the physicians to be present at the examinations of those who were to be made freemen. They were held in the Apothecaries' Hall at Blackfriars, into which, after sixteen years in hired premises, they now moved. Unhappily the examination provided matter for new ill-feeling. Within a year the College 'much disliked' the clause in the Apothecaries' charter by which the Society was to summon the president: they thought it

---

[1] See above, p. 255. The authorities for the case are printed partly in full and partly in summary in Underwood, pp. 258 ff.

[2] The date was 13 June 1632: MS. Sloane 3914, fo. 74. For the text of the freeman's oath prescribed by the council, which embodies these provisions, see Underwood, p. 263.

[3] 25 June 1632: text in Underwood, p. 255.

[4] For full details see Underwood, pp. 84–86, 327.

unbecoming to his dignity and they considered that the apothecaries' officers should wait upon the College.[1]

The lords of the council ordered the attorney general to have the proposals of the College put into execution. The apothecaries, little daunted, said the new clauses were unlawful and gave out that if they were not allowed to amend the physicians' prescriptions much harm might be done.[2] The College had to investigate a story about a poisonous prescription, which seems to reveal nothing very definitely except some laxity in procedure at St. Bartholomew's.[3]

At the summer comitia of 1633 there was a full-dress debate on the sinister dealing of the apothecaries, and the means of opposing it. Dr. Foxe, Dr. Ramsay and others offered some new suggestions. The first was 'to reserve something to be putt to everye Medeceyne by the Doctor; which the Apothecarye shall not knowe'. Of this we may say that it would have been extremely tiresome for the doctor and destructive of any wholesome relation between him and the pharmacist. The second was that apothecaries who would be conformable to the College should be given an exclusive right to make up the 'colleagues' bills. Whether at this stage this was meant to cover prescriptions of the fellows and candidates only or all authorized practitioners in London cannot be said for certain. In either case it was unrealistic in view of the existing temper of the apothecaries, and exposed to legal attack in view of the common law against restraint of trade. The third proposal was on the face of it unworkable: that the patients should not pay their apothecaries' bills until the doctor had viewed them and fixed the prices.[4]

In the winter of 1633-4 both sides were defiant. The apothecaries took counsel's opinion on the two questions about the oath and examinations, and two apothecaries called out to Dr. Brouart as he passed by in the street, asking why doctors should make physic, it being the apothecaries' art[5]; one of them, Robert Holland, had given trouble for years and was mixed up with Buggs[6]; the other was the rich and bustling Cooke, who was to become in later years a special object of detestation to the College. It was not long before Cooke was accused of practising,[7] but the College meant to attack on the whole length of the front.

---

[1] 15 April 1633.   [2] For their spirited reply see Underwood, pp. 47, 263-4.
[3] 4 July 1632. For an account of the incident see Underwood, pp. 255-6.
[4] 25 June 1633.   [5] 17 January 1633/4.
[6] Several entries from 7 September 1627; Buggs mentioned 23 December 1633.
[7] 18 October 1634 and subsequent entries.

The new phase of the contest started with a dispute among the apothecaries about a medicine called milk of sulphur.[1] The Company had censured one of its members on the complaint of another that he had supplied some of this medicine wrongly prepared. The College made this a test case. The mixture was not in the *Pharmacopoeia*. It was only a disguised form of flowers of sulphur. By the president's direction Harvey made a speech to the master and wardens. He explained and justified the demands of the College, which he summed up as sufficiency in the understanding of their art, honesty in rightly preparing their medicines and conscience in charging for them so that the prices might not be burdensome to the poor. He declared the opinion of the College that it was within the discretion of any doctor to order for his private use any medicine that was not in the *Pharmacopoiea*, but subject to the judgement of the College on its merits, and that the promiscuous sale of such medicines should not be allowed. Nor should any other medicine not in the *Pharmacopoiea* be sold promiscuously until it was allowed and approved by the College.[2]

The Company did not express its assent to these principles laid down by Harvey. It failed to co-operate in any way. The censors, accompanied by Dr. Winston and Dr. Hodson descended on an apothecary to examine his stock of milk of sulphur: he behaved abominably and threatened to call a constable. The College discommoned and summoned and sentenced right and left; but it was not content to exercise its own power. It appealed to the privy council, and set the attorney general in motion.[3]

The attorney general entered a *quo warranto* suit in the court of exchequer chamber, alleging that the apothecaries had violated their charter. The president sent a message to Apothecaries' Hall; the master refused to receive it. In September, however, the master and wardens came to the College for an attempt to reach agreement, but unsuccessfully. Both sets of proceedings, before the privy council and in the exchequer chamber, dragged on and the College took a very high line. It wrote that apothecaries' shops had multiplied so greatly since the incorporation that it was impossible for the Company to govern the apothecaries, let alone for the College

---

[1] The materials bearing on the disputes from this point to 1640 in the College Annals and the ampler materials from the Society's records occupy nearly fifty closely-printed pages (265–313) in Dr. Underwood's volume.
[2] 4 July 1634.
[3] 6 June; 4, 9, 11 July; 28 August; 18 October; 7 November 1634.

to govern the Company. The apothecaries then took a high line in their coarser way. When the president and censors appeared for their annual search they were obstructed and some of them even arrested. A prominent apothecary called Houghton, who had been committed to Newgate, brought an action for false imprisonment, as Dr. Bonham had done.[1] The College tried and failed to enlist the support of the City in the matter of apprentices' examinations.[2] It felt itself forced to address the king and council again.

From this point, November 1634, there followed marvellous twistings and turnings which may interest students of human nature or of the history of constitutional law, but are marked by no change in demands or ideas on either side. The attorney general was ordered to prepare the *quo warranto*; the apothecaries submitted and it was suspended; the College replied and the suspension was taken off. The apothecaries had to send their charter to the star chamber office and a hearing was appointed for 25 January 1636/7 but nothing was decided then. Twice the privy council referred all matters pending between the physicians and the apothecaries to strong committees of judges and law officers; each time the judicial proceedings were stayed, only to be resumed again. All this time the College stuck to its guns and refused to parley. Its own internal organization was adjusted to the needs of the struggle. On 28 August 1634 a committee, the committee for the college business, was appointed, evidently for this purpose, and it was kept in being, with some personal changes, until 1640. Some of the arguments on the College side became clearer. It had not misused the power of discommoning apothecaries: in forty years there had only been eight, of whom five had gone before the star chamber.[3] It had never exceeded its statutory power of search. No fellow kept an apothecary in his house, though they had a legal right to do so. Known things were sometimes described in prescriptions by unknown names, not in order to compel the patient to employ an apothecary who was in the secret, but to save the patient's reputation or for other reasons which could be no grievance to the apothecaries. If there had been delays on the side of the College in this litigation, it was due to the plague. Perhaps the apothecaries did not really mind about the delays. They were subjected during

---

[1] Houghton gave the College a good deal of trouble from 1627/8: he also was mixed up with Buggs (5 June 1635). In 1628 the Company fined him 10s. for failing to appear as a guest at the lord mayor's dinner (Barrett, p. 28).   [2] Underwood, pp. 84-85.

[3] Barrett (p. 55) says eight 'physicians', which is a mistake; but why forty years?

all these years to a powerful flank attack from the Distillers, who obtained a charter in 1638. The three sponsors were Mayerne, Dr. Cadyman, and Sir William Brouncker, the father of the first president of the Royal Society. These names in this connexion show that besides the questions at issue between apothecaries and the physicians, there were others which concerned them both as scientists and as business men.

The final stages of the contest did not come until 1639–40. At last a body of referees produced a report which decided all the questions at issue. On this commission there was Dr. Moundeford's son-in-law Sir John Bramston, now chief justice of the king's bench; there was Sir John Finch, chief justice of the common pleas, who had taken pity on Buggs. With them were the attorney general, Sir John Banks, and the solicitor general, Sir Edward Littleton. They granted almost all that the College asked, first of all the three clauses in the oath, then the poison clause, one on price-fixing (the master and wardens to do it, and the College to be notified), and the peaceable enjoyment of the College's right of search. Four amplifications of the Apothecaries' charter followed. They were not to have any right of search except by direction of the College of Physicians, and their oath of secrecy was not to bind them as against the College in the matter of medicinal compositions 'in which respect they are to be distinguisht from other Companyes'. They were to have a special relation and dependance on the College and to be regulated by it in matters of their profession concerning physic. They were no longer to have the power of summoning the president at the time of their examinations, on the contrary they were to attend at the College to be examined and to receive the written approbation of the physicians. They were not to call the president to be present at the making of their laws, but to go to the College and to receive their laws and ordinances from it. Lastly the privy council should deal with all the oustanding law-business, the suits brought by the College against Weale, Houghton, Buggs and others, and, on the other side, the arrests of physicians and the prosecution of some of them in the star chamber.

The privy council ordered the apothecaries to submit to these recommendations. They did not obey. Nothing but a *deus ex machina* could save them now; but deliverance was at hand. The god descended. The Long Parliament met, and to it the apothecaries appealed.

XV: REVOLUTIONS AND RECOVERY, 1640–60

THE College did not act as though the meeting of the Long Parliament was the beginning of a revolution. It lost no time in beginning to prepare its business, hoping for a confirmation of the last charter and the rejection of the claims of the surgeons and apothecaries. It adopted the thorough and expeditious procedure which had been used for the enquiry into home-grown tobacco, and, since the house of commons would obviously be extremely busy, it decided to start the business in the house of lords. But after four months of preparation the lords too were overwhelmed with greater matters, and the College stopped short of nominating any fellows to take the petition to the house.[1] Only one of the national events of that winter affected the College directly. Dr. Bastwick came back in triumph from his prison in Jersey, and even before the commons voted that he had been wrongfully imprisoned the College restored him to his status as a licentiate.[2]

In 1641 the College submitted its draft Bill to the house of lords. Besides asking for the confirmation of the old privileges and powers, this included several demands which were new at least to parliament. The fine for illicit practice was to be doubled, that is raised to £10 for each month. No one was to advise physic unless he prescribed it by written bill and put to it his name and the time, on pain of a fine of 40s., half to the poor of the parish and half to the informer. The annual allowance of corpses for dissection was to be raised to six. As the president and College had no express power to administer the oaths of allegiance and supremacy this power was to be granted, and also the power to administer an oath to observe the statutes and by-laws. There was nothing in the draft about the oath which had roused the opposition of the apothecaries, and they do not seem to have put in any objections, from which it appears that their susceptibilities had been spared of set purpose; but the

---

[1] 13, 24 November 1640; 19, 23 March 1640/1. There seems to have been only one meeting of the delegates and counsel to consider the apothecaries' rival petition, 18 December 1640; but on 1 July 1641, a censors' day, there was a discussion about the charters of both the Companies. [2] 18 December 1640.

surgeons immediately petitioned against the Bill. They said it would deprive them of the exercise of their profession; they repeated their old argument about the necessities of the sea-service; they thought the oath about statutes and by-laws contrary to law and reason; they even thought that six corpses would be too many.[1] Whether it was in consequence of this obstinacy or of the pressure of public business, the Bill went to a committee but the house took no further action.

By the summer of 1641, when the court of star chamber was abolished, the fellows must have known that there was danger for the whole structure of institutions within which they had worked. They had seen organized and successful political riots. They saw strange reversals of fortune. An impoverished French refugee licentiate, who was in arrears with his dues, profited from the reputation of his family in the Protestant controversial world to press his views about plague-precautions on the all-powerful commons. The College did not support him, but it treated him with much more consideration than he could have found a year before,[2] The discommoned apothecary Edward Cooke not only lorded it in his Company but came out as a minor demagogue, accusing the bishop of Rochester of unlawful practices in his cathedral.[3] Apothecaries who were summoned by the censors showed themselves obdurate.[4]

That the conditions were difficult appears from small indications, for instance that the December dinner in 1640 was frugal. The College carried on its business on a reduced scale but without interruption. When it came to civil war, however, the difficulties were more severe. Some of the fellows left London. Harvey, as the king's physician, was at the battle of Edgehill and spent the next four years with the court at Oxford. Sir Simon Baskerville was there too. Dr. Winston, believing that he had talked too much about something or other, fled to France. Lister and Mayerne had

---

[1] According to their petition they had made representations to the house of commons against the College as early as 17 March, though the Bill was only presented to the lords on 5 June.

[2] He was Louis du Moulin (Ludovicus Molinaeus): 4 November; 15, 23 December 1641. For him and his family see K. H. D. Hailey, *William III and the Whig Opposition* (1953), especially pp. 13–14 and A. G. Matthews, *Calamy Revised* (1934).

[3] Hamey 'Bustorum Aliquot Reliquiae', in the life of Cooke. The bishop's name was John Warner.

[4] Mr. Evans, 2 December 1641; Mr. Phyge (or Fige, a prominent surname in the Company) 13 December 1641; 7 January, 3 March 1641/2.

to attend the queen at Exeter. The movements of lesser men are less fully recorded, but no doubt some of them were called away. Edward Emily, then a candidate, wrote a letter before York in 1644 which shows that he was tempted to throw in his lot with the parliamentary cause.[1] The College as a body could not have done anything for the king if it had wished to. In London his authority was ended, and if the College was to perform its duties there it had no choice but to recognize the *de facto* rulers. In 1643 Speaker Lenthall wrote to ask for three physicians for the parliamentary army, and the commander in chief, the earl of Essex, recommended a young Padua doctor called Thomas Coxe for one of the places. The president called for volunteers, and Dr. Delaune and Dr. Sheafe came forward. In sending up their names the president expressed good hopes of Dr. Coxe from his reputation in the army, but was unable to give any other testimony to his sufficiency: he was duly appointed and subsequently became a fellow.[2]

A parliamentary ordinance of the following year required all Englishmen over the age of eighteen to subscribe to the Solemn League and Covenant, and the College administered this to its members and to such of the surgeons as demeaned themselves to come in after a discussion in their own Hall, which they thought was the proper place for them to subscribe in.[3] There is no list of fellows who subscribed, but we may suppose that the president and censors, who were present on the first occasion did so. They were Dr. Meverall, Dr. Delaune, Dr. Prujean, Dr. Hamey and Dr. Sheafe.[4] Even in these two incidents the government was acting exactly as legitimate governments had done before it, and the College was reacting as usual. So it did when anyone tried to tax it, and so apparently it would have done if its members had been called out for watch and ward.[5] When the revenues of deans and chapters were sequestrated the College, with expressions of regret, had to pay its rent to parliamentary commissioners instead of St. Paul's.[6] It reported to the City on the noxious nature of a newly imported drug called ramatroe, but the City as well as the privy council had consulted it on such matters before.[7]

---

[1] Hamey Letters, fo. 69.
[2] 26 June 1643. No doubt serving as an army doctor did not amount to taking sides, but Delaune at least was probably in sympathy with the Puritans.
[3] Young, p. 251.   [4] 5, 12, 19, 24 July 1644.
[5] 3 February 1641/2; 6 May 1643; 6 March 1642/3.
[6] 6 May 1063.   [7] 27 March 1643.

The machinery of justice was less disturbed, in London at any rate, than any other part of the constitution, and the only sign that the College found it inadequate was a proposal that it should ask the City sheriffs for a warrant to summon empirics.[1] Before and during the Civil War, however, the unlicensed practitioners pretty certainly had an easier time. Few accusations are recorded and fewer punishments. Only four women appeared in seven years. The only two cases worth comment are those of the empiric Robert Savory, who was accused of keeping an apprentice,[2] and Tobias Garbrand, an Oxford bachelor of medicine, who excused himself as a refugee from the part of England occupied by the king.[3] About the time of the outbreak of war ten doctors and two others were summoned, but none of the doctors and only one of the others obeyed.[4] In the middle of the war a letter was sent to the mayor of Rochester saying that Mr. Samuel Thomson held a licence from the College, but one Barrett did not.[5] No legal action could be taken, and perhaps no law was broken, when the apothecary and astrologer Nicholas Culpepper published his book *A Physical Directory or a Translation of the London Dispensatory* in 1649. This revealed to all men the secrets hitherto veiled by the Latin from all but the physicians and his fellow-apothecaries, a real blow for freedom.

A few surgeons were charged, but only one, an old offender called Hogsflesh, was sent before a court of justice.[6] None of the routine operations ceased altogether, though none of them went on with any vigour. Considering how violent were the religious animosities of that time we may be surprised how little the College heard about them. Mr. Pordage, confessing to six years practice, asked to be examined, and soon after that was convicted of malpractice in a fatal case. His priestly character was not mentioned.[7] A doctor of Rheims named Mark Belwood, had been in the Fleet Prison for some years. He was accused of malpractice, excused

[1] 5 December 1645.
[2] 'Guilielmus Dawson accusabat Robertum Savory empiricum burgi de Southworke eo quod in familiam suam admiserat Anibalem Dawson pro apprentisio in arte medicinali.' Savory came to anchor on 23 March 1652/3 with a special licence, printed in Munk, to practise with distracted people and in some other particular maladies. Was he the Savory of 1625?
[3] 5 August, 7 October, 4 November 1641; 6 February 1645/6.
[4] 7 July, 4 August 1642.   [5] 5 August 1644.
[6] 3 March 1641/2, 7 April 1642.
[7] 3 December 1640; 28 January, 4 February 1640/1, 26 March 1641: see above, p. 247.

himself and asked to be examined, but he refused the oath of allegiance, and we may infer that he was a catholic. The censors had pity on him and he was not fined.[1] A foolish and scarcely sane empiric Aaron Stretter, an Oxford bachelor of Arts, admitted to being in priest's orders.[2] When the Puritans were in power and ejected hundreds of clergy from their livings, some of them, as might have been expected, took to medical practice.[3] It seems impossible at present to tell whether some or all of these provided themselves with licences from the universities. The bishops were no longer exercising their office,[4] and the College does not seem to have been approached by any of the deprived. Nor did it take cognizance of a new kind of irregular practice which flared up all over the country. Among the excited religious enthusiasts there were many miracles of healing. Fortunately for the College none of the fellows interfered.

They stuck to their accustomed ways. The examining and approving of apothecaries' apprentices went on at reasonably regular intervals.[5] The library was inspected and keepers were appointed for it.[6] The most important matter in such a time was to make sure of the continued succession of fellows, and this was handled successfully. By 1642 it was happening fairly frequently (*saepiuscule*) that the number of fellows fell short of the statutory limit. The president, Dr. Meverall, believed that this largely resulted from the statute which made incorporation at Oxford or Cambridge necessary for admission. After argument on both sides it was decided that in future this requirement should be waived if the applicant bound himself in no less a sum than £60 to incorporate within two years.[7] Only one man seems to have taken advantage of this offer, but the vice-chancellor of Cambridge wrote nearly two years later asking for the concession to be withdrawn. According to him some applications for incorporating had been withdrawn and the university feared the medical faculty might be deserted. The president was, or so he professed, pierced to the heart by this

---

[1] 19 March 1640/1, 1 April 1641.   [2] 2 December 1641.
[3] A. G. Matthews, *Walker Revised* (1948), p. xxvii.
[4] This may be the reason for the granting of five extra-licences in 1640 (nine in 1640–2) in contrast with five granted in the whole previous decade, when there was never more than one in a year. There were more in 1643–6, the years of war. An extra-licence was refused on 2 September 1641 to George Binx, who came from Hesdin and had a Douai licence but was of English parentage. He was recommended to study the old writers on practice further.
[5] For the dates see Underwood, p. 334, n. 25.
[6] 5 May 1642; 30 September 1644.   [7] 30 September 1642.

distressing news, but could not agree that the College was to blame. The statute had not been abrogated and only the one exception had been made 'in these troublesome times'.[1] The College had already surmounted its immediate difficulty by admitting five new candidates.[2]

Towards the end of the year 1646 things began to change for the better. The fighting was over; the king no longer kept court; many men were able to return to their normal avocations and to London. Three fellows were elected and their places filled by three new candidates.[3] A statute was drafted and referred to the censors for preventing the absence of fellows which frustrated many of the meetings.[4] After that the whole of the statutes were revised by stages. It was decided that only Englishmen, not all Britons, should be able to become elects, that a fellow should be expelled if he were absent four times running without good cause from the stated comitia majora, and that the fellows' oath should be amended.[5] The beadle's share of fines was regulated. The number of candidates was raised to twelve; they were to visit the fellows as the licentiates did. The registrar's fine for absence was doubled.[6] The revision was completed on 31 May 1647.

Several manuscripts of these statutes have survived, the first complete sets since the *Statuta Vetera*.[7] Although it embodies all the changes of forty years the new code is by no means radically unlike the old. The arrangement is more systematic. Some of the verbiage is pruned. There are linguistic improvements throughout, and other changes of writing which, if not changes for the better, at least show that the revisers paid close attention to detail. The *presidens* becomes *praeses*; the *electi*, *electores*; the *bedellus* becomes *caduceator* again. There never was but one *caduceator* in London, though there were beadles by the dozen; but this attempt to restore the dignified title was unsuccessful.[8] There are a few passages where not merely the language but the substance reverses some intermediate decisions and restores what was in the earliest statutes. In the statute about consultations, although there are important

---

[1] On 22 October Robert Wright, a specially deserving young man, was admitted to the privilege. Even his Leiden degree was obtained only by paying a fee, after a very brief residence.

[2] 22 December 1643.   [3] 4 November 1646.   [4] 22 December 1646.

[5] 22 March 1646/7; 1 April 1647.   [6] 30 April 1647.

[7] See above, c. x. Appendix II, below, gives the text of the 1647 statutes. The dates given in the formulae for diplomas and summonses are 7 May and 14 June 1647.

[8] The last, isolated, occurrence of 'caduceator' in the Annals is on 22 December 1676.

new provisions, some words inserted in 1601 are now omitted. In that about avoiding delinquent apothecaries, there are two changes to correct definite slips that were made then.[1]

In the syllabus prescribed for the examination there is no change. In the procedure for conducting it there is one innovation: doctors of 'our' universities, that is Oxford and Cambridge, are to have the honour of being seated, which implies that all others had to stand.[2] The favoured few are to be examined in such a way as may not seem to put any indignity on their mother universities. Any censor or fellow who asks a question is to remove his cap, especially if a doctor is being examined. The ceremony of admitting fellows and licentiates is minutely described: they are to kneel before the president and place their closed hands within his, and he is then to pronounce the words of admission. This is the ancient form still practised at Cambridge in our own time; that it should appear here in writing suggests that there had been some recalcitrance about submitting to it. Once admitted the newcomer is to shake hands with each fellow and thank him.

The constitutional arrangements remain as they were except for the general raising of fines to meet the fall in the value of money and for some adjustments which, with one exception, need little or no comment. The exception regards presidential elections. The quorum of four elects is dropped, in spite of the rule that elects must live in London. The device of successive nominations for the office of president disappears, perhaps as a result of experience though perhaps it had never been used.[3] Although they were passed under the Commonwealth, the statutes of 1647 are on the whole more oligarchical and exclusive than the *Statuta Vetera*. Whether the general body ever exercised any influence over the annual presidential elections in any earlier time we do not know, but at least from this time forward the elections were on a very narrow basis: the eight elects were chosen for life and those of them who were present, even if they were fewer than four, chose one of their own number. In the comitia the same new politeness appears as in the examinations: anyone

---

[1] In 1601 *statuta Collegii* was substituted for *statuta regni*, though the latter had greater force and was fully justified. The physician was held as much accountable for what he himself knew as for what the president and censors brought to his notice. This was, to say the least of it, unpractical.

[2] This presumably dates back to 1621: see above, p. 240.

[3] See above, p. 173. A statute on the election of president was passed on 1 August 1626 and may have contained this provision.

who makes any motion or speech is to be uncovered and to address and defer to the president. No one is to interrupt except the president or the senior censor present, and so on. The censors must attend all *comitia minora*.[1] Provision is made for the appointment of committees; in doubtful and important matters at the president's discretion *delegati* are to be elected who are to discuss a matter from every point of view; but they are to report to the College, not to take any action themselves. At every meeting of comitia, major or minor, the registrar is to run through (*recenseat*) the acts of the preceding meeting in a clear voice, and when any necessary corrections have been made his minutes are to be written in the Annals. This gave the fellows a degree of control over the record which was not attained in some academic corporations until within living memory. Certainly in the seventeenth century it was not uncommon for the head of a society to indite and keep the *acta*, and it was possible for a wicked head to secrete or even falsify them. To this extent the College was more businesslike and more genuinely self-governing than some other august bodies.

One change was made in 1647 in the composition of the College. There were still to be not more than thirty fellows elected after examination, who must have been candidates for a year unless they had taught as required in Oxford or Cambridge; there were to be not more than twelve candidates, of British nationality with doctors' degrees and four years practice behind them. But the restriction to Oxford and Cambridge graduates had disappeared. The proposal which had been passed in 1642 and explained away by Dr. Meverall was now certainly statutory.[2] There would be trouble about it in the future; but for the present we need not suppose that it was intended to do more than ease a possible difficulty in recruiting. The licentiates were to be appointed, in words well-known in connexion with public offices, during good behaviour (*quamdiu se bene gesserint*). The ordinances suggested by the judges in 1607 in the matter of licensing are included.[3] But there is a notable sentence which may have been written a generation earlier and is certainly reminiscent of the imputation made against the College by the surgeons, by the apothecaries and even by Cambridge in the later years of James I. It was thought right (*aequum*) that the censors and fellows should admit all those to practice whom they found fit

---

[1] 1 August 1626.
[2] See above, p. 277. [3] See above, p. 211.

for it in knowledge and character (*moribus*), 'lest our College be accused of monopoly'. The College was to quote this sentence in evidence of its good faith in the printed *Case* for its parliamentary Bill in 1689.

The main interest of the new statutes lies indeed not in the constitution or the composition of the College but in what is laid down for its action. The *Statuta Moralia* are thoroughly revised. Those on consultation are stricter than before. If possible the first medical attendant is to remain in charge of the case, and all due care is to be taken not to impair his reputation. Discussion is to be in Latin. On the other hand there seems to be a relaxation in the first of the clauses about uroscopy: the prescriptions are to be given to honest apothecaries, but nothing is said about their being in Latin. It is no doubt merely to correct an oversight that the physician is now told not only to date his prescriptions but to add the patient's name and his own.[1] In the whole body of the statutes there is not a word to remind us of the seven years of tumult which the College had lived through. Nothing had changed in its purposes or its policy: now that London was settling down it meant to go on as before. It was a good omen when Dr. Paget gave the library Bacon's works in three volumes.[2] In the summer, three vacancies for candidates were filled on the same day and arrangements were made for revising the *Pharmacopoeia* with a view to a new edition.

There were set-backs, and some of them may have been due to public events. In 1648, for instance, civil war flared up again, though not for long, and the College was in arrears with its payments for taxation.[3] In 1650, before the last outbreak of fighting in England, some of the fellows were made to pay for finding and feeding horses and maintaining men, but Alderman Eastwick vigorously defended the privileges of the College, saved the situation and was thanked.[4] In most respects the life of the College seems to have returned to its normal course about the time of the revision of the statutes. A day was to come when no one wished it to be supposed that he had lived comfortably in the days of the usurpers, and the fellows may have conformed to the times more easily than they afterwards cared to remember. Six months after the execution of Charles I, Dr. Walter Charleton, one of his physicians, was living in London and had to

---

[1] Unless this clause goes back to 1603: see above, p. 177.
[2] 12 April 1647.   [3] 23 November 1648.
[4] Between 26 and 30 September 1650.

give an account of himself to the College. He was refused admission
as a royal physician, but he submitted to being examined, and
became a candidate.[1] Then for five years various impediments
prevented his becoming a fellow until finally he was rejected by
seventeen votes to twelve.[2] Even if he had not come into the fold
under Charles II and served for three years as president there
would be sufficient grounds for believing that this personally
attractive, though professionally not distinguished, doctor was
kept out by his royalism. Not that the usurping governments pressed
the College hard. Under the Commonwealth once, but only once,
there was an incident of the old kind. Two members of the council
of state, Bulstrode Whitelocke and John Lisle, asked the College
to take in Dr. Thomas Timme without examination, but they asked
in vain. Later he was accused of illicit practice and of ethical shortcomings, but in the end he lived it down.[3] When parliament toyed
with the latest scheme of Peter Chamberlen, a project for public
baths with a monopoly for himself extending also to the sale of bath-
stoves, the College was consulted but was not authorized to examine
the projector. It submitted a deliciously cautious report on the moral
dangers of public baths and the necessity for preserving the rights
of physicians to prescribe the salutory methods already in use in
private houses.[4]

In the course of some ordinary litigation, the College twice had
to go to the expense of obtaining new charters. Both are in the name
of Oliver, Protector, and both have the same purport, to exemplify
the Act of 14 and 15 Henry VIII.[5] They are connected with a
fantastic exercise of legal ingenuity by which counsel checked the
College in an action against one Barker at Guildhall. Serjeant
Maynard started the idea that the Act had never received the royal
assent in the proper form and so was void. Actually this was a
mare's nest. It ought not to have deceived anyone and it was disproved by an examination of the records, but the argument was
reproduced from time to time until well on in the nineteenth

[1] 6 July, 2 November 1649; 1 February, 1 March 1649/50; 5, 8 April 1650.
[2] 6 December 1650; 5 March 1651/2; 3, 11 May, 14 July.
[3] 6 December 1650; 27 February 1650/1; 6 June 1656. Timme became an honorary fellow in 1664.
[4] 30 September 1648. From about this time Dr. Peter Chamberlen seems to have been insane, but he marvellously preserved his prosperity and influence until he died in 1683 at the age of eighty-two.
[5] They are in Box 6 in the College Library, with other charters. The dates are 8 November 1656 and 18 December 1657.

century.[1] We need not linger over it, nor over the new charters, except to notice that the College was driven to deal with the *de facto* government, perhaps to an extent which it was uncomfortable to remember when the royal authority was restored.

During the civil wars the organization of medical services in the field and of hospitals received much attention, especially on the parliamentary side, and physicians were employed as well as surgeons.[2] The College, however, was scarcely involved at all. When the governments of the Commonwealth and Protectorate engaged in naval war against first the Dutch and then the Spaniards they made more use of physicians and apothecaries than previous governments had done, and so they weakened the surgeons' monopoly of naval medical services. The provision of surgeons' chests and the care of the wounded on shore passed largely out of the surgeons' hands. A gifted and energetic young fellow, Dr. Daniel Whistler, rose from a regional appointment in 1653 to a position of general control over the medical arrangements on shore, and justified his appointment. Paul de Laune, although in his seventies, sailed as physician general with the expedition which captured Jamaica, and his death there ended the vicissitudes of his not undistinguished career.[3] So far as we know neither of these appointments was made on the recommendation of the College, but they are signs that the government recognized the usefulness of the physicians' aptitudes as the College understood them, and this recognition, sometimes accompanied by more direct reliance on the College, continued throughout the other wars of the seventeenth and eighteenth centuries.

It was still necessary to be careful about ecclesiastical matters. William Morgan was debarred from the College by his Anglican orders.[4] In the case of Dr. Thomas Browne, of Padua and Oxford, the College did not go beyond the splendid tolerance of the Cromwellian protectorate, though it was more helpful to him than it had ventured to be to any papist before. Browne was elected a candidate but then declared his religion and was pronounced ineligible, but

[1] As for instance in J. N. Johnson, *Life of Thomas Linacre* (1835), p. 286 n. and Appendix XV, where the text of the 1658 charter is printed. On p. 288 Johnson explains the legal subtleties devoted to the words 'presidentis et collegii' in 1655 and 1695.

[2] For this subject in general see Sir Charles Firth, *Cromwell's Army* (1902), cap. xi.

[3] For details and references see J. J. Keevil, *Medicine and the Navy*, ii (1900), 13–56.

[4] 4 February, 3 March 1652/3; 22 December 1658. This was the William Morgan who became M.D. at Cambridge in 1652 (Matthews, *Walker Revised*, p. 40) and who had been a fellow of St. John's.

he was allowed to carry away a private and unsealed testimonial from the registrar.[1] The ruling elements in the College were as anxious as ever to keep on the right side of authority. Edward Emily, whom we know already to have been politically-minded, alarmed them when he gave the first Harveian Oration in 1656, by criticisms of the *res militaris* and the current régime. Apparently he objected to the rule of Oliver's major-generals then in force. His oration was read at a special comitia and then scrutinized by the censors. Though he escaped without even a reprimand, it was judged that in future the orations must be submitted in writing at least a month beforehand, and not delivered unless they had been previously approved by the president and one of the censors.[2]

Not only had the College recovered its energies: two incidents showed that its reputation stood high out of doors. The first was the arrival from Edinburgh of Dr. George Purves as a representative of a newly founded college of physicians there. He brought with him a letter signed by five of his colleagues, which was notably different from the Dublin letter of thirty-one years before, in that it praised the College for its discoveries of the hidden secrets of nature, admired by the whole world. The response was most friendly. The College referred to its preservation by Apollo from the dangers of recent years, and instructed the registrar to give Dr. Purves every assistance in looking through the statutes.[3]

The Edinburgh college seems to have been short-lived, but the other incident had lasting consequences. It was the admission of Henry, marquess of Dorchester as a fellow.[4] For the first time one of the aristocracy became a member, and that in itself was a promotion for the College. How the idea of electing him arose we do not know; but there is fairly good authority for the statement that Harvey was one of the fellows who conveyed the invitation.[5] Dorchester was a great reader, fond of the society of cultivated men. He had already been elected a bencher of Gray's Inn, and perhaps this made the precedent. Such was privilege in those days that a nobleman would doubtless have been accommodated in any society that he cared to join; but Dorchester was also an earnest amateur

[1] 5 December 1656: entry printed by Munk.
[2] 28 July 1656: entry printed by Munk.
[3] 4–7 May 1657. The Edinburgh signatories were Robert Burnett, George Rayns, Henry Henryson, Robert Cunningham and James Calhoun.
[4] 22 July 1658.
[5] This is stated by Goodall in a manuscript quoted at length by Munk.

physician. The fellows cannot have intended to give their blessing to his medical opinions and prescriptions, and he was admitted as *socius honorarius*. This seems to have been the first use of the phrase 'honorary fellow' in England. The Oxford colleges do not appear to have had honorary fellows until the nineteenth century.[1] In creating this new status the physicians do not seem to have defined what it amounted to, or foreseen that they would make use of it again within a few years. Accidentally it anticipated a future development, and this, as we shall see is also true of the marquess's membership in others of its aspects.

Some years after his election Dorchester made a gift of a hundred books to the College library.[2] It may be that the library, which was entering on a new and more publicly known existence, played a part in attracting his interest to the College. In 1651 Dr. Ent and Dr. King were put in charge of it when, as it seems, their predecessors had served only six months of their annual term, possibly to make ready for important changes. A few days later a very short and practical letter from an anonymous benefactor was read. He asked leave, with such others as he should choose, to build for the College (of which the letter implied that he was a member) a library and a repository for simples and rarities 'such a one as shall be suitable and honourable to the College'. The offer was immediately and gratefully accepted.[3] Books and money due to the library were called in.[4] It became known that this act of generosity came from Dr. Harvey. In 1654 the Harveian Museum, as it was to be called, was ready and there was a simple but impressive opening ceremony.[5] Statutes or regulations were duly made, with details about the committee, the librarian, custody, cleaning, readers and the recording of gifts to the value of 40s. or more. It was to be open on Friday from two to five, but only till four in the winter, and on the days of comitia or at other times at the discretion of the librarian. In addition to the fellows donors of £5 or more might use it, and others admitted with due precautions by the committee. It was to be primarily a medical

---

[1] C. V. Cox, *Reminiscences of Oxford*, 2nd edn. (1890), p. 321 says that they began to do so 'some few years' after the cathedrals began to appoint honorary canons about 1841. In 1664 the Royal Society, decided to make Sir John Cutler an honorary fellow, but he seems to have been enrolled in the ordinary way (Minute of 16 November 1664 in Birch). In the eighteenth century, if not earlier, there were honorary freemen of boroughs, and the City companies began the custom at least as early as 1659: see below, p. 270.   [2] 9 April 1655.
[3] 23 December 1650; 25 June, 4 July 1651.   [4] 30 September 1657.
[5] 2 February 1653/4. 'Musaeum Harveianum' is the first English name of this kind, followed by 'Musaeum Ashmoleanum' and others.

library, but other subjects were to be included, of which the most suitable were held to be geometry, geography, cosmography, astronomy, music, optics, zoology, physics, mechanics, and voyages. Chemistry and botany are not mentioned separately but were probably included with medicine.[1]

These statutes have more than a merely local interest, and the library itself attracted support from scholars outside the College. The flow of gifts increased. Sir Richard Napier of All Souls, a doctor but not a fellow of the London College, gave the Greek commentators on Aristotle in thirteen volumes which cost him £25.[2] A sumptuous English Bible was acquired.[3] The great John Selden bequeathed eleven Oriental manuscripts to which Dr. Rant's brother added six Arabic books.[4] After a few years Edmund Castell, the Semitic scholar, was applying for access to Arabic books for himself and for Mr. Thomas Murray.[5]

Besides the library there was an elaboratory outside the College building, which was also called a chymicall repository. A Mr. Johnson was appointed as chemist, and instruments were purchased for him. He seems to have continued his work as long as the building remained standing,[6] and it would be pleasant if we could believe that he was engaged in chemical experiments. For this, however, we have no warrant. His business was to prepare medicines, and, though some of these were standard specimens for inspection and tests, it seems that most of his work was to make chemical medicines for use by the fellows in practice. The apothecaries are said to have opened their first laboratory in 1623. In 1641 their master, the hated Edward Cooke offered them £500 to build on waste ground by the waterside at Blackfriars.[7] Their purpose was, one might say, industrial. Mr. Johnson's seems to have been much the same but perhaps his appointment should not be regarded as a move against the apothecaries. Being already a freeman of the City, he was allowed to incorporate in the Society in 1654, but he was made to promise that he would not meddle with Galenical medicines.[8]

During this period of recovery there is indeed little to report which throws light on the attitude of the College to science and

---

[1] 19 June 1656. The drawing of the regulations began on 4 August and 1 September 1654.   [2] 30 September 1652.
[3] 4 April 1653.   [4] 9 April 1655; 1 February 1655/6.
[5] 28 March 1659; 5 February 1659/60; 16 April, 25 June 1660.
[6] 26 June, 24 October 1648; 23 January 1650/1 (£20 for anatomical and chemical instruments).
[7] Barrett, pp. 58–59.   [8] Underwood, p. 334, n. 26.

thought. The new edition of the *Pharmacopoeia* was thoroughly and deliberately prepared; it was entrusted to a new publisher Mr. Boutell instead of the unsatisfactory Marriot; the prefatory letter to King James was retained, and it was published in 1650 with a list of the fellows and candidates.[1] A Frenchman called Punctaeus or Puntaeus (? Jean Pointau), a veteran among the empirics, asked for a certificate for his balsam, already approved by French universities and by Oxford. Rather surprisingly it was given and renewed after ten years. The precedent was followed for another empiric called Vincent Lancelles.[2] In 1652 it was decided that for the future the Gulstonian lectures should be given in Latin. Perhaps this was intended to veil their purport from surgeons, apothecaries or other unlearned hearers.[3] On requesting approbation for his book on fevers William Slatholm of Buntingford was told that there was nothing new or distinguished in it and so the decision whether to publish or not must rest with him.[4] The College twice issued open pronouncements, beginning 'Be it known to all whom it may concerne', on medical questions, the first to approve Dr. Charleton's treatment in a difficult case, the second to condemn a colocynth purgative administered by a woman of Covent Garden.[5]

Although there is no trace of it in the Annals, the fellows were affected by the new vigour of medical and scientific thought in London in the time of the Protectorate. The Protector had a court, but it was modest and colourless in comparison with the radiant Whitehall of the old days, and altogether there were few social distractions for the physicians who gravitated to the capital. When Lord Dorchester joined the College the official newspaper praised him for giving the nobility of England 'a noble example how to improve their time at the highest rate for the advancement of their own Honor and the benefit of Mankinde'.[6] Here and there, particularly in Gresham College, there were more or less informal meetings at which scientific questions of all sorts were discussed. Afterwards, when memories of them had become confused, these meetings became famous as preliminaries to graver and more formal

---

[1] 30 September 1647; 4, 28 June; 27 July, 23 November 1649; 10 January 1649/50.
[2] 3 October 1651; 5 April 1661; 6 March 1656/7. Punctaeus appears in the list of 17 February 1631/2 as an unlicensed practitioner.
[3] June comitia 1652 in Brit. Mus. Sloane MS. 3914 fo. 31v.
[4] 7 November 1656.
[5] 5 March 1651/2; 12 August 1652.
[6] *Mercurius Politicus*, 22–29 July 1658. This was probably written by the editor, Marchamont Nedham, of whom we shall hear again.

proceedings. Among the fellows who were prominent in the subsequent developments, such as Glisson, Ent, Jonathan Goddard
Whistler and Merret, all of whom were in London, several were
active in the preliminary stage, and none can have been unaware
of what was on foot.[1]

On the prosaic level of College business they had useful work to
do, but few excitements. The new statute about absenteeism was
enforced against the increasingly crazy Peter Chamberlen and
against William Goddard, the latter fruitlessly trying to get the court
of king's bench to re-instate him.[2] Dr. Frazier was in France with
the royal family and had to be expelled, but his return was provided for and came about in the fullness of time.[3] The membership
was kept up, though not without difficulty in the earlier years.[4] At
the Michaelmas comitia of 1650 there were present thirty-seven
fellows, ten candidates (forty-seven out of fifty in the printed list)
besides seven licentiates and three extra-licentiates. Finance was
difficult, but a succession of legacies came in from fellows. In 1640
the elder Hamey, though only a licentiate and not always well
treated by the College, had set a good example with £20; Regimorter,
Catcher and Smith each left the same sum, and, if Wilson did
nothing, the good ex-president Foxe bequeathed £60, which his
nephew made up to a round hundred.[5]

At this time there are notices of charitable gifts by the College.
Dr. Grent died, leaving his widow very badly off, and the College
voted her half the sum it was to receive for the new *Pharmacopoeia*.[6]
William Sainte Barber, a doctor of Caen and a licentiate, had fallen
into poverty and the College gave his orphaned family £5, but
put it on the ground that some years before he had presented an
anatomical figure.[7] On the previous day it had given advice *gratis*
to a poor youth suffering from *gutta serena*. It is curious that such
things should appear now in the Annals and it may or may not be
significant. Licentiates indeed had complained of their poverty often
enough in the past, but they had complained when they had to pay
their dues. Prosperous people have been known to behave like that

---

[1] For an account of the present state of knowledge on this much-controverted matter
see *The Royal Society, its Origins and Founders*, ed. by Sir Harold Hartley (1960),
especially the first essay by Professor D. McKie.
[2] 23 November 1649.   [3] 26 September 1650.
[4] On 4 and 15 June 1647 it was decided to elect two new fellows after which Dr.
Wilson and Dr. Coxe were elected.
[5] Wilson ('ne teruncio quidem') 15 November 1655.
[6] 13 December 1649.   [7] 28 September 1659.

on similar occasions in many walks of life, and it is more than possible that Sainte Barbe had a harder time than Diodati. Grent was physician to St. Thomas's Hospital, thrust in by royal mandate, but he is alleged to have been too great a fool to have any other practice, so that the times were not to blame for his poverty.[1] Nor need we suppose that the terms of the grant to Sainte Barbe implied a grudging spirit. Professor Jordan, the historian of English charitable giving, has analysed the wills of nine London physicians in the period 1480–1660, who together left £7,376 of benefactions in their wills. The doctors, he writes, were much less rich than their lawyer contemporaries but more generous in charity.[2] It seems most unlikely that the poor youth who happened to be mentioned was the only one to benefit from free advice, and we shall have occasion to remember him in a later chapter.

The one respect in which there was no recovery worth mentioning was in the contest with the physicians' rivals. The law still stood firm: Dr. Buggs failed in an action to recover the king's share of his old fine.[3] But the College was able to make little effective use of its powers. It certified to a justice of the peace that Mrs. Lane (perhaps not the old criminal) had given 'funestal' treatment in a fatal case of small-pox.[4] It set in motion one prosecution, but perhaps not more.[5] When it engaged a new solicitor it charged him to inform it of unlicensed practitioners.[6] Once it decided that all who set up bills were to be summoned, and six months later it looked into the question of those who had doctor's degrees but no licences, of whom seven were accounted for.[7] In 1655/6 there was a general discussion on how to repress the empirics and the unlicensed physicians, distinguished as two separate classes. At the next meeting many candidates attended to complain of the unusual insolence of the invaders, and Dr. Greaves, made a set speech on this theme. A committee of the elects and eleven others, half of the whole number of fellows, was appointed to organize an offensive. There were disagreements about tactics, but unanimity was reached on two points: all those who openly displayed advertisements were to be arrested and prosecuted at law, and the remainder of the

---

[1] The allegation is Hamey's, printed by Munk.
[2] This was 31.73 per cent. of their disposable wealth: W. K. Jordan, *The Charities of London* (1959), p. 56. It would be reasonable to add the gifts made to the College itself by its benefactors from Linacre, Caius and Caldwell down to Harvey during their lives.
[3] Goodall, pp. 259–60.   [4] 6 February 1651/2.
[5] 13 October, 3 November 1654.   [6] 28 June 1649.
[7] 1 July, 6 December 1650.

medicasters were to be sued in the court of exchequer. But differences still remained, and in the end, as had happened so often before, there was no visible result from all this talking.[1] An empiric was forbidden to practise on the historic ground of Knightrider Street itself.[2] A new committee was appointed, this time of five.[3] Needless to say in those days when the City was almost the steadiest factor in national affairs, the two organized Companies of rivals held their heads high. Hardly any surgeons were interfered with. It is interesting to notice that, perhaps owing to the absence of bishops, one extra-licentiate was authorized to practise surgery as well as medicine.[4] One person accused of malpractice was described as *chirurgo-pharmacopoeus*.[5] The apothecaries were busy in these years defending themselves against interlopers and vindicating their rights of search. The College went on examining their apprentices and holding its visitations. They practised audaciously and the College grumbled, but hostilities were suspended.[6] Two physicians indeed were *personae gratissimae* at Apothecaries' Hall: Dr. Merret and Dr. Wharton, along with the minister of the parish, were admitted honorary fellows at a feast day in 1659.[7]

The recovery of the College had been in progress for some eleven years, during the last seven of which England had been internally at peace, when the protector died and confusion came back. Under a quickly changing succession of unstable régimes no one knew what to expect and hardly anyone knew what to do. From the summer of 1659, when the remnant of the Long Parliament reassembled, the College repeatedly discussed how it could preserve its privileges. The military authorities again demanded payments from fellows for providing mounted and unmounted soldiers. There were troop movements in London and a renewal of civil war seemed imminent. The College was given to understand that it could buy back its exemption from military and civil taxation by a cash payment—to whom we are not told—of no less than £150.[8] The registrar did not confide to the Annals any admission that this blackmail was paid, and the treasurers' accounts have perished, but it seems more than likely that he parted with the money. It would have been just as useful at the bottom of the sea, for in the spring of 1660 King Charles II came back to enjoy his own.

[1] 3, 31 March 1655/6; 4, 25 April, 2 May 1656.   [2] 5 February 1657/8.
[3] 25 June 1658.   [4] Thomas Williams of Eltham, 11 February 1659/60.
[5] Edward Randal, 5 March 1657/8.   [6] 9 April 1655 a discussion.
[7] Underwood, p. 335, n. 27.   [8] 30 July 1659.

Table of Fines in the Statutes of 1647

Absence from comitia		2*s*.
Refusing office of president unless physician to the king		40*s*.
Refusing office of consiliarius unless physician to the king		40*s*.
Refusing office of censor unless physician to the king		40*s*.
Consiliarius not ready with advice unless for urgent cause		3*s*. 4*d*.
Absence of censor from comitia minora unless for cause certified to president		10*s*.
Disorder in comitia		2*s*.
Not wearing academic dress on prescribed occasions		5*s*.
Revealing secret of any importance		10*s*.
Accusing colleague	first offence	£4
	second offence	£8
	third offence	expulsion
	restoration after third offence	£10
Not ascertaining treatment of first doctor		20*s*.
Bad manners at consultation		5*s*.
Consulting with empiric		40*s*.
Revealing name of medicament		40*s*.
Corruptly bargaining with apothecary		40*s*.
Associating with apothecary, unless approved, after warning		10*s*.
Refusal to conduct anatomy demonstration	not more than	£20
Absence from anatomy demonstration		3*s*. 4*d*.

XVI : HARVEY

THE Edinburgh physicians who praised the services of the College to medical knowledge, in concert as they said with the whole world, may have been thinking of the long line of writers from Linacre and Caius, but we may doubt whether they would have mentioned the uncovering of the mysteries of nature hidden through earlier ages if it had not been for the renown of Harvey. He died only a few weeks after their letter was written, in his eightieth year. Riolanus of the Paris faculty, the only critic of his work whom he answered in writing, also died in that same year 1657, and he died unconvinced; there were still mutterings of dissent here and there on the Continent, but it was substantially true, as Hobbes had written, that Harvey, saw his discovery of the circulation of the blood accepted in his lifetime.[1] When he printed it he gave the College a share in the credit. On the title page of his book *De Motu Cordis* he described himself as physician to the king, and he very properly dedicated it to his master Charles I; but he also described himself as 'Professor Anatomiae in Collegio Medicorum Londinensi' and wrote a second dedicatory letter to the president and fellows. By this he made Dr. Argent and his colleagues known in every centre of serious physiological study. He made them known not only as a body to which he owed a formal acknowledgement, but as one before which he had explained and experimentally demonstrated his innovation, in which he had answered doubts and objections, and whose approval gave him confidence in making it public. Harvey's relations with the College are therefore of importance in its history.

He came to the College with excellent qualifications, though with no extraneous advantages over the general run of its members. His father, a man of substance, was described as a Kentish yeoman at a time when the yeomen of Kent were proverbially prosperous.[2] He was the eldest of seven sons, and five of his younger brothers became wealthy merchants in the City. While they were beginning to make

---

[1] *Elementorum Philosophiae sectio prima De Corpore* (1655), *Epistola Dedicatoria*. For instances of late (and worthless) writers against Harvey see the life of Joseph Browne in the *Dict. of Nat. Biog.*
[2] *Oxford Dictionary of English Proverbs* (1935), p. 16.

EXERCITATIO
ANATOMICA DE
MOTV CORDIS ET SAN-
GVINIS IN ANIMALI-
BVS,

GVILIELMI HARVEI ANGLI,
Medici Regii, & Professoris Anatomiæ in Col-
legio Medicorum Londinensi.

FRANCOFVRTI,
Sumptibus GVILIELMI FITZERI.

ANNO M. DC. XXVIII.

V. Title Page of Harvey, *De Motu Cordis* (1628)

their way he had gone from a good school, the King's School,
Canterbury, to Caius College, Cambridge, with its medical associations, and thence to Padua. Padua not only had its wonderful old
tradition; it was still the greatest medical school in the world, and
Fabricius ab Aquapendente, one of the great anatomists, was
teaching there. Harvey as a student did well, he took his doctor's
degree before he was twenty four, returned to England and became
a Cambridge doctor in the same year. His *Lebenslauf* was a model
of orderly success. He took a house in London, and, as we have
seen, applied for a licence to practice. It was duly granted after a
delay, in no way reflecting on his fitness, which may have been due
to the desire of the College to keep room for one of the physicians
of the new king, James I.[1] In the month following his admission as
a candidate Harvey married the daughter of a fellow of the College,
Dr. Lancelot Browne, one of the late queen's physicians. His own
turn for election as a fellow came in 1607. By that time he was a
made man. In 1609, after recommendation by the king and the
president and several senior fellows of the College, he became
physician to St. Bartholomew's. By 1618 he was one of the royal
physicians and in 1623 he was promised a place as a physician in
ordinary when it should fall vacant.

In the College he moved on from office to office with the same
regularity. He was censor for the first time in 1613 and again in
1625 and 1629. In 1627 Mayerne declined the office of elect as a
foreigner and, if the truth were told, as no very assiduous member
of the College, so the appointment fell to Harvey. In 1628 he was
treasurer, to which office he was re-elected in 1629. Soon afterwards
the king commanded him to accompany his young cousin the duke
of Lennox on his travels abroad, and Harvey resigned the treasure-
ship in a becoming manner, after entertaining the College to a
magnificent dinner in his house.[2] He left behind him a gift of £20
towards the redemption of the Amen Corner lease. But his success
with the College was not obtained by the minor arts of popularity.
We have seen already that he was regular in attendance at comitia,
much in request for committee-work and for negotiations.[3] There

[1] See above, c. xi, p. 197.
[2] According to the then accepted view of the royal prerogative the king had the right
to order any of his subjects to carry out any service. This was strikingly exemplified in
the case of Sir Thomas Overbury in 1613: the offence for which he was thrown into
the Tower (where he was murdered) was merely that he refused a diplomatic appointment. It might be difficult to say exactly how or when the rule ceased to operate.
[3] See above, cc. xi-xv.

are other entries in the Annals which show that in College business he had a will of his own. It would indeed be forcing the evidence to mention here that he was fined £6. 13s. 4d. in 1611 for not giving his admission dinner: a fine was not necessarily a punishment and might be in the nature of a friendly composition, and there may have been some obstacle to his giving the dinner.[1] Excuses are not so easy to find for a later lapse, when he and Dr. Winston were fined 10s. each for failing to accompany Dr. Herring on his deputation to Lord Keeper Williams.[2] If he was in the wrong then, at any rate he erred in good company. On another occasion, in even better company, he may have had some difference with others of the fellows. He and Dr. Atkins offered in writing their resignation as elects, and Sir William Paddy joined them; but the president and the other four elects considered their reasons inadmissible and so they stayed on.[3] Possibly this incident had something to do with a statute approved some months later, that whenever it could conveniently be managed one of the censors should be an elect.[4] Once Harvey and Dr. Argent seem to have been in a minority of two against a decision of the College. In 1640 John Cadyman, the son of the catholic fellow who was a physician to the queen, was admitted a licentiate in the ordinary way. In the next month the commander-in-chief asked the College to choose a physician for the army which was preparing to meet the Scots in the Second Bishops' War. The name of this very young doctor was proposed, and all the fellows present signed his appointment except these two. May we conclude that they were standing out against a job?[5]

Harvey became Lumleian lecturer in 1615 and retained the office until the year before he died. No deputy seems to have been appointed for any of the periods when he was away from London. Besides his journey with Lennox he went abroad on other occasions and accompanied the king several times to Scotland and the north of England. During the Civil War he was in Oxford from 1642 to 1646, after which he lived in the town or country houses of his brothers, none of them very far from London, but he did not resume his attendance at *comitia*.[6] The exact dates of his comings and goings are not known, but it seems certain that he did not deliver a full course of lectures in every year of his tenure. Towards

---

[1] Morrow of Palm Sunday 1611.   [2] 15 January 1623/4. See above, p. 192.
[3] 20 September 1633.   [4] 16 July 1634.   [5] 1 May 1640.
[6] That his movements were restricted at least for a time is shown by his application for a pass permitting him to visit Lady Thynne in 1650.

the end the College once discussed whether the two salaried anatomical prelections, that is presumably the Lumleian and the Gulstonian, should be combined into one.[1] This suggestion may, however, have arisen from the difficulty of collecting the Lumleian lecturer's stipend: Harvey was authorized in 1640 to take legal proceedings for this purpose, and again in 1647 to do so by attorney.[2] We know very little about the College lectures. The licentiates, candidates and fellows in their first year were supposed to attend, but we do not know how regular they were, and we do not know whether favoured outsiders were admitted as they were in later times. Licentiates had to attend for their first five years, and it was possible to remain a candidate for a good many years, so that perhaps no one suffered much from a suspension even of a year or two.

No contemporary has left any account of Harvey as a lecturer, but from everything we know about him we should expect that he was a first-rate teacher. His famous lecture note-book of 1616 confirms this as far as the lecturer's own notes can, for he wrote down principles for his own guidance which show that he knew the difference between lecturing and writing and the use of demonstrating in conjunction with the lecture.[3] These notes were not a text for reading but a repertory to select from, less suitable for Lumleian lectures than for the Latin show-lectures at the College dissection, which all the fellows attended. They were embellished with many references showing Harvey's mastery of the ancient and modern literature of his subject and with ingenious, homely parallels written down in English and perhaps to be spoken in English. The notes, possibly for his Lumleian lectures of 1627, which also survive, have much less of the learned apparatus, no doubt because they were meant to give ordinary instruction. The earlier notebook is famous because in it Harvey states his

---

[1] 12 April 1652. The Lumleian must have been one of the 'duae praelectiones stipendiariae'. The original college dissection, continued, though not without intervals, but was not endowed and so is unlikely to be the second.

[2] 24 November 1640, 31 May 1647: resolutions printed by Munk. The proceedings cost Harvey at least £500 and did not come to a satisfactory conclusion until his successor Sir Charles Scarburgh had incurred further expense. (Munk, i. 127, from R.C.P., MS. 158 fo. 9.)

[3] *Prelectiones Anatomiae Generalis* (1886)—text with facsimile; the standard edition, with translation, by Dr. Gweneth Whitteridge, which also includes the other quite unadorned anatomical note-book of Harvey in Brit. Mus. MS. Sloane 486, was published after the present work was set up in type.

fundamental conclusion about the circulation of the blood. When he published this discovery in the little Frankfort book of 1628, he wrote that he had laid it before the College, by ocular demonstration and in words, for nine years and more. Why did he not say twelve? The answer seems to be simply that Horace advised authors to put down their works to mature until the ninth year.[1] It looks as if Harvey chose 1616, when it came to his turn to conduct the dissection, to make a formal announcement of his discovery to the College.

Where we can check Harvey's statements by other evidence they generally turn out to be true though a few of them may not be exact. There is a strong presumption that in the twelve years when the new doctrine was before his colleagues but not before the world he freed them from the objections of very instructed and learned anatomists. We need not suppose, because he does not give us any grounds for supposing, either that these objections were of any importance or that the clearing of his doctrine from them involved any modification of the doctrine itself. We have no means of knowing what the objections were, or who raised them, or on what occasions, formal or informal. Still less have we any reason to suppose that anyone contributed to the formation of Harvey's opinion. So far as we know he was an indefatigable and at this time a solitary worker. There seems to be no record of his employing an assistant or an amanuensis while he was working on the circulation. He always showed great respect for his predecessors, and, though he was aware that he was breaking with views which had ruled unquestioned for centuries, his work seems to have been a continuation of theirs and not to have resulted from the explicit formulation of a new problem. We cannot be sure of this, because we have no information about the steps by which his thought advanced; but his known qualities of keen visual perception and firm intellectual grip were such as could bring him to this result, which is essentially the detection of a physical fact, without the help of discussion. We might even venture to suggest that Harvey in a famous *obiter dictum* disparaged intellectual team-work. He said of Bacon: 'He writes philosophy like a Lord Chancellor.'[2] This was a very good remark, but it needs explanation. It is about what we call science rather than about what we call philosophy, and it is usually taken to mean simply that Bacon was not a good scientist

[1] *Ars Poetica*, l. 388.   [2] J. Aubrey, *Brief Lives*, ed. A. Clark (1898), i. 299.

or that he was a mere amateur. No one ever became lord chancellor without some positive abilities and we have seen that as lord chancellor Bacon had to consider medical questions. Harvey may well have conceded something to his breadth of vision or to his belief in the value of science. But Bacon was the great advocate of organized and collective research, and Harvey's remark may imply confidence in the individual investigator as against the statesman's project of a great institution for scientific research.

Much has been written about the reception of Harvey's discovery, but to little profit, since in the long run it had to be accepted. According to David Hume 'it was remarked, that no physician in Europe, who had reached forty years of age, ever, to the end of his life adopted Harvey's doctrine of the circulation of the blood'.[1] The reader is free to believe this or not as he pleases. Within the College there were some who still preferred their Galen. Dr. Winston was professor of physic at Gresham College, and in 1659, four years after his death, a course of anatomy lectures, purporting to be his, was published: it does not include the new discovery.[2] That the same is true of the second edition (1632) of Helkiah Crooke's compilation is not surprising.[3] Sir Wilmot Herringham drew attention to the questions put to Gerard Boet in 1632 in the presence both of Crooke and of Harvey himself. They show no trace of the new teaching.[4] This was an examination on a set book, Galen *De Inequali Temperie*, and the examiners seem to have thought that their duty ended with testing Boet's knowledge of the text. The statute about the examinations remained unchanged, except in points of Latinity, throughout Harvey's lifetime, and it is not impossible that Harvey was satisfied with it as it stood, with its overwhelming emphasis on Galen, passing over all later authors in silence. At any rate he had taken a more active part than most of the fellows in the revision of the statutes in 1626, and there is nothing to indicate that he tried to change the syllabus. The College may therefore have intentionally examined its postulants in beliefs which it knew were superseded.

It cannot have taken such a line in dealing with publications. Dr. Primrose, the Franco-Scottish licentiate, had been a pupil of

---

[1] *History of England* (ed. of 1786), c. lxii, towards the end.
[2] *Anatomy Lectures at Gresham Colledge.*   [3] See above, p. 204.
[4] In *Annals of Medical History*, iv (1932), 491. The date of the examinations was 11 June 1632, and the examiners were Dr. Argent (president), Drs. Clement, Foxe, Winston, Hodson (censors), Harvey and Crooke.

Riolanus and came out openly against Harvey in several publications to which Harvey did not reply. He also attacked Dr. Drake, a younger man who had graduated at Leiden with a thesis upholding Harvey's view. When Dr. Drake submitted a short treatise against Dr. Primrose's arguments, the College tamely declined to express either approval or disapproval and left the responsibility of publication to the author.[1] But this neutrality had no effect on the campaign. In the same year one of the most promising of the younger fellows, Dr. George Ent, came out with a book on Harvey's side, with commendatory verses by Baldwin Hamey, who was also one of the younger men but had a very conservative cast of mind.[2] Ent it was who afterwards persuaded Harvey to publish his second major work *De Generatione Animalium*. While he was in Oxford Harvey had made the acquaintance of another gifted young man, Charles Scarburgh, who worked with him on embryology and was to succeed him as Lumleian lecturer.

Whatever reserves and hesitations the older fellows may have felt about Harvey's ideas, they had none about his benefactions. The banquet and the £20 before he set out with the duke of Lennox were a foretaste. After he left Oxford in 1646 he seems to have considered what he could do for the College. He was not unmindful of other institutions that had a claim on him. In his will he remembered his native town of Folkestone besides Caius College, the poor in St. Bartholomew's, and Christ's Hospital, another of the charitable foundations governed by the City.[3] But it was for the College of Physicians, now that he was old and rich and childless, that he did most. We cannot tell what feelings of gratitude and of hope may have prompted him, but it seems a certain inference that he expected and intended the College to be a home of medical science. First he modestly and anonymously made his offer for a library and a repository for simples and rarities.[4] When it was completed it was a noble building of Roman architecture, rusticated and with Corinthian pilasters, having a large room for the comitia below and the library above.[5] It was officially named after him, and it seems inappropriate that the inscription outside it mentioned only the

---

[1] 19 April 1641.
[2] The respectful reference to Harvey's discovery in Hamey's College anatomical lectures of 1647/8 is printed on p. 17 of the translation of the *Lectures on the Whole of Anatomy* by C. D. O'Malley, F. N. L. Poynter and K. F. Russell (1961).
[3] The text of the will is in his *Works* (1847), lxxxix.
[4] See above, p. 285.   [5] Aubrey, p. 297.

names of Dr. Prujean and Dr. Edmund Smith, who supervised the building.[1] Perhaps, however, this was another instance of his modesty.

After the ceremonial opening the College elected Harvey president. It is to be feared that this was a tribute rather to his bounty than to his genius, but the offer was made and received with perfect dignity. The great man's health was failing, and he could scarcely have undertaken such a burden; but while declining it he recommended that Dr. Prujean should be continued in office, at whose hands he then accepted the office of consiliarius. He made the College a parting gift, which had an intimate character, for it was that of his inherited estate of some fifty acres at Burmarsh near Hythe on the Kentish coast. One of the purposes of this was characteristic. There was to be each month a small collation for those who attended the comitia, and each year a general feast for all the fellows. Here Harvey shows that he valued the social life of the College as Dr. Caius had valued it. On the same day as the dinner there was to be a Latin oration. The orator was to be chosen by the two senior censors and the two senior elects, the same person never being chosen for two years running. He was to deliver his oration publicly[2] in the College, commemorating all its benefactors by name, with an exhortation to follow their examples, and another exhortation to the fellows and members to search and study out the secrets of nature by way of experiment.

Harvey was not the first Englishman to institute an annual dinner or oration in memory of benefactors; indeed some such commemoration was a regular function in many older colleges, in some of which it was still accompanied by vestigial religious observances; but the Harveian orations, changing their emphasis with the variations of the times, have never lost their value. Once a year a fellow reminded the College as impressively as he could of its own purposes and those of the profession. Before the end of the eighteenth century more than fifty of the orations were printed. From them the learned world could judge how the College maintained its standards of civilized intellectual intercourse and professional service. For the historian they provide an illuminating series of

---

[1] The inscription said the building was due to their 'suasus et cura', which seems to imply that they had advised Harvey on the form his benefaction should take.
[2] This does not mean that the public were to be admitted, but only that the oration was to be a corporate function of the College, delivered under its authority or on its behalf.

considered, if usually very conventional, statements, sometimes accompanied by unconscious revelations.

We shall see in the sequel how the College responded to the exhortations to seek out the secrets of nature; but it will be as well to notice here that in all probability Harvey did not intend to promote any new kind of organization for research. At the end of his life there were indeed several men in the College who had made or might reasonably be expected to make substantial additions to knowledge. He clearly had his own hopes of Ent and Scarburgh; Glisson, partly anticipated by Whistler[1] had already published his book on rickets in which George Bate, Regemorter and others assisted.[2] Among the younger men Jonathan Goddard, Thomas Wharton and Christopher Merret were showing promise, to say nothing of the many-sided genius of William Petty. But two things must have prevented Harvey from imagining that the College as a whole would become a research-institution, his own adherence to the old method of individual work, and his experience of the great inequalities between intelligent men in openness of mind and receptivity to new ideas. It is scarcely necessary to point out that he recommended experiment as a good but not as a new method: Galen himself was an experimental scientist.

If Harvey did not plan a revolution in research, still less did he contemplate a revolution in the treatment of disease.[3] He did indeed make important observations on midwifery though his friend Percivall Willoughby and he did indicate in a famous passage how far the consequences of his discovery might reach in every part of medicine, physiology, pathology, semantics and therapeutics itself.[4] But one of the distinctive qualities of his mind was his power of

---

[1] E. Clarke, 'Whistler and Glisson on Rickets' in *Bulletin for the History of Medicine*, xxvi (1962), 45/61, states the extent of the anticipation and adds a general, but not conclusive, defence of Whistler's character against the charges mentioned below, p. 339. Whistler's Leiden dissertation of 1645 is entitled *De Morbo Puerili Anglorum . . . the Rickets*, It is curious that his examiners should have thought it was a peculiarly English disease.

[2] These three are named on the title-page and sign the preface, which explains that about five years before the publication they used to meet privately for purposes of study along with Sheaf, Lawrence Wright (who died in 1657), Paget, Goddard and Trench. All eight were fellows of the College, but there is no warrant for calling them a committee of the College, and no hint that they engaged together in any practical research, although they exchanged written communications about rickets (*Tractatus de Rachitide*, The Hague, 1682).

[3] For this subject see Sir Geoffrey Keynes, *Harvey through John Aubrey's Eyes* (Harveian Oration, 1958) and Sir Charles Dodds, *A Riddle of the Seventeenth Century* (Linacre Lecture, 1960).

[4] *De Motu Cordis*, c. xvi towards the end.

keeping to the point, and he left no programme of practical applications for the new physiology to which he made one cardinal
contribution and many others of no little moment. He destroyed
the foundations of the humoral pathology as a system, but of his
own practice we know next to nothing. A few of his prescriptions
survive, but they are too few and too commonplace to prove anything of interest. It is said, and it may be true, that 'after his booke
of the Circulation of the Blood came-out, . . . he fell mightily in his
practize',[1] but it has never been suggested that this was due to
anything new in his methods of treatment. There are several traits
which suggest that, outside his scientific investigations, Harvey's
nature was conservative: such a conclusion might indeed be
drawn from the present chapter as a whole. The system of medical
education, insisting on a close textual knowledge of the standard
authorities, inculcated conservatism, especially in the theoretical
and systematic parts of the study, and in its examinations the College
allowed no deviation from this approach. There was still much
scope for anatomical and physiological investigation in continuation
of what Harvey had done and, on a rather different plane, two major
problems were unsolved, those of animal heat and the function of
the lungs. As it turned out these could not be solved until factors
of a different plane, not considered by Harvey, were brought to
bear. This expansion of the field of physiology occupied the last
quarter of the seventeenth century and much of the eighteenth.
While it was still in progress and the outcome could not be foreseen,
it remained true that among the many humours or liquids in the
body there were four major humours, somehow involved in the
vital processes and somehow involved in diseases. It remained true
that some of these humours could be controlled. The blood could
at least be drawn off by puncturing a vein. Injection or evacuation
through the few available orifices could add to some of the others
or detract from them. Medicines could produce known effects. The
accepted explanations of these effects were so roundabout and so
tenuously related to the facts that they were not obviously harder
to reconcile with the new physiology of the blood than with the old.
So there was no reform of treatment during Harvey's lifetime. A
generation later it was already often brought to the reproach of his
great discovery 'that it seemed to illustrate the *Theorie of Medicine*,
yet it made no improvement in the practice thereof.'[2]

---

[1] Aubrey, i. 300.   [2] A. Broun, *Vindicatory Schedule* (1691), Preface.

Note on Harvey's Conservatism

It will have appeared sufficiently plainly from the foregoing chapter that Harvey, though he was one of the greatest of scientific innovators, was conservative in many other respects. Any indications of the limits of his conservatism throw light on his mind, and the purpose of this note is to point out two of them in widely different matters.

The first concerns his personal habits. John Aubrey wrote that he saw Harvey ride in 1654 or 5, presumably in London: 'he rode on horseback with a footcloth to visit his patients, his man following on foote as the fashion then was, which was very decent, now quite discontinued'[1]. A foot-cloth was an ornamental cloth laid over the horses's back and hanging down to the ground on both sides. Nicholas Culpeper, the contentious apothecary, cannot have been alluding to Harvey when he asked several years before: 'Is it handsome and well-seeming in a Common-wealth to see a Doctor riding in State with a footcloth and, not a grain of Wit but what was in print before he was born.'[2] But by then the fashion seems to have been already dying. Baldwin Hamey wrote that the last two presidents of the College who used foot-cloths on their rounds were Foxe who died in 1642 and Argent who died in 1643.[3]

The second point concerns chemistry. There is no reason to suppose that Aubrey's erratic memory misled him when he wrote that Harvey 'did not care for chymistrey, and was wont to speake against them with an undervalue'.[4] On the other hand there is a scrap of evidence which suggests that in his last years Harvey was not known in the College as an opponent of chemistry in the old Galenic style. Christopher Terne, who was elected a fellow in 1655 wrote: 'with old *Doctor Winston*, and *Doctor Wright*, all our dogmaticall Gallenists, as they call them, died.'[5] Winston died in 1655 and Wright in 1657.

---

[1] *Brief Lives*, i. 302. Aubrey's notes were scribbled down mainly in 1680-1, and the earliest of them date from 1674.
[2] *Physical Directory* (1649), to the Reader.
[3] Munk, i. 113 n.   [4] *Brief Lives*, i. 320.
[5] C.T., *Some Papers writ in the year 1664 in Answer to a Letter concerning the Practice of Physic in England* (1670), p. 19.

VI. Silver Tazza, the Porter's Staff (1679) and Badge, Hamey's Bell and
Antimonial Cup

XVII : FROM THE RESTORATION TO THE FIRE OF LONDON, 1660–6

THE king had been settled in Whitehall for ten weeks or so before the College took any official steps to celebrate his restoration. No doubt most of the fellows were loyal and even jubilant, but perhaps the new government made some enquiries, as other governments had done in critical times, into the political reliability of the fellows. Under the protectorate, whatever discontent individual fellows may have harboured, others had conformed. Some had sat in parliament.[1] The College as a body had prospered, and to some extent it had reflected credit on the unlawful régime. As it happened three of the fellows had been physicians to Oliver Cromwell himself, but of these Dr. Wright and Dr. Bathurst were already dead and the nimble George Bate made sure of his position in good time. He was present at the extraordinary *comitia majora* on 17 August 1660, when the president and twenty one fellows mustered to give expression to their joy and reverence. They wisely decided to make presents to the returned Osiris. Dr. Hamey took the lead. He had, the reader will remember, taken the Solemn League and Covenant, and he had added to his riches by practising throughout the troubles, not repelling the republican leaders.[2] He had prudently remitted cash by secret means to the exiled monarch. He now offered the College from his private collection the horn of a unicorn. The comitia at once accepted it as appropriate for the occasion; the president and consiliarii had it fitted with gold mountings, and on 3 September the king received the College. The lord chancellor, Sir Edward Hyde, introduced them; Dr. Alston made an elegant speech and the king knighted him on the spot. The unicorn's horn was then presented, and the king accepted it with a smile (*hilari vultu*). He may have been sceptical of its antitoxic powers, or he may have heard of

---

[1] Bathurst, Petty, Jonathan Goddard.
[2] His story, repeated, by Munk and Keevil, of the Puritan with the pox reads like a fairy-tale and in any case cannot have anything to do with Henry Ireton whose career was quite unlike that ascribed by Hamey to his patient.

the unicorn as an emblem of chastity.[1] In any case he closed the audience by promising his support for the medical art and for the College itself.

In the following summer the College set itself to improve the favourable opportunity for acquiring new privileges. Except for the disappearance of the court of star chamber and for minor changes, the public institutions with which it now had to deal were as they had been in the time of Charles I. The objective therefore was once again to petition for a charter. A committee of the consiliarii, the censors and two fellows began the work.[2] Its final outcome was the sealing of the charter on 26 March 1663.[3]

With a profuse expenditure of words this document confirms the powers of the College and tidies up its constitution. It changes the corporate name to 'the President Fellowes and Comonaltie of the Kings Colledge of Physitians in the Cittie of London', an enhancement of dignity.[4] It raises the number of fellows to forty. We might imagine that this change was a consequence of the growth in the number of practitioners in and about the City, but we shall find evidence that it had a different origin. An increase from thirty plus the royal physicians to forty all told was not large. The increase of the number of elects from eight to ten, which followed, was proportionately rather greater; it enlarged the body which elected the president, but perhaps it was also meant to strengthen the president's power among the fellows. Another addition was made to his power by giving a casting vote to him or the vice-president (as the pro-president was now called) in all elections or other proceedings. The power to expel, which the College had exercised and in which the court of king's bench had upheld it,[5] was now defined: the fellows were to be elected for life unless they were removed for evil government, for misbehaviour in their office or place, for non-residence without leave under the College seal or the king's

[1] At Windsor there was already the unicorn's horn brought back by Frobisher from his second voyage. Dr. Thomas Browne mentioned it in bk. iii, c. xxiii of his *Pseudoxia Epidemica*, and as this was published in 1646 the College in general probably had no illusions on the subject; but in 1661 the duke of Buckingham promised to bring the Royal Society a piece of unicorn's horn: Birch, *History of the Royal Society*, i (1756), 16.
[2] 25 June 1661.   [3] Text in Goodall, pp. 62–118.
[4] From the middle of the eighteenth century it has been the law that a corporation is not bound by a charter unless it accepts it, the authority quoted being R. *v.* University of Cambridge (1765), and further that it need not accept the charter as a whole but may pick and choose from its contents. See below p. 374 for the question whether the College accepted this charter of Charles II. For the inconsistent practice of the College in using the name 'Royal' see L. M. Payne in *British Medical Journal*, 1960, i. 123–4.
[5] See above, p. 288.

privy seal or for the like reasonable cause. That the privy seal was to give leave of absence was a sign that the College was not to be immune from interference from above, and it was not the only sign. The fellows were to take the several known oaths of allegiance and supremacy.[1] Since the early days of the College, the legal advisers of the Crown had often had to consider the means of controlling corporations, and no doubt it was they who now inserted the provision that there were to be four visitors of the College. They were to be the lord chancellor, the two lords chief justices and the chief baron of the exchequer, the successors of the high authorities to whom legal questions regarding the College had been referred in former times. Any two or more of the visitors might hear and determine appeals against any judgement, decree or sentence of the College. Though their other visitatorial powers were not specified, there were such, known to the common law. It would be an advantage to the College to have complaints against its decisions adjudicated upon by its own visitors instead of in the expensive and unpredictable courts of law.

There were several clauses which would conduce to more efficient working. No offender was to be charged when more than a year had passed since his offence. A 'court or convocation' was to have a quorum of fifteen, including the president or the vice-president. Every sentence was to be approved by the next court, and registered. The penalty for illicit practice was raised to £10 for each month. The list of practisers whom the College was to supervise was drawn amply, including all who sold anything that was to be used for medicines. The area of the College's jurisdiction was extended to seven miles from the city of Westminster as well as London, which took it further out to the west and north west and south west.[2] The number of bodies of criminals for dissection was raised to six. The value of land that might be held in mortmain was raised to £200 per annum. The right to grant licences to extra-licentiates was granted in terms which seemed to imply that neither the archbishop of Canterbury, nor the bishops, nor the universities had any such right. Not a word was said about any of them. On pain of a fine of £5 for every month all those who were desirous of practising then or thereafter 'in any parts of this our kingdom'

---

[1] See above, p. 240.
[2] In 1629 the area for the Barber Surgeons' Company had been given the same extent: earlier it was three miles.

outside the seven-mile limit were to be licensed by the president and elects or four of them. Nothing was done to clear up the obscure question of who exactly were the members of the College: so far as we know this question had never been raised within living memory or for long before it. The fellows were to be chosen out of the commonalty or members, and the College was to make wholesome and reasonable laws, orders and so forth for all other physicians as well as for the vendors of medicines. Another clause continued a principle first introduced in 1647. Except for the fines for illicit practice in town or country, all other money raised by fines was to be paid, after deducting the charges incurred in recovering them, to the poor of the respective parishes in which the offences were committed. The king promised his consent to an eventual Bill in parliament for confirming this charter.

As was usual the charter contained the names of the fellows. The first thirty-five of the forty call for no comment: they were the existing fellows and none was omitted. After them came five new names, and something must be said about each of these. The order in which they appear would presumably become the order of their seniority in the College. First was James Hide (or Hyde) who was to become regius professor of medicine in Oxford in 1665. Then came Humphrey Whitmore, an Oxford doctor experienced in practice, Robert Waller of Leiden and Cambridge, who had been admitted a candidate in 1653, and Peter Barwick a candidate since 1655 from Cambridge, who is said to have written in support of Harvey on the circulation. The last name was that of Robert Morison, a botanist of considerable note, who had taken his degree at Angers when he was a royalist refugee. This was a respectable list, and it looks as if pains had been taken to balance the claims of the two English universities. As was to be expected from the mood of the moment, the list was distinctly connected with the Restoration. Morison was a royal physician; Barwick's wife was a relation of Archbishop Laud, and his brother, the dean of St. Paul's, had been a daring agent of the king. What it was that specially recommended the other three we do not know, but it may well be that they were befriended by some of the officers through whose hands the charter passed on its way to sealing. In any case there was no precedent for such an influx of new fellows who were not examined and did not even produce certificates of their degrees. And, strange to say, Dr. Waller was the only one who came forward for admission in the ordinary way. Dr. Whitmore was made an honorary fellow in 1664, and Dr. Barwick came in as a royal physician in the following year, but Hide and Morison were never reckoned by the College among its members.

The list indeed had caused confusion. At the June comitia after the charter was received Dr. Timothy Clarke got up. He was a candidate, a year senior to Dr. Barwick. He made an angry speech in English, complaining that outsiders had been put over the heads of the seasoned candidates. Another of these, Dr. Burwell, briefly dissociated himself from this protest and said that it was for the elects and the fellows to rule, for the candidates and licentiates to obey. The president and Sir Francis Prujean rated the mutineers, and they withdrew defeated; but at Michaelmas they raised their point again. They were told that what had been done could not be undone; that the great business of the charter could not have been put through in any other way; that no precedent had been created for the future. Nevertheless they won. At an extraordinary meeting two days before the next Michaelmas comitia it was unanimously agreed that notwithstanding the statutory limitation of numbers six candidates should be admitted as fellows. In October, after some adjustment of numbers, actually seven were admitted of whom Dr. Clarke came first and the submissive Dr. Burwell second.[1]

In the meantime the charter had fared even worse out of doors. In the winter of 1663–4 the Bill for confirming it was duly carried to Westminster, and, since the charter of James I had never been confirmed by parliament, not only the new privileges were recited but those of 1617 as well. Nothing came of the Bill.[2] Its failure seems to have been accepted as irremediable, and the College behaved as if it had not accepted the charter. The number of elects was not increased; the new name of the College was only occasionally used; the extension of the seven-mile limit seems to have been a dead letter; the fines were not given to the poor. If the College accepted any of the provisions of the charter they were very few.

An incident followed which may or may not have had practical consequences, but which indicates a new attitude to professional standards. At the quarterly comitia in June 1664 Dr. Timothy Clarke came forward as the spokesman of all the candidates. He

[1] 20 October 1664.
[2] Abortive conferences (and plans for them) with the surgeons are mentioned on 29 April and 22 December 1663 and 4 April 1664, with the apothecaries on 29 April, 5 May and 22 December 1663, 4 April and 25 June 1664, but with no details.

complained strongly that the medical art and the dignity of the physicians were suffering at the hands of the apothecaries and, by way of remedy, he asked leave for himself and his associates to practise pharmacy, to prepare useful medicaments and to prescribe them. If he is correctly reported his third request was superfluous, for they could prescribe already; but the other two were revolutionary. For the physician to become his own dispenser was to depart from the immemorially received division of functions; it was to do something which the apothecaries could use as an accusation. The laboratory in the College had, to be sure, made a small departure from the old system; but it seems to have been limited to unusual preparations. For practitioners each to prepare his own medicines would be a direct threat to the apothecary's livelihood. The outcome shows what a degree of exasperation the College had reached. It resolved unanimously that it would redound to the honour of the College, to the advantage and security of the art and to the health and economy of the public if every candidate and licentiate prepared and compounded his own medicines. The candidates were thanked for their helpful advice.[1] In the nature of the case we cannot tell how many suited the action to the word; but it would appear that some at least took on this new and toilsome, if remunerated, work.[2] It was an untried weapon against the apothecaries, a declaration of unrestricted war. We may suspect that in the eyes of the public it blurred the contrast between the two sides in the contest. A physician who practised pharmacy needed strong arguments against an apothecary who practised medicine. They were both doing the same things except that the physician was supposed to dispense only for his own patients.[3]

The Apothecaries, who were advised by eminent counsel, seem to have behaved with moderation and good sense. When they first saw the draft charter they thought of an amendment by which the College should give due notice before carrying out its search; but they did not persist in this transparent attempt. They stated their objections to the proposals for an oath and penalties compelling

[1] 25 June 1664.
[2] Christopher Merret did so, either then or later: see below, p. 343.
[3] An able pamphlet of 1665, T.M., *A Letter concerning the Present State of Physick* advocates dispensing by physicians and urges the College to set up committees on anatomy, diseases and *materia medica*. It is specially interesting because it is written by a member of parliament who justifies the rejection of the College Bill. Of the three members with the initials T.M. the best known was Sir Thomas Myddleton, the son of the Sir Thomas mentioned on p. 240 above, and he may well be the author.

them to adhere to the *Pharmacopoeia* or the prescriptions of physicians. When the proceedings on the Bill began they proposed an amendment which would have satisfied both themselves and the surgeons, but the College would not accept it, and, although it was modified, it failed. When the Bill itself was dead and the College was understood to have no intention of reviving it, six months after its belligerent resolution, the Apothecaries proposed on 27 February 1664/5 that there should be a conference of three from their Company with three physicians. This was accepted: Dr. Micklethwaite, Dr. Wharton and Sir Richard Napier represented the College. The Apothecaries proposed that it should not accept as fellows, honorary fellows or licentiates any who kept apothecaries' shops. Here they were in a strong position, for unless this was granted the physicians could not logically justify the exclusion of shopkeepers from practice. The physicians on their side proposed that apothecaries should not practise and that they should give an assurance that they would prepare prescriptions faithfully. The negotiators made some progress towards agreement, and this seems to have been the one and only moment after 1614 when there was a chance of rebuilding amicable relations between the two bodies on the old foundations. But the work was not concluded when the plague broke out and the papers were put away. They were never used again.[1]

Until this time the College had been the only learned society in London or in England with a royal charter outside the universities. Its original purposes were professional and practical, but it consisted of learned men and they enjoyed learned intercourse within it. Its library, as we have seen, facilitated something of the sort for educated men in general. Its scope was not narrowly medical, and it was prized even by citizens who knew very little about it as an ornament to the City, a symbol of intellectual pursuits. Now the College ceased to be unique: the granting of the first charter of the Royal Society in 1662 set up another learned body beside it. Physicians indeed had a great share in the new foundation. They were the only students of any natural science who had any organization of their own. Since the new society confined itself to natural knowledge, leaving aside both theology and law, the physicians as a body had a higher academic standing than the rest of its members, and quite apart from their formal position, they provided

[1] Barrett, pp. 74–77. For a more detailed account see Underwood, pp. 345 ff.

it with some of its most active thinkers. Its birth is commonly and rightly dated from the meeting in Dr. Goddard's room at Gresham College on 28 November 1660, after Christopher Wren's regular weekly lecture on astronomy. This was the culmination of the groupings and regroupings of scientists in Oxford and London which we have already noticed. The twelve men who met decided to consolidate their ground, 'according to the Manner in other Countryes, where there were voluntary associations of men into Academies for the advancement of various parts of learning. So they might do something answerable here for the promoting of Experimentall Philosophy.'[1] Of these twelve Dr. Goddard and Dr. Petty were fellows of the College, Lord Brouncker had a medical degree.[2] When their society was fully constituted there were more than twenty physicians among its fellows, about a fifth of the whole number.

The Royal Society from the first was unlike the College in many ways. It had no jurisdiction and no administrative functions. Experiments were carried out and discussed in its meetings. It was three times as large, and this contributed to its prestige by making it known. It was not merely a learned body. Although it included most of the best English scientists and mathematicians of the time there were also a good number of fellows who were not scientists at all, such as political noblemen, engineers, shipbuilders, the poet Dryden and the journalist Sir John Birkenhead.[3] Any peer might become a member simply by paying his dues. This too gave it influence, and brought to bear on its early endeavours the force of many converging interests. It may be doubted whether the example of other countries contributed much to its constitution, but its outlook was European and there were eminent foreign scientists among its first members. Its legal form followed the same English tradition as that of the College: it was incorporated by charter. We may guess that the reason why the College of Physicians received the name of the King's College was that this put it on the same plane with the junior foundation.

There was never any formal negotiation to mark out spheres of influence between the two. To begin with they seem to have expected friendly co-operation. The Society looked forward to

---

[1] Journal-book of the Royal Society, i. 1, quoted by most of its historians.
[2] Wren was an anatomist among other things, but the first charter of the Royal Society seems to be mistaken in describing him as a doctor of medicine.
[3] See the annotated list by Dr. E. S. de Beer in *Bulletin of the Institute of Historical Research*, xiv (1937), 79 ff.

holding its meetings in the College, and in return it offered membership to the fellows of the College on similar terms to those for the
peers, though in the expectation that the former would carry out
'works or tasks' allotted to them.[1] In the first charter the Royal
Society was given the right to obtain the bodies of executed
criminals for dissections, on the same terms as the College and the
'Corporatio Chirurgorum'. In the winter of 1663-4 it acted on this
authority and Dr. Charleton conducted a dissection of a muscle,
with instruments bought for the purpose by the Society. Dr.
Goddard was made convener of a committee of physicians for
arranging similar demonstrations in the future, and later, on the
suggestion of Boyle, this committee was asked to prepare what we
should call a programme for anatomical research. In the following
spring the Society set up eight committees for different subjects, of
which one was the anatomical committee consisting of the great
men Boyle, Hooke and John Wilkins and all the physicians of the
Society. Sir George Ent became chairman, and the committee
arranged to meet twice a month at his house in the College. It
decided on three questions which were to be considered at the
next dissection of the Society, to be held at Gresham College. This
was organized research of a kind which the College of Physicians
had never undertaken, and showed no disposition to undertake.
Some of the fellows may well have scented encroachment; but there
was no excuse for obstruction, nor is there any evidence that it was
attempted. The College records do not once mention the Royal
Society; but there is at least one sign of friendly relations. The
committee for trades, of which Merret was a member, met in the
College building.[2]

There was never any quarrel. Some years later a pamphleteering bruiser called Henry Stubbe, who practised physic in Bath,
turned his mercenary pen against the Royal Society. Baldwin
Hamey was afterwards alleged to have been the paymaster because
it 'grieved him to foresee a Rival Society treading so close upon the
heels of the Aesculapians'. But if Hamey did this he did it privately
and on his own responsibility.[3] The College stood by silently

[1] Minutes of meeting of 12 December 1660 in *Record of the Royal Society*, 3rd edn.
(1912), p. 11.
[2] Minutes of the council and Society, 20 January 1663-12 October 1664 in Birch.
[3] For Stubbe and his controversies see the two articles of Miss R. H. Syfret in *Notes
and Records of the Royal Society*, vii. 207 ff. and viii 20 ff. (1950). That Stubbe sometimes hired out his pen is proved by the entries relating to his pamphlets in *Calendar
of State Papers, Domestic, 1672* and *1672-3*.

while the Royal Society conducted and published researches into many aspects of medical science, some of them deservedly famous. In 1668 John Locke, a physician and a close associate of Sydenham, became a fellow of the Royal Society. A generation later he stood as high in European reputation as the Society itself, but he was never admitted to the College of Physicians of London, and never sought admission or a licence for his occasional practice there.

The comprehensiveness of the Royal Society in the matter of membership may also have a bearing on a major innovation in the College, the broadening of its basis by the election of a large number of honorary fellows. For this, however, there were several reasons. When Lord Dorchester joined the College he was once incidentally referred to as an honorary fellow, but it was evidently not expected that others would be appointed and nothing was done to lay down the rights and obligations appertaining to this status. A few years later another election followed which was similar, though not identical, in character. Among the celebrities who came back to England from foreign parts at the Restoration were the inseparable friends Thomas Finch and Thomas Baines. They were both physicians but they did not practise, and they were on their way to places of dignity in the great world. They had links with Eliab Harvey, the richest and most influential of the Harvey brothers, and it was on account of the services rendered to it by Eliab and his ever-honoured brother William that the College elected Finch and Baines as fellows.[1] They were not called honorary fellows but are referred to once as extraordinary fellows. A few months after their admission they obtained the leave of the College when they went abroad again[2]; but except for that their position was much like Dorchester's. They were not examined and they were supernumerary to the fixed establishment of fellows, two departures from the statutes which amounted to a relaxation, if only a slight relaxation, of the old standards. Four fellows went so far as to cast negative votes, and the minute laid it down that this election was not easily to create a precedent.

The thin end of the wedge was now in the crack. At the special comitia when Finch and Baines were admitted as fellows Dr. Baber, who had just then been appointed a physician to the king,

---

[1] 26 February 1660/1: this entry is given in full by Munk. For the lives of these two remarkable men see A. Malloch, *Finch and Baines* (1917).
[2] 30 September 1661.

asked whether the College was willing to admit Dr. William Quartermaine as an honorary fellow. This was a different sort of case, but it had obvious attractions. Quartermaine was a Cambridge doctor and he had passed his first two examinations for candidate; no doubt he would have passed his third if he had not gone to sea. For the present, however, his case was deferred, and it never had to be decided in this form because he too became a royal physician and was admitted as such.[1] For three years nothing more is recorded about honorary fellowships; but then a special meeting passed a resolution which prepared the way for creating them on a larger scale and for two quite new reasons. In order to repair the finances of the College and to strengthen its authority it was decided to co-opt (*adsciscere*) grave and learned men holding the degree of doctor, under the title of honorary fellows. There were in London numerous medical doctors, the resolution explained, who were suitable in age, in character, and in their reputation as men and scholars but to whom it would appear a hardship to undergo a public examination. All men of this stamp were to be eligible as honorary fellows by a majority vote in the comitia majora and were then to enjoy the licence to practise in the City and suburbs and all the other privileges of fellows.[2]

These read like wise words. All through the century there had been worthy men who had been excluded from the narrow circle of the fellows, and whose resentment might well have been charmed away by such liberality as this. The elder Baldwin Hamey, whose son was now an elect and consiliarius, could have taken advantage of it; perhaps too Dr. Bonham of painful memory. The number of such men had grown with the growth of London, and so had the difficulty of enforcing the old rigid rules against them.[3] If the new resolution was generous, it also meant that the College was facing facts. To be sure it departed from tradition so abruptly that difficulties of one sort or another would inevitably arise. Curiously enough we hear nothing about the greatest of these difficulties until ten years later,[4] and of the minor obstacles which the College foresaw we have

---

[1] 1 March 1660/1, 20 September 1661; but the latter entry only says that he was unanimously admitted a fellow, and it seems that on 22 December 1663 the king wrote to the president recommending him for the precedence due to a royal physician: *Cal. of State Papers Domestic 1663–1664* (1862), p. 95.
[2] 1 September 1664.
[3] As before the numbers in London and Paris seems to move roughly on parallel lines. Raynaud, pp. 20–21 calculates that in Paris in 1640–70 there were about 110 physicians to 540,000 inhabitants.   [4] See below, p. 340.

only a puzzling glimpse. When the special comitia met to pass a statute regarding honorary fellows and to approve the form of their oath of admission, a rumour was already circulating in Oxford and Cambridge that the College was about to do something which would infringe the privileges of the universities. This was indeed a reasonable inference from the licensing clause in the new charter; but not from the new proposal. Latin letters were drafted, and fellows were deputed to carry them and explain, the sociable Dr. Whistler for Cambridge, Dr. Stanley and Sir Edward Greaves for Oxford. The letters were not to be delivered immediately and for weighty but unspecified reasons they never were delivered: it seems from the later course of events that the murmurs in Oxford and Cambridge died down.[1]

The form of the honorary fellows' oath, which follows *mutatis mutandis* the relevant parts of the fellows' and candidates' oaths, shows that they were to have no part in the jurisdiction or elections of the College, but they were to have access to the statutes.[2] They were to be bound by suitable general promises of loyalty and by some specific obligations. When necessary they were to join with the fellows and candidates in contributing money. They were not publicly to carry out or to announce any dissection of the human body in London or within seven miles except in the College or in a place assigned by the president and elects: which may imply that the College was jealous of other competitors in anatomy besides the Barber-Surgeons.[3] They were to make no contracts for dividing money-receipts with apothecaries. They were to have no intercourse with empirics nor with any others not approved by the College. Their deportment in consultations was prescribed, with explanations, though much more briefly than in the corresponding statute for the fellows. They were to pay an entrance fee of £20.[4]

The first list of honorary fellows is full of surprises. It may not include only those who adhered at the first opportunity, but it seems to have been completed within a few months.[5] There is nothing to show whether the College invited them to join or left it to them to apply, nor whether any were unwilling whom it would

[1] 16 September 1664, with texts of the draft letters.   [2] Text in Underwood, p. 353.
[3] There is nothing to show whether the Royal Society or private teachers or both were in mind.
[4] December 1664. Westminster is not mentioned in the reference to the geographical limit.
[5] Dates of degrees are not given for the last eleven names and universities for only four of them, so that these names seem to have been later additions.

have accepted. In any case it is a long list; there are seventy-three names. All except a few paid their fee, so we may reckon that they handed in something like £1,400, in addition to which they jointly presented a cup valued at £100 and entertained the College, with some guests from outside, to a magnificent banquet. The plan certainly succeeded in its first purpose of recruiting the finances. But the list is not entirely made up of London residents fitted for membership of the College by seniority. It has no consistent arrangement, and unfortunately little is known about some of the names and nothing at all about two or three, but here and there a group come together who seem to be connected by some common characteristic. The first name of all is that of John Frear of Huntingdonshire, the son and the grandson of two catholic fellows of the College, who took his Padua degree more than fifty years before, and doubtless would have been a fellow if he could have taken the oaths of allegiance and supremacy. Freedom from this obligation opened the door to catholics. Since they were to exercise no public function and the atmosphere at court was favourable to them the College no doubt thought that this would not provoke any objections from the state. There seem to have been other catholics in the list, two court physicians[1] and probably others.[2] Six either then or later held royal appointments. It is known of a few that they practised in London, but there are so many obscure names that it is impossible to assess the proportion of this element to the whole number.[3] On the other hand there are several of whom it is certain that they practised not in London but in the provinces, and it seems likely that this must be true of a good many others. The third name in the whole list is that of the most famous English provincial practitioner of the seventeenth, indeed of any century, and it seems to be presented as the name of a great man, for the registrar did not set down this man's university and the date of his degree as he did for all the others down to the sixty-second: he simply wrote the name of Dr. Thomas Browne.

[1] Sir Theodore de Vaux and Dr. William Waldegrave.
[2] Walter Needham afterwards enjoyed the favour of King James II and may well have been a catholic: see below, n. 3. Munk identifies the Robert Bidgood of the present list with John Bidgood. If the identification is correct the same is true of him. Aaron Gourdan or Goorden, a doctor of Rheims, fought shy of the oath on 7 November 1640.
[3] Gourdan, Diodati, Burnet, Argell and Needham certainly, Timme, Gelsthorp, Glover, Clarke and others probably practised in London. Burnet had been rejected on his third examination in August 1650: Brit. Mus. MS. Sloane 3914 fo. 31 c.

It is not surprising that the College paid attention to the provinces; indeed it had been slow to do so. The discovery of England
had gone forward steadily throughout the century, and its pace had
been accelerated by all the comings and goings of the years of
disturbance. Several of the more active fellows had travelled up and
down the kingdom and had become aware at first hand of the
increased numbers and improving status of the provincial physicians.
There are two kinds of provincial practitioners in the list, country
doctors and university doctors. From Oxford there was Sir Richard
Napier, and three Oxford doctors who are named together later on
may well have been university residents at this time. One of the
three certainly was still there, Thomas Willis, who was already
rising into European reputation. The Cambridge regius professor,
Francis Glisson, was already a fellow, but his brother Henry appears in this list. It seems that the universities did not interpret the
creation of honorary fellows from the provinces as a preliminary
to the licensing of foreign doctors to compete with their own licentiates. There may even have been some understanding that the
College would not exercise its provincial jurisdiction. The return
of the bishops had restored the old licensing machinery, and,
whether for this or for some other reason, the number of extra-
licences granted by the College, after rising sharply in 1661–4
declined after that to something like its old very low level.[1]

By adding all these men to its nominal membership the College
gained friends who were committed to supporting its influence and
reputation and also to conformity with its ethical standards where
these were stricter than those of other physicians. Those who lived
in London received a licence to practise there, with an indefinite
promise of other privileges, which can scarcely have meant more
than the right to use the College buildings and attend lectures.
Although they were apparently not to pay any annual fee, their
entrance fee was far higher than that of candidates or licentiates,
and clearly what they paid for was an honour, a distinction. It is

[1] The numbers are

1631–9	5	
1640–2	9	Cessation of episcopal licensing.
1643–6	nil	Civil War.
1647–51	3	
1651–9	10	Protectorate.
1660–4	21	Restoration, &c.
1665	2	Plague.
1666	nil	Fire of London.

Another sustained increase began in 1674.

an important fact in the history of the College that it was sufficiently strong and respected to be able to confer an honorary title on which the recipients and the public set such a value. The price was certainly not excessive: the right to wear a scarlet gown cost several times as much. In 1691 (when there had been no marked change in the value of money) an extra-licentiate who had been in good practice for eight years or so journeyed to Oxford from Somerset to take his doctor's degree: the main fee was £56 12s. and the entire expedition cost him more than £92.[1] But did the College lose nothing by its action? It did give a little more impetus to a change in its purposes of which there were other manifestations about this time, not all of them wholesome. It associated its new blood-brothers not with its work but with its social enjoyments. That, however, was no great matter. It would be much more serious if we had to judge that the College was derogating from its strict standards of fitness to practise. The examination system may have been misguided and by this time the curriculum was at least obsolescent; but it was administered strictly. The honorary fellows escaped examination. For them the only prescribed test was the production of a degree certificate.[2] A majority vote in comitia did not provide any security against the defects of foreign and even English degree-examinations which had distressed the College when it framed and revised its statutes from 1585 to 1647. The flag was no longer flying high.

Whether the College made serious efforts to re-assert its authority within the seven-mile limit seems uncertain, and there were obstacles in the way. Generally speaking the medical profession settled down quickly in the mutual reconciliation, such as it was, of the national parties; but the national unity was restored on certain conditions which were comparatively rigid, and some of these had a bearing on the structure of the profession for rather more than two centuries to come. First of all the archbishop of Canterbury and the bishops were restored to their old functions. Episcopal licensing began again, as we have seen, and a few clergymen received licences. At least in some parts of the country, the

---

[1] *The Diary of a West Country Physician A.D. 1684-1726*, ed. by E. Hobhouse (1934), pp. 147–8.
[2] That the certificates were produced may be inferred from a small detail: for the two graduates of Rheims, but only for them, the dates of their degrees are given in the Roman form by Kalends and Ides.

bishops seem to have licensed more physicians than ever before.[1] Whether they accounted for a larger proportion of the whole number, or merely had a share in the general increase of numbers cannot be decided from the facts which have hitherto been published. The Church did not confine its interest in medicine to licensing. In 1665 Archbishop Sheldon asked all the bishops for returns of the names, degrees and qualifications of all practisers of physic, their places of residence, whether they were licensed and by whom and how they appeared to be affected to the government and to the doctrine and discipline of the Church of England.[2]

Other measures concerning the relations of church and state had an indirect effect on the College. Subscription to the formularies of the Church of England was already a condition of taking a degree at Oxford or Cambridge so that Roman Catholics and protestant nonconformists could neither study medicine there nor incorporate on degrees from continental or Scottish universities. Thus they could not become fellows of the College. The College statute excluding those who were only graduates of other universities was rescinded in 1834; but the exclusion from Oxford and Cambridge lasted unaltered until the eighteen-fifties. The church settlement of 1662 closed their doors to many holders of opinions which had previously been permissible there. Another consequence of the Act was that nearly a thousand clergymen had to vacate their livings, in addition to several hundred who had already gone. Out of this number fifty-nine took to the practice of medicine. Some of the younger and abler started at the bottom and qualified in the regular way. Of these there were several who ultimately became fellows of the College, two of whom, Edward Hulse and Richard Morton rose very high in the profession. Some received episcopal or university licences. The rest joined the ranks of the intelligent amateurs, who were still not undeservedly respected in out-of-the-way places.[3] There were eminent men to keep them in countenance by giving advice though they did not practise for fees, such as the Puritan leader Richard Baxter and the scientist Robert Boyle.

In one instance the College was unable to overcome the legacy of hatred from the Civil War. Among the rising physicians of

[1] See E. H. Carter, *The Norwich Subscription Books, 1637–1800* (1937), especially pp. 6, 136, 140. Lists of those who subscribed to the oaths may include some who were licensed not by the bishop but by other authorities.

[2] R. R. James in *Janus*, xli (1936), 97 ff.

[3] A. G. Matthews, *Calamy Revised* (1934), p. lvi, and the biographies in the volume.

London was Thomas Sydenham, an Oxford bachelor of medicine, who had begun practice there in 1655 and broken it off to study at Montpellier. In 1663 he was examined three times in the ordinary way and admitted as a licentiate. After that his name occurs only once in the College Annals during his lifetime. In 1687, two years before he died, he had to apply, in accordance with a recent change in the law, for the permission of the College to issue a second edition of one of his books. By that time he was not only the leading English physician and the leading English medical writer, but in reputation throughout the world he stood second only to Harvey. He did not make his application in person but sent his publisher with a copy of the book. The president and censors expressed themselves as more than willing to grant the application, but they applied their rule by which the censors must read the text. The president was Dr. Charleton, whose best-known literary work was a proof that Stonehenge was built by the Danes.[1]

Sydenham was a Dorset gentleman. All of his brothers who grew to manhood served in the parliamentary forces in the Civil War. Two of them were killed, and their mother was murdered, it was believed by a royalist major. One brother survived the war and was reputed a dangerous man. It seems that Thomas Sydenham himself served and fought in the army,[2] but there are many uncertainties about his military and also about his civilian career. He was intruded as a fellow of All Souls by the parliamentary visitors after they had purged the college; but, for reasons unknown, he resigned his fellowship long before the Restoration. Somewhere in his history as a young man lies the reason why he took no doctor's degree until he was over fifty and was thus ineligible to be a candidate or a fellow of the College. The College may or may not have come to regret that he was ineligible; Sydenham may or may not have been contented with the status of a licentiate, which was all that his son after him enjoyed; but Amen Corner was no longer the meeting place of all the wisest physicians of London.[3]

[1] 7 October 1687. The censors were Barwick, Elliot, Pitt and Bateman; Burwell, the registrar, was present.
[2] His name has not been found by the exhaustive study of army-lists for Sir Charles Firth, *Cromwell's Army*, 2 vols. (1940). The only definite evidence seems to be that of his petition of 8 March 1653/4: *Cal. of State Papers Domestic, 1654* (1880), p. 14.
[3] The evidence of Andrew Broun, *Vindicatory Schedule* (1691) cannot be accepted without some correction. He does not understand (p. 80) that the College approved the second and not the first edition of the *Schedula Monitoria*, merely because it was after the publication of the first that it became the licensing authority, and he seems to be

The prospects for carrying on the ordinary business of the College were not altogether unfavourable. In 1664 it received a token of confidence in the bequest of £250 from the merchant druggist Francis Tryon. With part of this money it was to purchase a rent-charge of £10 a year. Whenever there was a vacancy for a physician at St. Bartholomew's, St. Thomas's or Bethlem Hospital, the president and elects were to submit two names to the governors and if either of the two was chosen he was to receive the £10 as a contribution to his stipend, not an augmentation. Unless and until such an election was made the £10 was to be shared out equally between the four censors. The balance of the £250 after buying the rent-charge (that is £50) was to be disposed of at the discretion of Dr. Hamey. Tryon hoped that others would follow his example, and after a lapse of years Dr. Hamey did so himself; but, as we shall find, the hospitals did not yield to the temptation to surrender their control over their own appointments. They were on the threshold of a new phase of their history which was also a new phase in the history of medical teaching and organization. It was in 1662 that members of the staff of St. Bartholomew's instructed pupils there, an example followed at St. Thomas's by 1695, and so there began, in the capital which had no university, the English tradition of clinical teaching in the hospital wards. So far as can be known the College was not consulted and expressed no opinion. As it had never been responsible for medical education before admission to practice, it probably took no interest in the whole matter. Dr. Micklethwaite, who was physician to St. Bartholomew's and in 1644 Gulstonian lecturer, cannot have seen any reason for troubling the comitia with it.

So little is recorded about the judicial functions of the College in the years after the Restoration that in all probability they were not exercised with any vigour. There was a grave charge against an unlicensed practitioner and one, less grave, against an apothecary, but they were not followed up.[1] The apprentices came to the College in due succession to become apothecaries. Only one matter was referred to the College by a public authority. One Eustace Burnaby had invented a method of preparing French and pearl barley, which

wrong on other points; but he knew Sydenham and I find it impossible to disregard the allegation that there was an attempt to banish him from the College 'as guilty of Medicinal *heresie*' (p. 83).

[1] 2 November and 7 December 1660; 24 March 1661/2.

was expected to be useful in the American plantations. The attorney general sent him to the College, which gave its approval, and he got his patent for fourteen years; but this was no great compliment to the College, for the question whether it was a new invention was also referred to the Apothecaries' Company, and, it would appear, to some druggists and grocers.[1] The expelled fellow Peter Chamberlen the third was busily petitioning for patents for his own inventions but the College heard nothing of them.[2] The College made some progress, but very little, towards fulfilling an ambition in which it did not succeed for the present: in an abortive draft Bill for the licensing of the press it was proposed that the College should be sole censors of books on Physic.[3] There was in fact no business of any importance until the spring of 1665 when the tranquillity was broken by a most gratifying ceremonial occasion.

On 15 April in that year the College was honoured by its first royal visit. It was indeed high time that the king came to see his College in person; he had twice proposed to visit the Royal Society and, though he never carried out this intention, he had given the newer foundation unmistakable signs of his favour. If he owed amends to the elder sister he paid in the most gracious way that could be imagined. The anatomical praelector for the year was George Ent, the friend of Harvey. At his third and final lecture in the Harveian Museum the king was present. The president, Sir Edward Alston, expressed the gratitude of the College. So did the lecturer, on whom the king conferred the honour of knighthood there and then.

This was the happy prelude to years of disaster. The second Dutch war had begun already, and the king sent the lord mayor a letter to remind him of the exemption of the College from watch and ward[4]; but a worse enemy was in the field. This was the year when the last and greatest London epidemic of the plague began. In May the privy council asked the College once more to prescribe precautions and remedies, which it did, printing its advice and sending copies in the hands of suitable deputations to the council and the lord mayor. It also advised that special physicians, surgeons and apothecaries should be appointed for plague-patients.[5] By June the gravity of the emergency was evident, and the College

[1] 26, 30 September 1662; *Cal. of State Papers, Domestic, 1661–9662* (1861), p. 506.
[2] Ibid. *1665–1666* (1864).   [3] Ibid. *1661–1662* (1861), p. 45.
[4] 26 June 1665. In this war, as in the preceding and following Dutch wars, the physicians and the surgeons worked well together.   [5] 17 May.

nominated eight physicians of whom the lord mayor appointed two, Dr. Hodges, a candidate, and Dr. Witherley, an honorary fellow.[1] They stayed and did their duty, and all survived. Nathaniel Hodges earned much honour both for his services and for the books in which he published his observations. But, like the prosperous inhabitants who provided their livelihood, a good many physicians took the only certain precaution: they retired to the country. Dr. Micklethwaite, who was physician to St. Bartholomew's incurred reproach for deserting his post; but others were not ashamed of going.[2]

These plague-years saw the culmination and the collapse of a movement against the College which broke off short when it came to action, but made a considerable stir in its earlier phase of print. From an early date in the history of the College there had been books and pamphlets in which physicians or their methods were satirized or defended, but it was not until the Restoration period that the College itself became a subject for authors and pamphleteers. This was due less to any change in the College than to the rise of pamphleteering and of a public which provided it with an audience.[3] First in this field was Marchamont Nedham, the first journalist who influenced English public opinion by newspaper articles. We have come across his paper *Mercurius Politicus* already.[4] It was the official newspaper of the Protectorate, and the Restoration temporarily shut the editor out of political activity. After fleeing the country and returning with a pardon he set up in medical practice near Temple Bar, having made some sort of study of physic in his young days. In 1665 he published his *Medela Medicinae*, in which he attacked the College and complained of the neglect of chemistry for anatomy. According to Nedham four champions were set on by the College to reply. This seems to be quite untrue, but four

[1] 12 June: Wyberd, Conyers, Brooke, Hodges, Deantry, Davies, Harrison, Witherley.
[2] Writers who mention their own flight are Sydenham, who was not wanting in courage, and George Castle, who departed from a provincial town (not named) where he was then practising. In the anonymous and duplicated but not printed catalogue of an exhibition in the College on 7 April 1952, Commander J. J. Keevil gives a valuable study of the whole question, concluding that at least 24 physicians remained in the City of whom 17 were already fellows of the College or were elected later.
[3] C. Merret, *Collection of Acts of Parliament, Charters, Trials at Law and Judges' opinions concerning Grants made to the College of Physicians* (1660), was not a published pamphlet but a work of reference privately printed for the use of the College. The title-page says that it was commanded by Sir Edward Alston and he is sometimes mistakenly credited with having compiled it.
[4] See above, p. 287.

replies there were. The first two were by a recently elected fellow, John Twysden, and a candidate, Robert Sprackling, the third by George Castle, who was not a member but dedicated his little book to Dr. Millington, his colleague as a fellow of All Souls, where Nedham had once been a chorister. The fourth was the *Vindiciae Medicinae et Medicorum* of good Dr. Nathaniel Hodges. Thus in two years the public became accustomed to reading about the College and this sort of commentary was a normal accompaniment of its existence for the next two centuries.

This publicity made the College to some degree sensitive to the opinion of some people outside, though who they were and to what degree their opinion made itself effective would be hard to say. The pamphlets are interesting for many incidental touches which give colour and detail to our picture of medical life; but few of them are worth reading for their literary quality, and most of them re-iterate, with more or less of learned citation, well-worn arguments on one side or the other of three of four simple controversies. The first line of argument against the College was that it was too con-servative, that the fellows did not keep up with the new medical knowledge or with new diseases and supposed new phases of old diseases like the scurvy. To this its defenders had their choice of two lines of defence. They could praise the achievements of the College itself in investigation, or they could admit that they were conservative and justify themselves. George Castle showed himself well-read in the modern authors, including Descartes, and criticized Nedham's views about modern diseases acutely; he also stated the conservative case with candid common sense. Even if the superstructure were demolished, he wrote, there were many rules of the art which would remain as unshaken foundations because they were not based on any hypothesis contrived by human brains. It was much easier to prove the efficacy of mithridate, treacle and diascordium than to give the true reason of their composition. Improvements in the theory of physic had not much altered practice: the indications for purging, for instance were founded not on the notion of the four humours, but upon long observation. So were most of the doctrines of the therapeutic part of physic: 'We know the Ligature in letting of blood was alwayes used by the Chyrurgions, though the reason of it was never understood before the circulation was discovered.'[1]

[1] *The Chymical Galenist* (1667), especially pp. 127, 141, 196.

The second main line of attack was against the tests of competence. Nedham, being not only an empiric but also an experienced if inconstant champion of political freedom, wanted physic to be a free profession, and he generalized stoutly: 'If any Society of men be armed with power to regulate, censure or suppress whom and what they please, the most ingenious Labourers must be left to the mercy of others less laborious and be discouraged, or condemned, as others have been before them, if it please their Infallible Masters.'[1] The answer was repeated with many variations, of which two deserve mention. Occasionally there is an appeal to foreign examples, but only by way of mentioning some recent measure of a well-governed country, not a systematic proof that no civilized country gives unlimited freedom to practise.[2] More frequently the defence of the closed profession passes over into the argument that a liberal education, or in other words a university education based on the classics, makes the best physicians. Now that this idea has sunk into almost complete discredit, it is necessary to point out that in those days, although no one perhaps gave it adequate expression or freed it from its look of arrogance, it was on the whole true. When wide questions of public policy arose in connexion with epidemics, or when general supervision was needed for the surgeons and apothecaries of the fighting services, physicians were called in.[3] They gave as good advice as was to be had, and they were better able than their less literate allies to put their opinions down on paper and do business with the courtiers and politicians. Their writings do show a wider view and a greater power of systematic thought than can fairly be attributed to their critics; some of them even show a receptivity to new ideas.[4]

It seems to have been at the beginning of the year 1665, several months before the alarm of the coming plague (which everyone

---

[1] *Medela*, pp. 272/8.

[2] N. Hodges, *Vindiciae Medicinae et Medicorum* (1665), pp. 16 ff. gives some recent edicts promulgated in Brussels.

[3] Their position is neatly defined in the case of Dr. Hans Sloane, when he sailed in 1687 as physician to the West Indies fleet: 'the surgeons of all the ships must be ordered to obey his directions': Sir Gavin de Beer, *Sir Hans Sloane and the British Museum* (1953), p. 31.

[4] The other replies to Nedham are R. Sprackling, *Medela Ignorantiae* (1665) and J. Twysden, *Medicina Veterum Vindicata* (1666). Both Nedham and Twysden contributed further to the controversy and in 1676 Twysden's brother Sir Thomas, as a justice in the court of king's bench gave judgement against Nedham in an action against the College: Goodall, p. 273, Annals (without date), 1684.

knew to be a hot weather disease) that Nedham and some other introchemists set about forming a society. One of them, one of the self-taught practitioners and writers of pamphlets advertising their authors and decrying the Galenists, was an Irishman, Thomas O'Dowde. His services and sufferings in the cause of the late king had not been sufficiently rewarded to content him, but he was one of the grooms of the chamber to the king, and so had access to people about the court. It seems to have been largely through his activity that an imposing list of signatures was appended to a short and general statement which promised countenance and support for the proposed incorporation of a noble society for the advancement of hermetic physic. The list was headed by Archbishop Sheldon, and there were thirty-seven other names, nearly all of them names that carried weight. The proposal itself was much less impressive. It accused the College, without naming it, of maliciously and ignorantly hindering the general understanding of chemical medicine, and it announced the intention of applying for a charter. What the new society was to do was indicated only in the vaguest terms: it was to be 'capable of such Constitutions and Discipline, as shall answer the ends herein propounded.' Thirty-five names followed, the first being that of an expelled fellow of the College, William Goddard. Several of the other signatories were doctors of medicine, but among the rest only two or three were equal in distinction to Nedham and O'Dowde.[1]

Before the month of May some of these promoters appeared before the privy council. Though Nedham claimed that ear was given to them with princely grace, which seems to imply that the king was there, they got no charter and the proceedings were not so much as mentioned in the council's register. Nevertheless on 28 June the Society of Chemical Physicians published a broadsheet advertising their medicines prepared 'in pursuance of his Majesties Command, For the *Prevention*, and for the *Cure* of the PLAGUE'. Whether they meant some specific, perhaps oral command, addressed to them, must remain in doubt: there is no trace of such a command in writing. But the body of the broadsheet destroys their

---

[1] It is unnecessary to give any references for this and the two following paragraphs except to Sir Henry Thomas, 'The Society of Chymical Physitians, an Echo of the Great Plague of London, 1665' in *Science, Medicine and History*, ed. E. A. Underwood (1953), ii. 56 ff. This witty and learned article deals with the bibliography of the subject with masterly neatness, but its conclusions are vitiated by the assumption that the Helmontians represented scientific progress and the College, 'the closed shop'.

claim to public gratitude. It states that, as the plague has increased in spite of the use of Galenic medicines, they have held several meetings and devised medicines appropriate to the present pest; but instead of publishing the recipes as the College had already done for its own remedies, some of which were chemical, it merely gave the names of eight 'doctors' and the addresses where they would sell their preparations, with directions how to use them 'at reasonable Rates'. William Goddard, Everard Manwaring and George Thompson had a right to the title of doctor, but Nedham, O'Dowde and perhaps all of the other four had assumed it, as they maintained with a perfect right.[1] They had the courage of their delusions; but one of the victims of the plague was Thomas O'Dowde.

It may be that but for the plague the society would have become a rival to the College,[2] but it seems unlikely. Its influential supporters melted away. Its own members quarrelled and accused one another. The College as a body took no notice of it. Mr. Johnson, the chemical operator at Amen Corner did indeed launch a pamphlet against it, and no doubt some of the fellows knew what he was doing; but the hermetics' attack was misdirected. The College was no longer inaccessible to arguments in favour of chemical medicines, and the society had few or none of the elements of permanence.

There was no meeting of the comitia between the quarter day in June 1665 and 17 March 1665/6. Dr. Christopher Merret, the keeper of the library and the museum, who had living quarters rent free in the College buildings, was one of those who sought safety by leaving London. Dr. Hamey, the treasurer, had foreseen danger to the possessions of the College, and (apparently while Dr. Merret was still there with his household) had persuaded the College to have its silver plate and its cash, including most of that paid in by the honorary fellows, locked in an iron safe, about a thousand pounds worth altogether. It was all stolen; no one knows by whom.

In the spring the plague was waning and the College met six months late to elect a president: it met six strong. At the June comitia twenty-seven gathered, Merret among them. In July some business was done. An elect was needed in the place of Sir Francis

---

[1] One of them, Thomas Williams, may be the extra-licentiate of that name, who practised medicine and surgery at Eltham in 1659/60.

[2] This is the view of A. Huyberts, *The Corner-Stone* (1670), p. 19: see below, p. 341, n. 7.

VII. The Mace (1684) and the Common Chest

Prujean, who had died, and in order to admit Sir Alexander Frazier to this office the statute was altered which excluded all but Englishmen.[1] Then came an unprecedented resolution showing both the loyalty and the alarms of the fellows: as a voluntary contribution for the war they would provide *arma*, weapons and perhaps defensive armour, not for their own use but to be available for others whenever they were needed.[2] That was all the business and there was no dinner that summer.[3] Then came the final blow, the great fire of London. It began down by the river on 2 September. As it spread on the following days Dr. Merret and the beadle did what they could. They removed some of the treasures to places of safety, the charters, the four volumes of Annals, the insignia of the president, a case of surgical instruments, the memorial inscription to Harvey, the portraits of Harvey and Foxe, and about 140 volumes from the library. On the fourth day the fire reached the College. The buildings and everything in them were destroyed.

[1] 12, 17, 26 July 1666.   [2] 12 July.
[3] Dr. Wharton paid £20 to be let off, 25 June.

XVIII : FROM THE FIRE TO THE
POPISH PLOT, 1666–79

IT took the College twelve years to provide itself with a new home that it could be proud of. No time was lost in the first days of the disaster: twenty-one fellows met with the president in comitia on 1 October. The president, Sir Edward Alston, had a friend called Sir John Langham, a Turkey merchant, a City alderman and a baronet, to one of whose sons he gave his eldest daughter in marriage. On this day and on many others afterwards the College met in Langham's house; there were other days when it gathered, especially for *comitia minora* in the house of one or other of the fellows.

There were three possibilities: to rebuild on the old site, to build elsewhere or to buy some existing building.[1] The first was not so easy as it sounded. The old buildings were held on a forty-years lease from the dean and chapter of St. Paul's, which had only run for four years. St. Paul's would not sell a freehold site, but they could give a lease either of the old site or a new one. If the College were to build at its own expense it would need a fairly long tenure: it seemed reasonable to both sides that the old lease should be prolonged by four years. But St. Paul's had been burnt down too, and many of its papers had been destroyed. Among them were promises made before the fire by prospective donors towards the restoration of the dilapidated old cathedral. The dean and chapter thought the College had promised something, and made it a condition of prolonging the lease that it should renew its promise. There was no such promise. Dr. Hamey had actually given £100 and Sir Francis Prujean had bequeathed £50, but in its corporate capacity the College had done nothing, nor was it willing to do more than collect voluntary subscriptions from its members. That, however, satisfied the churchmen, but somehow the chance of staying on the old excellent site slipped by; the dean and chapter resumed possession and used the site to build houses for the canons, whose successors still reside there.[2]

---

[1] 25 June, 30 September, 23 December 1667.
[2] 11 September, 26 October, 12 November 1668. A curiosity of the lease of 1662 is that part of the consideration was free medical advice previously given and to be given by the fellows to the dean and chapter: Underwood, p. 353, n. 19.

The College was still to have legal business over surrendering its lease, but even before this began there was a new muddle. Sir Edward Alston, when he was president, had managed to commit the College to buying an unsuitable piece of ground in Cannon Street. At the cost of £150 paid to the sellers, some fees to the lawyers, and amused exasperation among the fellows, this mistake was undone.[1] In the spring of 1669 another offer was rejected, this time of a site in Warwick Lane, further east than the old College and even closer to St. Paul's. Beside this, however, was another site which gave satisfaction and, hesitating to the last minute, the College bought this from Mr. Hollier, lithotomist to St. Bartholomew's, for £1,200.[2] Here it was to be seated until 1825. It seems that no one at any stage suggested moving further west. The westward movement of the well-to-do had already begun. The great rebuilding after the fire carried it further and a few of the fellows moved into the new streets of Bloomsbury and Westminster. One honorary fellow, the versatile Dr. Nicholas Barbon was financially interested in developing Soho. The physicians could hardly have foreseen that the City would cease to be the main sphere of their work and become a frontier region separating the London and Westminster of fashion from the wharves and mean streets of the East End. 'City business' indeed continued to be very profitable all through the eighteenth century, though the fellows moved westwards one by one. For the present they remained in the neighbourhood of Gresham College and of municipal bustle and prosperity. As the new halls of the City Companies rose from the ashes the physicians expressed emulous and even envious feelings at the proud palace of the Apothecaries at Blackfriars and the magnificent theatre of the Barber-Surgeons in Monkwell Street.[3]

Sordid as it is to think about money, the College condescended to do it, and did it to some purpose. At a very early stage the fellows made written promises to subscribe greater or smaller sums, and these were renewed when the work had to be taken in hand.[4] It was no small matter to collect all the money due from this source; it was only fair to call in arrears of payments for dinners and to give the honorary fellows and the candidates the opportunity of

[1] 11, 30 September, 18, 27 November, 22 December, 3 February 1668/9.
[2] 5, 23, 28 April 1669. Mrs. Hollier, presumably then a widow, extorted a further £20 on 25 June 1672.
[3] College appeal for funds, composed by the registrar Dr. Daniel Whistler, 30 September 1674.   [4] 25 June 1668, 28 April 1669.

sharing compulsorily in the good work. The pressure was maintained until 1677, by which time it had yielded £4697.[1] In addition to this the dean and chapter paid £550 for the remainder of the lease of the old College.[2] While the buildings were actually going up some parts of them had to be financed in another way. Besides the public rooms there were to be several residential houses, the largest of which was to be occupied by one of the fellows. Sir George Ent generously came forward. He paid for the building of the house; the College then leased it to him for sixty-one years, during which time it was to pay £54 a year, less £20 a year ground-rent, so that at the end of the time the house would become its property for this annual sum, without any capital outlay.[3] This plan originated with Mr. Hooke the surveyor, who had originally cast the builder for the part of the capitalist, and Sir George Ent came in when the builder backed out. Later in the year Mr. Hooke himself made an agreement of the same kind with the College, by which the College was to pay him £54 a year for the house on the north side of the site, and to receive an annual rent of one peppercorn in return.[4]

Then came a windfall. On 13 May 1674 the registrar reported that Sir John Cutler, the admired philanthropist and reputed miser, was minded to put up a theatre for the College at his own expense. The president and four fellows sped away to the rich man's house, where he feasted them and assured them it was true. A small committee was authorized to discuss the siting of this theatre with the surveyor-general of the royal works, Sir Christopher Wren, and Mr. Hooke. These two experts agreed in recommending the garden, east of the main block; but the benefactor preferred to have his building on the street, and he had his way. In the nineteenth century it was usual to credit Wren with a large share in the designing of the College and especially of the Cutlerian Theatre. This seems to be an example of the power of attraction inherent in great names: it may be that to all intents and purposes the building was Hooke's.[5]

[1] F. J. Farre, 'Short History of the College' (R.C.P., MS 118) iii. 110 ff.
[2] 22 December 1669, 14 February 1669/70.
[3] 7 April 1671, 30 September 1673 and *Diary of Robert Hooke*, ed. H. W. Robinson and W. Adams (1935), same date, which shows that the sealing took place at Sir George Ent's house.
[4] The papers relating to these leases are noted in the 'Descriptive Catalogue of Legal and other Documents in the Archives of the College' made in 1924 by Mr. Horace Barlow, pp. 210 ff.
[5] See the article by M. I. Batten in *Walpole Society*, xxv (1937), 89–90, which prints some of the relevant passages.

COLLEGIUM REGALE MEDICORUM LONDINENSIUM

VIII. The Warwick Lane Buildings

Physician college. warwick Lane
augt 28. 1821 —

IX. The Theatre in Warwick Lane

Mr. Hooke the surveyor was not a conqueror like Wren, but he was a scientist of the first order. Until our own time his achievements as an architect were not recognized as they deserved to be. His own diary from 1672 to 1680 confirms the College records by showing that he worked not only by surveying the ground, and engaging workmen but by advising the strong building committee. He made drawings for the theatre. From the time of Sir John Cutler's offer he and the College officers and committee were hard at work. A time-limit was fixed after which members who had not paid were to be expelled, and an appeal was addressed to the learned, rich and philanthropic, especially physicians.[1] The house on the north side was finished and Dr. Whistler, the registrar, entered on the tenancy.[2] Without any ceremony the comitia moved into the new *caenaculum* or assembly room.[3] Hooke was instructed to proceed with the houses flanking the theatre on either side on the street frontage.[4] Late in 1677 there was a paying-off of builders, when Hooke failed to keep his appointment, either because he slept too long in the afternoon or because he spent too long over showing one of Leeuwenhoek's microscopical books to his friends.[5] It was still necessary to find three fellows who would lend the College £100 each at interest, but the end was in sight.[6] On 21 January 1678/9 Dr. Charlton gave the anatomy lectures in the Cutlerian Theatre and the president, Dr. Micklethwaite, rounded off the occasion with a felicitous speech.

When John Evelyn dined with Dr. Whistler, whom he considered most learned and the most facetious man in nature, he wrote nothing in his diary about the architecture but he commented sadly: 'Tis pitty this Colledge is built so neere new-gate Prison and in so obscure an hole'.[7] This cannot be denied: Warwick Lane was narrow and the buildings were shut in all round; but as architecture they were a good specimen of the rational, brick-built style of the great rebuilding.[8] In the middle of the street frontage was the domed octagonal theatre, with houses on either side. The

[1] 30 September 1674. On 16 January 1676/7 the honorary fellows were told that the names of those of them who did not pay would not be included in the new *Pharmacopoeia*.
[2] 25 June, 22 December 1674.   [3] 25 February 1674/5.   [4] 13 April 1677.
[5] 21 November 1677; Hooke 27 November.   [6] 22 December 1677.
[7] *Diary*, ed. E. S. de Beer (1955), iv. 307: entry of 20 March 1682/3.
[8] There are many engravings of the court and theatre. For references to some of the more important and for reproductions of drawings (a preliminary drawing of the main block, drawings of the main block and theatre made in 1828 by J. C. Buckler) see the Walpole Society's volume mentioned in p. 330, n. 5. See also Plates VIII–X.

entrance was through carriage-gates under an archway to the open
loggia under the theatre, which projected into the paved courtyard.
The court was sixty feet by fifty, with the long sides parallel to the
street and the principal façade facing the entrance. This was the
front of the public rooms of the College, with a *perron* in the middle,
a statue of Charles II above it,[1] and on high a broad pediment and
a not ungraceful lantern. The wall had two orders of pilasters,
Ionic below and Corinthian above, with square-headed windows
in the lower stories and round-headed above; there were dormers
in the slated roof[2] and stone ornaments in the appropriate spaces.
The whole was well-proportioned and imposing. At the north end
was the fellow's house, which must have been commodious, since
it had three stories, besides a basement and attics and seven bays
of windows. Facing it were the two houses for the beadle and the
chemist, who had the same amount of frontage between them and
seem to have been provided for very amply; but the laboratory
was in the chemist's house, the beadle needed office-space, and
perhaps both of them took in lodgers.

The whole effect must have been exactly what the College hoped
for, dignified with a hint of opulence. Possibly the theatre did not
improve it, especially as the court was narrow for its height. This
theatre was an odd sort of structure, but there was something
pleasing about it, and the College poet celebrated it in lines which
have been quoted scores of times:

> A dome majestic to the sight
> And sumptuous arches bear its oval height;
> A golden globe plac'd high with artful skill
> Seems, to the distant sight, a gilded pill.[3]

The interior of the theatre was highly praised for its appearance,
arrangement and acoustics.[4] The principal rooms in the opposite
block were magnificent. The long room, sometimes called the long
gallery, or *caenaculum*, was on the first floor, and this rather than
the theatre was the usual meeting place for the larger comitia.[5] It

---

[1] This statute and that of Cutler which faced it across the court are the work of Arnold
Quellin and are now in the Guildhall Museum: see Katherine Esdaile and Margaret
Toynbee in *London and Middlesex Archaeological Society*, xiii (1956), pt. 1.

[2] The College decided on slates, not tiles or lead, on 2 April 1672.

[3] Sir Samuel Garth, *The Dispensary* (1699).

[4] J. Elmes, *Life of Sir Christopher Wren* (1823). For a plan and section see Plate X
to the present volume.

[5] The final decision was at Michaelmas 1695 when the College made up its mind that
the theatre was too cold in winter.

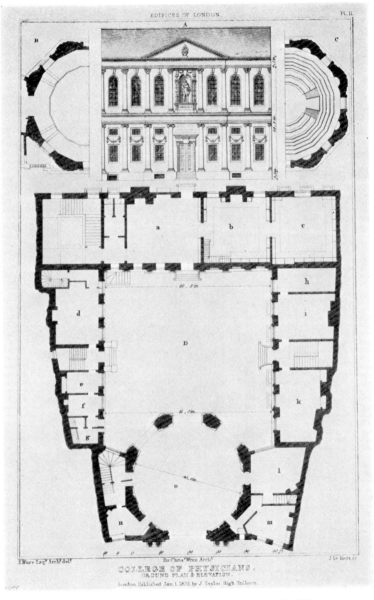

COLLEGE OF PHYSICIANS.
GROUND PLAN & ELEVATION.

London, Published Jan.1, 1825. by J. Taylor, High Holborn.

X. Plans and Elevation of the Warwick Lane Buildings

XI. The Censors' Room in Pall Mall East with Panelling from Warwick Lane

THE COLLEGE OF PHYSICIANS.

XII. The Long Room at Warwick Lane (1808)

XIII. Statues of Charles II and Sir John Cutler (1680) from the Warwick Lane
Buildings

was wainscoted, partly at the expense of the ever-beneficient Baldwin Hamey, and some of this splendid Spanish oak, with its fluted pilasters, lines the Censors' Room in the present College. In Warwick Lane the censors' room was on the first floor; the library, divided into two rooms with galleries round them, on the floor below. Altogether there was a great deal of space for a small society, but that was the token of prosperity in those days. Possibly some of it was unoccupied; but *caenaculum* originally meant a dining-room, so there were probably kitchens. The College soon became one of the regular sights for visitors to London. Foreign tourists were advised to give at least 3*d.* to the person who showed them round.[1] The presumptuous Companies were outdone.

Within a few years before and after the new doors opened there were changes in the intellectual dispositions of the College. The heroic generation of physiologists was dying out; by 1675 Glisson was nearing his end and only Ent survived him. There were a few younger men who did great things, but Mayow and Humphrey Ridley, the best of them, died ten years before Ent, and the science fell into a comparatively unprogressive phase in England as abroad. With chemistry vigorously moving forward the old ill-informed controversies of Galenists and Helmontians no longer interested the scientists, though cranks and hack writers still gnawed away at them. One of the greatest English thinkers of the age left a fragment of manuscript which seems to refer to these controversial writings, and gives a valuable indication of their relevance, or rather irrelevance, to the progress of medicine. John Locke began a treatise 'De Arte Medica' in 1669, but unfortunately only began it.[2] He had not yet taken his medical degree, and in later years he carried his studies further, but he already had much knowledge and no little experience. He wrote with a view to the improvement of the art, the establishment of a settled and certain practice, so that the list of incurable diseases might be shortened and the sad outcome of the others might be lessened. He hoped that this would diminish the distrust which some serious men seemed to have for the art itself and 'the disrepute which others'—surely Nedham and his like—'industriously labour to bring upon the practise of physick'.

---

[1] *Le guide de Londres* (1693), ed. W. H. Godfrey (1951), p. 7.
[2] The best text (though with a few unimportant errors) is in A. G. Gibson, *The Physician's Art* (1933), a wise and indeed beautiful book, pp. 13–26.

He admits that there are confessed *opprobria medicorum*, and he writes in the spirit of Bacon and the Royal Society, calling on the faculty to perfect the art by mutual assistance. He is far from disparaging the traditional writers,[1] though he rejects the tradition, the speculative theorems and the attempt to penetrate into the hidden causes of things. 'He that thinks he came to be skild in diseases by studying the doctrine of the humours . . . may as rationally believe that his Cooke owes his skill in roasting and boyling to his study of the elements.' He relies on observation, and he believes that there are already some diseases which are almost perfectly under the control of medicine, and for the most part yield to the skilful physician's hand guided by the established rules of his art.

Locke wrote of what he knew, for he was a close associate of Sydenham, watching him at work and noting both what he did and what he said. Sydenham, in his attentiveness to the patient, gained a new insight into one disease after another, with an accession of power in contending against them; but this was not merely a personal triumph. It was the application of the new principles which Locke marshalled in his argument, and while, on the one hand, it reminded people of Hippocrates, on the other it was part of a movement of thought among some of the best medical minds in Europe. Clinical teaching was established at Leiden when Locke was a child. It was beginning in the hospitals in London. The clinical tendency, as we may call it, shifted the fundamental attitude to disease, so that the old pathology, without being disproved article by article, was relegated to neglect. Locke had a clear conception of medical history. He believed the art as it then was to have risen (the numbering is his) on (1) Experience, (2) Method founded upon philosophy (which includes what we call science) and hypotheses, (3) Botany, (4) Chemistry, (5) Anatomy. But he, and we may add Sydenham, put their trust in clinical observation and doubted whether much more was to be hoped from scientific study even in anatomy. Anatomy could not reveal the organical constitution of an organ and that texture by which it operates. 'If therefore', Locke wrote in a later work 'anatomy shows us neither the cause nor cures of diseases, I think it is not very likely to bring any great advantage, for removing the pains and maladys of

---

[1] He gives a reference for this respectful attitude to *Novum Organum*, bk. i, xxxi–ii.

mankind.'[1] This we may note not as a hindrance to the reforming of methods of treatment by making use of such physiological discoveries as Harvey's, but as a measure of the distance which still separated science from practice.

The influence of the king and those about him was applied on behalf of *protégés*, as of old; but two of these were men of outstanding merit, and their need of this influence showed that the College was not adequately in touch with the elements of progress in medicine. Dr. Edmund King was a surgeon who attracted the attention of Charles II by his studies in chemistry; the archbishop of Canterbury gave him a Lambeth degree on which he incorporated at Cambridge, and a royal letter recommended the College to make him an honorary fellow, notwithstanding a previous letter forbidding the College to add any more to that category. This opened the way for a long debate on the constitutional effect of the new letter, and the majority held that it would be illegal to obey it. We may wonder whether they were actuated by hostility to Dr. King, who became a full fellow by the act of the next monarch and well deserved it.[2] Even more distasteful was the early life of Dr. Robert Talbor or Tabor. He came of educated people in Cambridge, where he was apprenticed to an apothecary; he did excellent work on the use of quinine as a cure for fever. After a doctor's quarrel resembling the contemporary battles over antimony by the bedside of King Louis XIV, he cured the king of a dangerous ague and he was made a royal physician. All the king asked of the College for Dr. Talbor was that he should not be molested or disturbed in his practice. The College unanimously but ungraciously decided to connive.[3] In a third case the *protégé* was not of the same stature as these two; he was a Mr. Russell against whom the College was proceeding, apparently for illicit practice; but it was ordered in the king's name to stop the proceedings and for two good reasons: Russell had been in practice in London for thirty years, and he had stayed at his post during the plague. The College obeyed.[4]

The court was not always in the right. A Dutchman from Gelderland named Gerhard van der Meulen applied for a licence

[1] 'Anatomia', quoted by Gibson, p. 8. For the respective shares of Sydenham and Locke in this and other writings see K. Dewhurst, *John Locke, Physician and Philosopher* (1963).
[2] 16, 23 January 1676/7, 25 June 1677. Munk prints the royal letter: for the earlier letter see below, p. 340.   [3] 3 May 1678.
[4] 21 January 1678/9, 7 December 1683. The latter entry appears to be misdated, probably through a typical error of Dr. Whistler.

to practise in cases of dropsy, relying on a war-time offer of privileges to subjects of the United Provinces who should come over.
This was refused and four years later he was prosecuted for illicit
practice. The Crown entered a *noli prosequi* for its half of the
penalty and recommended the College also to hold its hand; but
the College held on. A year later, however, this empiric was still
in practice and an obscure fellow of the College, Thomas Novell,
was accused of consulting with him.[1] A worse case was that of Mr.
Merry who was imprisoned and of whom the College was informed
that he was a person of no learning, of a mean and mechanical
education, that he had done much hurt by his ignorant and evil
practice and that he had been factious and turbulent. The earl of
Sunderland, secretary of state, wrote an off-hand note in this man's
favour giving no reason except that he was 'particularly recommended to me for an honest and ingenious man'.[2] But this was not
an official request and the College rejected it. The one other occasion when the College complied with a request from a great
personage was a special and domestic matter. The unhappy Dr.
Clench had made trouble in the College and outside it for years
until he was expelled. The lord chancellor put the final touch to
his restitution.[3]

In matters of wider scope the ministers did not evince a lack of
confidence in the College, but they did not entrust it with a single
task.[4] In the third Dutch war, as in the other two, physicians and
surgeons worked together, but this time the few physicians needed
were selected by the naval authorities themselves. Dr. Waldron
and the serjeant-surgeon accompanied John Evelyn on a tour of
inspection in 1672. After the war the College gave semi-official
help and support to schemes and experiments for sweetening salt
water which narrowly missed being of great service to the navy and

---

[1] 1 February 1677/8, 26 June 1682, 13 April 1683. The date of the alleged royal edict
is 12 June 1672. John Groeneveld who made a similar application on the same day was
admitted a licentiate on 5 January 1682/3 and afterwards had famous battles with the
College.   [2] 4 March 1686/7.

[3] 2 February 1682/3; 4 May, 13 September 1683; 16 June, 7 October, 22 December
1687; 4 February 1687/8. It must be held against the ministers that licences from the
king were granted to quacks to erect a stage and sell medicines: *Cal. of State Papers,
Domestic 1667* (1886), 5 October 1667 and R. R. James in *Janus*, xli (1936), referring to
1670. But they were not to administer internal medicines.

[4] Dr. Benjamin Worsley (who is unknown to Munk) was granted a patent of monopoly for fourteen years for a method which he had invented for cultivating and curing
senna in the colonies (plantations). The invention was approved by 'our physicians',
but this seems to mean the king's physicians, not the College: *Cal. of State Papers
Domestic, 1667–1668* (1893).

to all who sailed on distant voyages.[1] Signs were not wanting that
the reputation of the College continued to stand high with the outside world. In 1681 the physicians of Edinburgh, in consequence
of their local relations with the apothecary-surgeons, made another
and this time a successful attempt to obtain a charter. The example
of the London College influenced the development of their own,
especially through their promoter and first president, Sir Robert
Sibbald, who at the end of his life was a fellow of both. The London
College carried itself proudly. It began to use the name 'The Royal
College of Physicians'.[2] One of its acquisitions symbolized this
status. King Charles had presented a mace to the Royal Society,
silver gilt and much more massive than Dr. Caius's caduceus,
though in less admirable taste. In 1683 Dr. John Lawson delighted
the College by presenting a truly royal mace of similar pattern.[3]
There was another and far greater acquisition. Lord Dorchester
made it known that he intended to present his books to the College.
They amounted, according to a catalogue made in 1664, to more than
3,200 volumes.[4] They were reputed to be the finest collection on
physic, mathematics, civil law and philology in private ownership
in Europe. They were valued at some £4,000. In 1680, very shortly
before the donor's death, the question arose of providing accommodation for them in the College, and it was decided to begin a new
building at once.[5] For some reason, however, there were delays.
It was not until seven years later that Lady Grace Pierrepoint was
invited to view the fair library which the College had built for her
father's books, given by her.[6] It stood in the garden-space which
Wren and Hooke had recommended for the theatre, and it was the
final impressive addition to the Warwick Lane buildings.[7] The

[1] Keevil, ii. 100, 160.   [2] 26 June 1682.

[3] Morrow of Palm Sunday, minute in Munk, iii. 319. The present usage is that the
mace is carried before the president, who himself carries the caduceus.

[4] The catalogue, now MS. 199 at the College is classified under Mathematics, Civil
Law, Medicine and Philology.

[5] 8 October, 12 November 1680.

[6] 4 February 1687/8; the appointment of Dr. Charleton as keeper of these books
was proposed on 9 April 1688.

[7] In 1682 the College petitioned the City for approval of its new plan for the library,
which involved interfering with the City wall (Brit. Mus. MS. Sloane 3914 fos. 66ᵛ–67).
On 23 July 1686 the College committee requested Sir Thomas Millington to ask Sir
Christopher Wren 'to order his workmen to begin their worke about the library with
all speed'. For this, a further entry of 30 July and a letter of Wren dated 6 Aug. 1686
see the minute-book, Brit. Mus. MS. Sloane 3915 fos. 23–24ᵛ. On 22 December 1688
when a payment of £10 was authorized to John Scarborow 'for measuring worke done
for the College by the appointment of Sir Christopher Wrenn'.

College library was now far more than a medical library. Both in rarities and in commoner books it was no stronger in medicine than in various other subjects. That the College should maintain a general library, with treasures to impress both scholars and sight-seers helped to put it on a level with the colleges of the universities, and to define its standing in London. It may indeed have influenced many other institutions. Nowadays every profession may be expected to have a large and partly ornamental library at its head-quarters, and the example of the College of Physicians may have helped to establish this not invariably reasonable custom.

Not everything in the life of the College corresponded to this exterior splendour. It may be coincidence, but there may be a connexion between the loosening of private and public morals in the Restoration period and a deterioration in the behaviour of some of the physicians. It would be too harsh to include poor Christopher Merret's long quarrel with the College under this heading. He was something of a scientist, and he had done good service in College offices especially as the first Harveian Librarian. He had some excuse for thinking that he had a right to draw his stipend for life even when his library was burnt down, and his misfortunes explain if they do not excuse the litigiousness which led, as it was bound to lead, to his expulsion. No reason is given for a proposal to expel Dr. Atfield.[1] Some years earlier he and Dr. Lower had brought some grave charge against Dr. Richard Robinson, the senior candidate. When Robinson applied for admission as a fellow it was refused on the ground that he had never been educated at any university, so that his offence was probably some sort of deceit about his qualifications.[2] The College had been less vigilant in the disgraceful case of Thomas Frankland, who was in Holy Orders and had been proctor in Oxford, was actually censor and had a run of six years as a fellow before anyone discovered that his testimonials were forged.[3] Some of the lapses of manners might, of course, have happened at any time. Dr. Clench was fined £8 for accusing certain fellows of ignorance and malpractice, but he refused to pay. He was ordered not to act with Dr. Haworth nor to frequent his gathering (*conventio*) on pain of expulsion. In due

---

[1] 3 May 1689: not mentioned by Munk.
[2] 3, 13 April 1685: Robinson is not mentioned by Munk.
[3] 4 June, 22 December 1677, 26 June 1682. It appears from the minutes of the College committee for 22 May 1682 (see below, p. 349, n. 1.) that Frankland had taken bribes from one Bourn for conniving at his unlawful practice.

course he was expelled.[1] Good Dr. Hodges, only a fortnight before he died a prisoner for debt, had to employ counsel to defend him in a matter not of law but of ill manners.[2]

Some of the offences were perhaps characteristic of these times. Dr. Walter Needham was physician to the Charterhouse and a man of standing, but when he obeyed the censors' summons to submit his secret solar bezoardium for inspection they rejected it as noxious and, even after that, Dr. Pitt complained that he always pressed his medicine on patients and refused almost all consultations, thus injuring all doctors he had to do with.[3]

The worst case of all was that of Dr. Whistler, the hospitable occupant of the College house. Twelve times censor, registrar from 1674 to 1682, when he made a sorry mess of keeping the Annals, he was treasurer for one year and in 1683 president. He died in office and he was only two days dead when an extraordinary meeting in comitia was called to consider his notable peculations. Sir John Cutler was present.[4] The plutocrat saved the situation by buying the fellow's house and lending the money to pay all the College debts. He was to have five per cent. interest, which was low for those days, and his principal was to be repaid in seven years; but this could only be done by handing over all the rents, profits and perquisites due to the College, by stopping all salaries and fees whatsoever except those of the attorney and the beadle and by levying £20 at once from every fellow in lieu of providing a dinner in his turn and £5 from each candidate in lieu of his collation. The Elizabethan statute was to be revived by which the treasurer gave a bond to repay all College moneys that he received. Dr. Goddard nobly devoted his spare time to sorting out the accounts.[5] Thus did the learned and facetious Daniel Whistler afflict the College with seven lean years.

After the fire a long time passed before the comitia and the censors were able to do their business to much purpose. They stumbled over other obstacles besides the expense and labours of rebuilding. Keeping up the number of fellows presented no difficulty,[6] but

---

[1] 2 February 1682/3, 4 May, 13 September 1683; 16 June 1687. Is this the extra-licentiate Samuel Haworth, and was it he who was accused of illicit practice by Dr. Darnelly on 21 September 1683?

[2] 25 May 1688.   [3] 16 January, 13 February 1684/5; 18 November 1687.

[4] 13 May 1684.   [5] 1 October 1685.

[6] Five were elected on 29 July 1675 without prejudice to the rights of Dr. Trevor, who was awaiting election. By 1680 the statutory number had been inadvertently exceeded.

like a bolt from the blue there came a royal letter forbidding the College to elect any more honorary fellows. The letter said that there were several pretended physicians and graduates of foreign universities who endeavoured to enter the College as honorary fellows without incorporating at Oxford or Cambridge and without examination; that this was prejudicial to the fellows, and contrary to the statutes of the College itself and to the charters. The College must admit no such persons.[1] This was unanswerable, but it had been left unwritten for many years. There is no evidence that Oxford and Cambridge had prompted this measure in consequence of their jealousy of foreign graduates, and only one other reason has been suggested for the letter. The royal order is that no one is to be admitted unless, after he incorporates and before he is examined, he takes the oaths of allegiance and supremacy. The purpose therefore was to exclude doctors who were disapproved on religious and political grounds.[2] Except that unhappily it bears no date, a petition addressed to the College seems to explain how the incident began. In this twenty-four physicians of academical education resident in town propose to unite themselves to the College as honorary fellows. They express their willingness not only to submit to examination and to pay the usual fees but to contribute further to the rebuilding. They say that none of them is in ecclesiastical orders 'as hath been suggested'; but those who have taken their degrees in foreign universities cannot incorporate 'for severall reasons' and so cannot enter as candidates, while others are unwilling because of their seniority to become juniors as fellows.[3] Their names are missing, but it is a fair guess that one of the several reasons for inability to incorporate was unwillingness for reasons of religion to take the oaths required by the statutes of the English universities. Certainly the royal order came at a time when ministers aimed at tightening the system of oaths and tests. Whatever the reason for it, it was a set-back to the College.

Another check hampered action against unlicensed practitioners. One of them, an Italian called Damascenus, asked the president and College what their authority was, and ironically it was on the same day that a committee was appointed to consult with Sir William Jones, king's counsel, on the prosecution of an empiric.[4] They

[1] 25 February 1674/5.
[2] This explanation appears in the eighteenth-century College lawsuits.
[3] Brit. Mus. MS. Stowe 182 fos. 34–34ᵛ.
[4] 23 December 1672. I know of no prosecution since 1665, or indeed 1658: see above p. 289.

discovered that they could not prosecute because the crime was covered by an Act of Oblivion or general pardon.[1] Two years later Dr. Collins, junior, complained of an empiric and was given full permission to summon him for malpractice, but if anything followed it is unrecorded.[2] After another year there was a discussion on how to put beef into the repression (*nervose prosequendi*), but as of old it led to nothing.[3] On the contrary, when one more year had passed five brazen-faced doctors appeared and challenged the authority of the College.[4] The College resolved emphatically that it would stand on its rights, but it was puzzled. The ghost of Dr. Bonham was walking, for three of the five were Cambridge graduates. Of two Paduan doctors one claimed not merely liberty to practise but the right to be examined for candidate without incorporating. He gave in afterwards, incorporated as a doctor at Cambridge where he was already a member, and was received into the fold as a fellow.[5] The others remained impenitent.[6]

A pertinacious opponent of the College jurisdiction was Adrian Huyberts. After studying at Trinity College, Dublin he had served an apprenticeship to a Dublin apothecary, and in travels on the Continent he had picked up some knowledge of chemistry. He seems to have begun medical practice in London early in the reign of Charles II and to have had a few influential people among his patients. The College set the cumbrous machinery in motion, or as Huyberts put it persecuted him; but what makes his case interesting is the pamphlet in which he protested.[7] Besides developing the same arguments as Nedham, whom he mentioned, he threw together everything he could think of to discredit the College: they had admitted papists; the physicians, with some exceptions such as Dr. Wharton, had run away at the time of the plague, and

[1] The Act of 1660 (12 Car. II c. 5) covering offences since 1637.
[2] 13 April 1674.   [3] 25 June 1675.
[4] 2 June 1676: they were Drs. Swale, Masters and Hallwood of Cambridge, Butler and Stockham of Padua. Dr. Butler may be the Nicholas Butler who was rejected on examination on 1 September 1676 but became an honorary fellow in 1680.
[5] William Stockham or Stokeham: he applied to be examined in March 1679/80, but he was admitted in the quality of a royal physician in 1680.
[6] In April 1680 Sir Francis Pemberton answered a series of legal questions put to him by the College, one of which seems to have originated from this case, especially as it mentions Cambridge but not Oxford. He replied that foreign graduates had no licence as such anywhere in the kingdom, but about Cambridge doctors he was indefinite: Brit. Mus. MS. Sloane 3914 fos. 18-19.
[7] *The Corner Stone* (1670). A petition of Huyberts from prison is referred to in *Cal. of State Papers Domestic, 1670* (1895), p. 610. I do not consider that the evidence confirms Huyberts's statement on p. 19 of the pamphlet that there was a project for setting up a new and rival college of physicians, but that this was frustrated by the plague.

so forth. He complained of the exclusion of candidates and licentiates from the government of the College, and maintained that
apprenticeship to physicians should be permitted. In his view
there was no need for any regulation of medical practice except by
the law of the land, and no need for any licensing authority drawn
from the profession. Not content with the general statement that
corporations had been the great hinderers of progress in the medical
art, he endeavoured to show that the London College had no legal
right to exercise any authority, or even to exist. He resuscitated the
groundless contention that the Act of 14 Henry VIII was not a
true statute, that it had not received the royal assent and rested
on no true record.[1] Dr. Charles Goodall answered all this in a
sober and well-arranged reply dedicated to Sir Francis North,
then chief justice of the common pleas[2]; Huyberts, however,
fought on. The College obtained a verdict against him for £100,
and from the King's Bench Prison he petitioned the king. The
College replied with almost naïve frankness. He had not only
broken the law; he had questioned it. He had 'endeavoured to make
voyd and null all the grants and patents made and granted the sayd
Colledge' and had 'asserted that they were invalid and not to be
regarded'.[3] But he had failed, and it was a good many years before
the College needed to reaffirm its *raison d'être*.

There was a brisk exchange of derogatory pamphlets between
the College and the apothecaries. It began with two published by
Christopher Merret, honorary freeman of the Apothecaries'
Company though he was,[4] and Jonathan Goddard.[5] They repeat
the arguments that we have encountered so often, but neither of
them was prudent enough to keep to the beaten track; each went
out of his way to damage their cause. Merret immoderately claimed
that the apothecaries regarded him as an enemy because of late,

[1] See above, p. 282.
[2] *The College of Physicians Vindicated* (1676): it was only later in the same year that
Goodall was admitted a candidate.
[3] 23 December 1678.
[4] *Short View of the Frauds and Abuses committed by Apothecaries* (1669), 2nd edn.
(1670). At one stage of the negotiations of 1664 the apothecaries unsuccessfully asked
the College to appoint Merret as its representative to meet him: Underwood, p. 349.
[5] *Discourse setting forth the Unhappy Condition of the Practice of Physick* (1670).
The longer book of Daniel Coxe *Discourse wherein the Interest of the Patient . . . is
soberly debated* (1669) did not provoke immediate controversy. Goddard, p. 57, says that
his pamphlet was 'written about five years since'. For a pamphlet on the same subject
which Goddard is alleged to have published in 1668 see F. H. Ellis and L. M. Payne
in *Medical History* (1900), 187–90.

in order to save his patients' lives and purses he had dispensed his medicines gratis. He complained that 'of late years' when the censors dined with the Society at the dinner of a new master they were placed at the second table instead of being at the high table next to the master as of yore. His history of the progressive intrusion of the apothecaries into practice is ingenuous. First they stayed in their shops; then the physicians sometimes sent them to examine patients and report; next they accompanied physicians on their visits. So far there is very little in this that we need believe; but the end is historically sound, and Merret was unconscious that in writing it he made a damaging admission. In the plague-time, most of the physicians being out of town, the apothecaries took upon them the whole practice of physic, which they had ever since continued. Goddard wrote more urbanely, but he also was indiscreet. He admitted that some judged the separation of physicians and apothe-caries to be of unhappy consequence, and that the physicians had left the way open to the apothecaries by neglecting to understand medical materials and their preparation. He gave a very feeble reason for writing against the apothecaries and not against empirics 'though they do swarm so numerously in London': they do not betray a trust as practising apothecaries do. His motive for writing is unblushingly clear: the physicians' education was so expensive, their profession of such use and consequence that they deserved 'to get as great Estates, as are gotten in any Profession or way of Trading'. Thirty or forty years before, when the apothecaries kept within bounds, he wrote, the physicians got greater estates than now.

As a minor remedy Goddard suggested that the fines for offences against the law of medical practice should be increased to com-pensate for the fallen value of money; but the major remedy on which both writers agreed was that the physicians should prepare their own medicines, or at least the more important and secret of them. It seems indeed as if the two wrote with the concerted pur-pose of making this proposal. We saw that when it was raised within doors before the plague it led to a promising attempt to patch up relations between the two parties.[1] Now, having been made in public it was publicly answered. There is no need to summarize the replies, or Merret's rejoinders. We learn from one of the replies that the apothecaries were intentionally neglecting their duty of bringing their apprentices to the College to be freed,

[1] See above, p. 308.

and the same able writer tells us that when the College had a public laboratory in Amen Corner they sold 'as base medicines and preparations' as any other chemists in London.[1] But on the whole these subsidiary writings tell us what we should expect.

The Society of Apothecaries knew nothing about the original two books until they were on sale. Justly aggrieved it sent a deputation to enquire whether these insulting works were printed with the authority or consent of the College, who were told that as the books appeared under the authors' names it was not fitting that the College should either be questioned about them or reply. None the less the College agreed, we may say had to agree, to a discussion between representatives of both sides. To this the apothecaries brought a badly drafted proposal that the physicians should not prepare or compound medicines, that they should not deprive the apothecaries of their friends and acquaintances by pretence of any private arcanum or otherwise (in other words deprive them of patients). Further the apothecaries offered to join with the physicians in frequent searches, and to co-operate in promoting a new Act of Parliament against empirics and all illegal practisers and makers of physic. The counter-proposals of the College amounted only to a detailed restatement of their well-known position, and they denied that they had ever forbidden the sale of medicines without their permission or indeed the sale of wholesome medicines under any conditions. The College considered the apothecaries' proposals, re-appointed its committee and apparently forgot the whole matter.[2] The apothecaries were less inactive, but their movements do not seem to have troubled the College. They built a laboratory, and they submitted for the approval of the College a paper on the use proposed for it and on the particular chemical medicines to be made there.[3] Unfortunately from about this time the Annals deal very incompletely with the apothecaries' affairs, and we know from the other side that trouble was brewing, but for the present there was no official quarrelling.

[1] (H. Stubbe), *Lex Talionis* (1670) *Campanella Revived* (1670). Other titles are C. Merret, *Self-Conviction* (1670), *The Accomplisht Physician, the Honest Apothecary and the Skilful Surgeon* (1670), *A Short Reply to the Postscript of H.S.* (1670); Dr. C. T., *Some Papers written in 1664* (1670); *Medice Cura Teipsum* (1671). A complete list would include several tracts scarcely worthy of notice.

[2] 28 March; 21, 25 June 1670; Barrett, p. 82; Underwood, p. 358.

[3] 23 December 1672; Barrett, p. 86. The king's chemical pharmacist Nicasius le Febure had been appointed to serve the College on 1 October 1666. His chemical physician in ordinary, John Archer, was examined for a licence on 27 June 1670 in the English language, but failed.

In matters relating to medical thought and science little activity can be traced. The third edition of the *Pharmacopoeia*, which appeared in 1677, was almost a reprint of the last edition, with a few new medicines added.[1] The College thanked Willis for the dedication of his *Pharmaceutice Rationalis*[2] but it paid little heed to the principles laid down in it. In 1673 most of the fellows present at the Christmas comitia promised to subscribe at the rate of £5 to Robert Morison's projected 'Historia Plantarum'[3]; but that is all that appears on the credit side, while against it must be set the reduction of the anatomy lectures from six to three.[4] Except for the new buildings the College had little to congratulate itself upon for the next thirteen years or so after the fire.

[1] 30 August 1676. Boulter, whose name comes last in the list of booksellers on the title-page, a nephew of Sir John Cutler was appointed on that account on 25 June 1677 to publish all other works of the College. He was re-appointed on 10 April 1682.
[2] 13 April 1674.   [3] 22 December 1673.   [4] 21 June 1678.

XIX : FROM THE POPISH PLOT TO THE REVOLUTION SETTLEMENT, 1679-89

BEFORE the Cutlerian Theatre was opened national events took a turn which was to involve the College in the worst shocks it ever endured. In 1678 the horrible suspicions of a Popish Plot roused the old, dormant antagonisms within the nation. On 29 March 1679 the house of lords ordered the governors 'now in towne' of the College, of Doctors' Commons and of the Heralds' College to expel from their bodies all such persons as should not receive the sacrament as protestants and subscribe to the oaths required by law. The king had ordered the College to administer the oaths eleven years earlier,[1] but of late there had been no prying into the religion of the members. When the lords' order arrived the beadle was immediately sent to summon two fellows, Dr. Betts and Dr. Short, who were suspected of being papists.[2] Dr. Short obeyed the summons, but there was no quorum for the comitia.[3] Dr. Betts, who was a royal physician, did not present himself, and no one seems to have interfered with either of them further. In the ensuing political and religious strife the College seems to have sided with the king and the catholic duke of York against the whigs. When the whig offensive was exhausted the College came out openly on the side of authority. For the first time in its long history, or the second time if we count the Restoration as the first, it took notice of a political event. It congratulated the king and his brother on their escape from the Rye House Plot. Someone told the bishop of London, the stalwart Henry Compton, something about this resolution and he hastened to pass it on to Sir Leoline Jenkins, secretary of state. A few days later he wrote again to retract: he had read the resolution, heard what passed at the meeting, and found that he had been entirely misinformed: all was as it should be.[4]

---

[1] Royal Letter of 23 December 1668 in Annals 1679.
[2] 4 April 1679.
[3] 14 April 1679. For an abortive proposal in parliament that no papist lawyers, physicians or apothecaries should be suffered to stay in town above a week see *House of Lords Papers, 1678–1688* (1887), pp. 64, 92.
[4] 23 July 1683; *Cal. of State Papers Domestic, 1683 July–September* (1934), p. 214.

The College did not know how closely it was watched; but everyone knew before long that it was time to walk warily. The plot gave authority all the excuse it needed for a concerted movement of repression. For the time being this movement passed the College by. It had given no offence and there was no reason why the government should take any notice of its affairs. Indeed if there was any connexion between these affairs and the public events of the few remaining years of Charles II, a point which must remain uncertain, it was of a different character. The vigorous ministers who now set about restoring the king's power meant to curtail the liberties of the subject, but from their own point of view they were reformers. Certain personal links suggest that their zeal for clearing up the political scene may have stimulated like-minded men to activity within the College. Others of the fellows grumbled at their claim to have 'the spirit of government'[1]; but the new energy and the new imitation of French methods opened up some new lines of thought. It is significant that a pamphlet of 1685, in a list of seventy-five proposals for economic, social, legal, constitutional and miscellaneous reforms, includes a lying-in hospital on the model of Paris, a foundling hospital as in Paris and Rome and a free dispensary for the poor as at Rome.[2]

After the long spell of depression which followed the fire the College came to life again in the year 1680. The first sign came in a batch of questions submitted to counsel in order to settle doubts about the permissible limits of what might be done. There were the old problems about the licensing power, the number of fellows and the right to expel, and there was nothing novel in the replies to these; but there was also the question whether the College might create 'degrees among the fellows themselves' by appointing a committee for general purposes. To this Sir Francis Pemberton replied that they might, and though no such creation followed immediately, before very long the standing committee was set up, to become the centre of the new activity.[3] In the meantime the obstruction in the way of electing new honorary fellows was removed.

[1] This is Dr. Bernard's phrase: see below, p. 373 n. 2.
[2] *England's Wants*, reprinted in *Somers Tracts*, ed. Sir Walter Scott, 2nd edn. ix (1813), 218 ff. For the influence of Catholic examples in charitable foundations see the present writer's *Later Stuarts*, 2nd edn. (1955), p. 158.
[3] The questions and answers are in Brit. Mus. MS. Sloane 3914, fos. 18–19, and another copy ibid. fos. 23 ff. This manuscript forms part of Charles Goodall's collections relating to the College and was given to Sloane by Dr. John Bateman, president in 1716.

The device was simple: they should be honorary fellows by examination. The examination was needed to satisfy the law, but it was to be taken by invitation and at a single sitting. No doubt the result would be a foregone conclusion. Several elections followed quickly.[1] A few years later the entrance fee for honorary fellows was raised to £100 besides gratuities.[2] When the next batch of elections was decided on the conditions were restated: there was to be one examination and the applicant must have been a doctor of Oxford or Cambridge for at least five years; the entrance fee was to be £50 and there was to be an annual payment of 40s., equal to that of candidates and licentiates. Later the lord keeper, probably not as senior visitor but as the head of the court of chancery, actually intervened to make one of these conditions easier. By whom he was prompted we do not know, but he cut out the five years' stipulation: an Oxford or Cambridge doctorate was to suffice.[3] For licentiates the conditions were made a little more stringent. No one was to be admitted to examination on the ground that he was a refugee from religious persecution unless he produced authentic written evidence of the fact and no alien was to be offered admission by examination, which perhaps means examination without the other statutory qualifications.[4] This may have something to do with the credentials of the Italian catholic Henry Morelli, who took the oath of supremacy before two justices of the peace and swore that he had never been a priest.[5]

In the spring of 1682 the standing committee, simply called 'the committee', came into existence. With the four censors and the treasurer five other members sat, one of whom, Dr. Charleton, was elected chairman, to be succeeded at Michaelmas by Dr. Coxe and a year after that by Dr. Whistler. Five were to be a quorum. For

[1] 25 June, 27 August, 30 September 1680. Munk gives the names of thirteen doctors admitted on 30 September. Of these two were nonconformists, Nehmiah Grew and his half-brother, not brother-in-law, Henry Sampson, an ejected minister. Of the others four owed their English degrees to royal letters, one to letters of the Protector Oliver and a sixth to an archbishop of Canterbury. One, Robert Wittie, had retired from provincial practice and was 66 years old. For him see F. N. L. Poynter, 'A Seventeenth Century Medical Controversy' in *Science, Medicine and History*, ed. E. A. Underwood (1953), pp. 72 ff.   [2] 22 December 1684.
[3] 8 December 1678; 13 April, 25 June 1685. Lord Chancellor Jeffreys seems to have obtained an amendment further relaxing the rule in order to open the way for his nominee Nehemiah Cox: 29 November; 8, 9, 16, 22 December 1687.
[4] 2 April 1683: 'Nemini posthac alienigenarum examinationem exhibitum iri quo in Collegium adoptetur.' Two protestant refugees approved in 1688 were Dr. Dufray and Dr. Gombault.
[5] 5 February 1682/3, 25 June 1684: text of entries in Munk.

the first five years or so the personnel of the committee does not throw much light on its ideas; they seem to have been men of various types and opinions who were willing to meet once a week and work at preparing agenda for the comitia and at other necessary business.[1] They evidently wanted to make sure of their ground in all directions. Not long after their first meeting several different counsel were plied with questions about the College jurisdiction and discipline to which they sent duly reassuring answers.[2] Several promising measures followed, and after a time the committee strengthened its position by imposing a declaration of secrecy on its members, so that the fellows as a body should not know what it was doing until it declared its hand in full comitia.

One small change obviously made for efficiency. In 1682 for the first time a nominal roll of the College was printed.[3] It included the licentiates and must have been sold to the public; the profits went to the beadle, who no doubt kept the lists up to date. Some specimens of these lists, printed on single sheets, survive in old libraries.[4] They made it harder for impostors to claim that they had a right to practise. There were other and more important efforts against the irregulars. The fine for collaboration with them was raised to £10.[5] Dr. Charles Goodall published his accurate and methodical book *The Royal College of Physicians of London founded and established by Law* (1684). This gives the texts of the charters

---

[1] Two committee minute-books are preserved at the College: (1) MS. 274a which runs from 18 March 1682 to 7 (?4) October 1697 but has no entries between 20 June 1690 and 4 October 1697 except a loose sheet for 29 September 1697; (2) MS. 274 which runs from 9 October 1693 to 24 June 1697, and, in a different series at the other end of the book, from 22 October 1689 to 15 July 1692. In the British Museum MS. Sloane 3915 are the minutes from 20 March 1682 to 4 October 1697. This volume was given to Sloane by Dr. Bateman and was perhaps copied from those which remain with the College. In the present work footnote references to these minutes are given in the form: Committee, 4 October 1697.

[2] College case on subscriptions for the buildings, questions and answers of Holt, Pollexfen and Saunders in MS. Sloane 3914 fos. 20–26ᵛ.

[3] A few years earlier the secretary of state's office cast a suspicious eye at the Peacock in the Strand which professed to keep away from state affairs but provided information ('advertisements') of all sorts, covering robberies, publications, the residences of physicians and artists, medicines, prices of goods &c. *Cal. of State Papers Domestic, 1666–1667* (1864), p. 433.

[4] 26 June 1682. On 10 April 1682 £5 was voted to William Morgan for the dedication of his map of London on which the arms of the College appear with those of other subscribers, though less prominently than those of the Royal Society. Before long the lists were reproduced by journalists and in books of reference. From 8 June 1694 to 8 November 1695 they appear at intervals in J. Houghton, *Collections for the Improvement of Husbandry and Trade*. From 1682 they are in J. Chamberlayne, *Angliae Notitia* and its successors.

[5] 2 April 1683, 30 September 1684.

and Acts of Parliament, the legal reports of cases, and an historical account, drawn mainly from the Annals, of the other cases in which the College had exercised its jurisdiction down to the year 1647. That is to say it made public in a convenient form the original sources on which the College based its legal claims. It brought up to date and amplified the work done by Merret in 1660.[1] Dedicated to Lord Keeper Guilford and prefaced by a statement of approval by the president and censors it was more effective, at least for educated readers, than all that the pamphleteers had volunteered on behalf of the College. One venial charge against it must be admitted. It says nothing about the cases in which the College failed to make good its claims, those of William Trigge, Dr. Barker, Stepehen Trigge, and Fettiplace before and that of one Reade during the Commonwealth. But there is no reason to suppose that the grounds of the decision in these unreported cases were such as to invalidate the claims. Dr. Goodall also gave the College, for the use of the censors and delegates, a handsomely bound transcript of the Annals in two volumes.[2]

Before his book was published Dr. Goodall, in association with the beadle, was authorized to consult the rising barrister Mr. John Holt about the possibility of moving against the empirics and impostors in a new theatre of war. A country doctor called Parham had written to a junior fellow, Dr. Briggs, about their inflictions all over rural England; but no action followed and perhaps the sagacious Holt or the beadle, experienced in pursuit, pointed out insuperable difficulties.[3] In town the hunt became more lively.[4] Thomas Botterell, an extra-licentiate, had moved in, and he had to take out his licence for the City.[5] The shameless Huyberts was still in practice, but seems not to have been charged, though a German called Harder or Hardowe, who lived like Huyberts in Lincoln's Inn Fields, was apprehended. Lord Arlington wrote on behalf of Harder, it seems with effect. The Jew Dr. Sylva was begged off by Dr. Brooke on condition of ceasing to practice and paying the costs of the suit against him.[6] But out of half a dozen others charged in 1683 one was prosecuted in the courts and at

---

[1] See above, p. 322 n. 3.   [2] 7 November 1684.

[3] 14 September 1683. Dr. Briggs also had a complaint from Dr. Gostlin, the master of Caius, about stupid and unskilful men licenced for country practice, apparently by the College; 1 June 1683.

[4] Committee 5, 12 March 1682/3, proposal to strengthen the wording of the statute and to raise the penalty to £10.

[5] Entries in Munk.   [6] 4, 8 November 1681; 9 February 1682/3.

least two convicted by the censors. In 1684 the College called on the president and censors to summon all practitioners in physic and empirics in town and effectually to prosecute all such as refused to be examined or, upon examination, were found not to be fitly qualified.[1] Dr. Collins and Dr. Goodall were put in charge of prosecuting the empirics, but of their doings we have no record.[2]

The sector of the enemy front occupied by the surgeons was quiet. One of them was summoned for illicit and evil practice,[3] but another was examined and admitted to practise medicine.[4] Nor were the apothecaries attacked in public. Three of them appeared in interesting contexts. Dr. Robert Swale, one of the brazen five of 1676 had an extra-licence, but he was prosecuted, presumably for venturing into London. He was ill, and on this ground his father-in-law prevailed on the College to drop the prosecution. This father-in-law was an apothecary.[5] Thomas Crichloe, an apothecary of Grantham, was examined for an extra-licence. He had been a member of the Society of Apothecaries, but he brought a document to prove that he had taken his discharge, so that he was not applying for permission to practise as an apothecary and a physician at the same time. In any case he failed in the examination.[6] A month later came another application which was not so easily disposed of. John Badger was an apothecary and he was also a Cambridge bachelor of medicine though only by royal mandate, not as the result of a course of study. He applied to be examined for a licence, but he brought no discharge. His business was deferred, no reason being given in the Annals, but in 1683, in July, August and September, he was examined three times and satisfied the examiners. He paid his formal visits to the fellows. Then he was asked to defer his admission as a licentiate and to qualify as a candidate, which meant taking his doctor's degree. He acquiesced. In 1684 he gave up his employment in pharmacy and set himself to become a Cambridge doctor. The College had not heard the last of him.

Behind the scenes the College committee deliberated on a plan for fencing off one area of medical practice from the apothecaries. It was a plan for reviving the College laboratory. Very little is

[1] 26 June 1684.
[2] Committee, 9 December 1684; Annals 22 December 1684.
[3] 7 March 1683/4.
[4] 5 December 1684: Thomas Hobbs. Munk does not mention that he was a surgeon.
[5] 10 March 1679/80, 1 February 1683/4.   [6] 2 November 1683.

recorded about the laboratory in the new building and the resident chemist Mr. Huyck, Hewk or Hukes. If he had operated to much purpose there might have been less uncertainty, even at that date, about the spelling of his name. At any rate he died six years after being appointed, and in 1679 and 1680 the College negotiated with his widow about the value of College property in her possession and the value of such equipment of his own as the College was to take over. In March 1684/5 a new scheme was proposed. A committee should draw up rules which were to be approved in full comitia. These were to be subscribed to by all the members—that is fellows and licentiates—who should know or use the medicines which the Committee decided to have prepared. Twelve members were to undertake the management in turns, the first six being such as had spent some time in chemical preparations. The operator should be one who did not understand drugs or chemistry, yet was fit to follow the directions given to him. Those who subscribed to the rules were to form a fund by contributing 20s. apiece. Medicines were to be made and stored in a repository, the purpose of each one being entered in a book, and they were to be sold by an apothecary or apothecaries appointed by the College, who should be supplied with them when there was occasion. The proceeds of the sales were to be used in the first instance for repaying the initial levy and continuing the supply. If there was any considerable profit it was to go towards paying off the College debt.[1]

This plan was meant to keep in the hands of the appointed apothecaries the supplying of the secret or recondite medicines which they, and no doubt some patients, believe to be the most efficacious. It anticipated that some of the members would not wish to come in but would prefer to take the apothecaries into their confidence. By doing this they would give the apothecaries opportunities of profit, and it was in the power of the apothecaries to make a return by introducing them to business. From this it was a short step to a relationship between the apothecary and the physician like that between the general practitioner of later times and the consultant. The College as a body was averse from anything of the kind; but by proposing a scheme which did not involve the use of College funds, nor any corporate action by the College, the committee perhaps sought to avoid both dissension within doors, and legal challenge from outside. What might have been the outcome

[1] Committee, 10 March 1684/5.

cannot be known, for the execution of the plan seems to have been postponed. Perhaps it was frustrated by the next national crisis.

King Charles II was dead and the College drew up its address of condolence and congratulation to his brother. Nine fellows presented it and kissed the royal hand.[1] The quiet accession of a catholic sovereign was a triumph for the monarchical principle but the extremists of the old opposition committed themselves to the desperate venture of Monmouth's rebellion. Two physicians and three surgeons landed with the rebels. After the battle of Sedgemoor Dr. William Oliver was clever enough to escape to Holland, and to await better times. His practice in Bath, where he ended his days in peace, is still commemorated in the excellent biscuits which bear his portrait. One of the surgeons, Joseph Gayland, also got away, to become in the course of time a doctor and a fellow of the College; but Dr. Benjamin Temple, an extra-licentiate of the College, was caught. According to his friends it was the merest accident that he was there at all, but he suffered the dreadful penalties of high treason. Whether this counted against the College we do not know, but for other reasons its fortunes were involved in the now intensified reaction. When King Charles set out to destroy his opponents in the last years of his reign he had a constitutional programme. Aiming, as his father had done, at absolute monarchy he set himself to overcome not only the resistance of parliaments but the foundations of their power. He and some of his ablest advisers understood that parliaments became strong because they drew together in one place forces which developed throughout the country under the immemorial régime of territorial self-government and chartered liberties. Most of the borough members of parliament were elected by the municipal corporations, and Charles remodelled these corporations so that they should elect such members as he wanted. He set the *quo warranto* procedure in motion against the charters of the boroughs. It was successfully tested in minor places, and then in 1683 the charter of the City of London was declared forfeit. After that no charter was safe, and the law officers did not confine their attentions to the boroughs. It is scarcely an exaggeration to say that chartered liberties in general were reviewed with an eye to bringing all bodies corporate into subjection.

For the fellows of the College these proceedings were not simply a distant spectacle. They had on their hands a dispute with the

[1] 24, 25, 27 February 1684/5.

City about the ownership of part of the Warwick Lane site, and while they were trying to arrange satisfactory terms the City charter was seized and the City no longer had any legal right to negotiate.[1] Some of the City Companies forfeited their charters, primarily because their liverymen were the parliamentary electorate of the City. Among them were the Apothecaries, whose misadventure gave the fellows something to think about.[2] Their own turn was coming, but when it did come it seems that the authorities did not descend on the College as outraged masters, but with a willingness to respect its needs, at least as far as the law and their policy permitted. The lord chancellor was the senior among the visitors of the College, and business concerning it came into his hands in more than one of his capacities. The holder of this great office was Lord Jeffreys, the leader in the assault on the charters. In 1685 a College matter was referred to him by the privy council. Baldwin Hamey had followed the example of Francis Tryon, which he himself had inspired.[3] He had bequeathed an annual sum of £10 to be paid towards the stipend of the physician of Christ's Hospital, if duly elected as one of two persons whose names were submitted to the governors by the College. Dr. John Downes, a fellow both of the College and of the Royal Society, was in office as physician and claimed his money, but the College repeatedly refused to pay it.[4] Jeffreys after hearing counsel for the Hospital and the College, decided for the Hospital. The earl of Sunderland, as secretary of state, ordered the College in the king's name to pay.[5]

It seems probable that there was some connexion between this incident and a grave announcement which the president now made in comitia.[6] He said that, to his knowledge, a *quo warranto* was to be issued against the College charter at the beginning of the law term. It was unanimously decided to anticipate the blow by surrendering the charter.[7] No doubt it would have been hopeless to resist, but the president seems to have had reason to believe that submission

[1] Text of petition approved 3 September 1687.
[2] On 9 December 1684 the College committee instructed the beadle to take copies of the Surgeons' and Apothecaries' new charters before they should pass the seal.
[3] See above, p. 320.
[4] Submission of the names of Dr. Hodges and Dr. Downes, 17 August 1682.
[5] Letter of 13 October 1685.
[6] Possibly the exposure of Dr. Whistler's shortcomings in the previous year had also attracted the attention of the government to the affairs of the College.
[7] See the Annals, 19 October 1685. *The Case of the College of Physicians, London*, 1689 presented to parliament by the College, says that 23 out of 27 fellows present voted for the surrender.

would not be disadvantageous to the College, at least as he understood its interests. He was Sir Thomas Witherley, an East Anglian
and a Caius man, of whose character unfortunately we know next
to nothing.[1] He was in office from Michaelmas 1684 to Michaelmas
1688, and he seems to have acquired influence by working with
a party within the College. Having appeared first as one of the
honorary fellows of 1664 he became an ordinary fellow in 1677 by
virtue of being second physician to the king. It seems that he was
something of a reformer. During his tenure as president there was
activity in almost every direction, for instance in revising the statutes,
suing unlicensed practitioners and asserting the rights of the College
against its opponents. But it looks as if his policy was to work with,
for and under the ministers, and he may well have been satisfied
or even pleased to pay the price at which the favour of the ministers
of James II could be obtained. He may also have been a weak man,
hurried along by the active party. Whatever his feelings may have
been, he exchanged the old charter for another which conferred new
and obviously desirable powers but imposed one notable limitation.

The new charter was not dated until 11 March 1686/7. It is in
English and has every appearance of following the lines of a petition
or draft put forward by the College.[2] For some unknown reason
it drops the word 'Royal' from the title of the College.[3] As it was
intended to supersede the charter of Charles II it included all the
rights which he had granted. It regularized the practice, which had
already been adopted, of appointing a committee for general
purposes. Within one month of the appointment of the elects those
who had appointed them were to have power to elect a committee of
ten, of whom the president was always to be one. They or any five
of them might meet whenever they thought fit, to consider and
enquire into any matter concerning the College, but they were to
report to the next quarterly comitia ('meeting and convocation')
and they were not granted any executive powers. One substantial
new function was given to the College, one which, as we saw, it

---

[1] See Venn. He had perhaps taught at Holt School in 1660–4, and we know from
Sir Thomas Browne's *Hydriotaphia*, c. ii, that in 1658 he lived at Walsingham.
[2] For the text of the charter see below, Appendix III. In *Cal. of State Papers Domestic,
February–December 1685* (1960), no. 1817, is the reference of a petition from the College
to the attorney general. Mr. Henry Guy, who was thanked for his good offices in relation
to the charter (Committee, 25 May 1687) was presumably a barrister concerned with
drafting: see below, p. 360, n. 3.
[3] Possibly to avoid legal cavil about the identification of the earlier College without
adjective and the Royal College of Charles II.

had kept in view for a quarter of a century.[1] After the expiration of the Act of 1662 (14 Car. II, cap. 33) for the licensing of the press, no printing or publishing on physic or surgery or the practice thereof was to be permitted without the approval of the president and censors. The Act did not expire until 1693, having been continued in this same year 1685,[2] but the College was already exercising this power. By a private and in the beginning secret arrangement Archbishop Sancroft had transferred to it his authority for licensing such books, which it continued to do until the Act ran out and with it the whole system of censorship.[3]

A major change related to the number of fellows: the maximum was raised to eighty. This was a real reform. It went a good way towards solving the problem with which the creation of honorary fellows had merely tinkered, that of making room for all the London physicians who were fit to be fellows. The list of fellows in the charter shows that the College had surveyed the field thoroughly. Altogether there were seventy-six, thirty-six of whom were newcomers. Four were already candidates, twelve were honorary fellows and three were licentiates. There were some prominent men, such as Hans Sloane and Tancred Robinson, fellows of the Royal Society, and John Radcliffe. There was one name, afterwards suitably prominent in the College, of a doctor who had been an apothecary and had not received any university education. This was Francis Bernard, who had been apothecary to St. Bartholomew's Hospital, had earned praises there for his conduct during the great plague and was appointed physician there, on the strength of a Lambeth degree and incorporation at Cambridge. In 1680 he became an honorary fellow of the College. At the same time he ceased, by royal order to be a liveryman of the Society but he was still a freeman, and by becoming a fellow he was the first man to be lawfully both an apothecary and a London physician. His career was exceptional; it could hardly make a precedent; but it shows that there was not yet a complete barrier between the two branches.[4] At least two of the new fellows were sons of members of the College.[5] One of these last was a Roman catholic, as were Dr. Mendez and Dr. Conquest. One of the others may perhaps be classed as a protestant nonconformist.[6] There are several of whom little or

---

[1] See above, p. 321.   [2] 1 Jac. II cap. 17. (S.L.)   [3] 25 June 1687.
[4] For his activities in the College see vol. ii of the present work.
[5] Edward Betts and Lancelot Harrison the younger.
[6] Richard Griffith, but it seems more likely that he was a Roman catholic.

nothing is known (which is no proof that they were insignificant) and it may be that if more is discovered the list will be seen to reflect the tolerance of the king. He was pursuing his unpopular policy of admitting religious dissidents of all kinds to offices, provided they would side with him.[1] Taken as a whole the list represents a strong reinforcement for the College.

There was, however, the price to pay. The king's toleration did not extend to political opponents; very much the contrary; and four of the existing fellows of the College were omitted from the list in the new charter. Almost certainly they were struck out from a list submitted by the College.[2] One of the four, Richard Morton, was probably politically unreliable. As we saw, he was an ejected clergyman, and he received his Oxford doctorate on the nomination of the prince of Orange. It is not easy to guess how the others had offended. Timothy Clarke had done signal service in charge of the arrangements on shore for the naval sick and wounded in the third Dutch war, and the king was a naval man; but, as we know, Dr. Clarke was noted for speaking out, and he may have done himself harm by it. The other two were Dr. Torlesse, an unlucky man in other ways too, and Dr. Rufine, a figure so dim as to be almost invisible. Some honorary fellows were left out. Of these William Denton had been a shining courtier in his day, but he had written uncompromisingly in support of the penal laws against catholics; Henry Sampson was another ejected minister; Nehemiah Grew, the great botanist, was the son of a prominent nonconformist divine; Thomas Gibson's second wife was a daughter of Richard Cromwell, the protector; William Burnet was the brother of the famous Gilbert Burnet, now a proscribed political exile.[3] No doubt there was something against Sir William Langham of Puritan Northampton and Daniel Coxe. The College was purged, but not once and for all: for the future fellows were to be *fideles*,[4] the charter providing that the king, his heirs and successors might by order in council amove the president or any other fellows, elects,

---

[1] Munk has no particulars of Dr. Eglenby, who appears in the list of 1687 as a licentiate. I take him to be Dr. William Aglionby, F.R.S., who was later alleged to have been a papist: see my note in *Notes and Queries*, 12th ser., ix. (1921), 141–3.
[2] The number of names in the charter is four short of the new maximum and in the list in the Annals the four names follow those of the fellows, with the heading 'Fellows left out'.
[3] See T. E. S. Clarke and H. C. Foxcroft, *Life of Gilbert Burnet* (1907), p. 186. This fact was not known to Munk or to J. F. Payne, who wrote the life of Thomas Burnet in the *Dict. of Nat. Biog.*   [4] 29 March 1686/7.

censors or other officers or members. Moreover, unlike all the previous royal charters from the foundation, this contained not a word about confirmation by parliament.

The charter, symbolic of the confidence of the dominant section of the College, was the signal for energetic action. First among the new plans, and ultimately the most fruitful of them all, was a project for rendering free medical services to the poor in co-operation with the City authorities; but from the beginning this plan was beset by difficulties. There were preliminary steps, but for the time being they led to no visible results, and we need not detail them until we come to the revival and execution of the project several years later.[1] In almost every one of the old fields of College endeavour something was undertaken. With legal advice Sir Thomas Millington and Dr. Goodall drafted three new letters 'of great consequence', which were then issued by the king and the privy council, one to the College, the others enjoining the lord mayor and other authorities to assist it according to law.[2] A notice was inserted in the *London Gazette* calling on all London practitioners to submit to the College.[3] At the suggestion of Dr. Burwell the College petitioned for leave to print the letters and such statutes and orders as it had made in pursuance of the Charter concerning the practice of physic, and the prayer was granted.[4]

The College, after suffering in silence for more than a century, addressed a stern letter to every bishop. The bishops were told that there was a great increase of ignorant and unlearned practitioners, that the king had lately ordered the College to suppress them forthwith, that the bishops' power to examine was transferred by the Act of 14 and 15 Henry VIII to the president and three elects. The College therefore humbly requested the bishops to send all applicants for their licences to London to attend upon the president and elects.[5] Since the time of Henry VIII travel from the provinces to London had become safer and quicker and cheaper, but bishops and vicars-general had not become less tenacious of

[1] 29 July 1675; 27 July, 23 August 1687; 13 August 1688; Committee 22 August 1687; 11 May, 1 June 1688. For these proceedings see vol. ii of the present work.
[2] Committee 1, 8 June 1687.   [3] No. 2325, 1 March 1687/8.
[4] 4 February 1687/8. No reply was made to a reminder, in the same petition, of the desire of the College to have its censorship of books included in the licensing legislation then being considered. The text *His Sacred Majesty's Letters to the College of Physicians* (1687) is followed by a short account of the rights and functions of the College.
[5] 29 November 1687, 4 February 1687/8. The bishops' licensing power and their exercise of it were criticized in N. Hodges, *Vindiciae Medicinae*, (1665), pp. 72 ff.

their rights or less careful of their fees. Only one prelate is known
to have fallen in with the wishes of the College, Thomas Cartwright,
bishop of Chester. On receiving the letter he immediately ordered
his secretary to register it. He also had Dr. Compton, whom he had
licensed, recalled and ordered to bring a testimonial from the
president and elects. But Dr. Compton did nothing of the sort,
perhaps because he was not afraid. Just a year later Cartwright,
King James's stoutest supporter among the bishops, fled to join
his master in exile.[1] Whether the other bishops paid any attention
to the letter from the College, and whether it hastened the obsoles-
cence of their licensing power are still matters for research; but
the letter certainly did not put a stop to its exercise.[2]

No less that fifteen new statutes were passed.[3] In five of them
(nos. 1, 3, 4 and 5) relating to secrets, consultations, and controversies between physicians there was little change from the old
except that the fines were increased, no doubt to fit the diminished
value of money. The second statute, which was first discussed four
years earlier, imposed a fine of £10 for consulting with any empiric,
or any physician rejected by the College or forbidden to practise
or unlicensed unless he were a salaried royal physician or a country
doctor who had come up for advice.[4] The sixth made refusal to
pay subscriptions, as well as refusal to pay fines a ground for expulsion. There were two statutes concerning apothecaries. As
experience had shown that apothecaries acquired a false knowledge
from doctors' prescriptions, which they used for their own gain,
it was ordered that no member should add 'directions' to his
prescriptions, except in hospitals. They were to be left with the
patient himself or addressed to his home, and the medicaments
were only to be ordered by their proper, known or distinctive
names. Thus medicasters were not to nose out the purpose or use
of the remedies. The fine for a breach was 20s. (no. 9). The wording
does not clearly bring out the point that 'directions' meant instructions for the use of the medicine written in Latin and so usually
intelligible only to the physician and the apothecary. Directions in

[1] Brit. Mus. MS. Sloane 3915 (C.P. Committee Minute Book), fo. 62.
[2] Bloom and James (1935), pp. 62, 65 give instances from 1697 and 1715 from Essex,
which was in the diocese of London.
[3] 16, 25 June, 27 July, 23, 30 August, 28 September; 8 December 1687. Dr. Underwood points out (p. 359) that a leaf of the Annals has been removed immediately before
that recording the comitia of 16 June, and suggests that something significant may
thus have been cut out; but the committee minutes afford no support for this suggestion.
[4] Committee, 5, 12 March 1682/3.

English, which the patient could understand, were not forbidden and so the statute came to be known as the statute for English directions.[1] Another statute (no. 8) laid it down that any surgeon or apothecary seeking membership was to be fully released from his obligations to his Company before examination or in any case before admission.

Before the next group of statutes was considered it was resolved that before any grave business was dealt with the registrar should read out the passage about good order in the existing seventh statute. The new enactments which followed were seven in number. The first of them (no. 10) imposed the penalties of 40s. for a first offence, £5 for a second and expulsion for a third on any who should make use of an apothecary who had been reported by the president to comitia majora as found guilty by the president and censors of practising or failing to obey a repeated summons. Fellows, candidates and licentiates were to denounce practising apothecaries without respect of persons; failure to do this was to be punished as a breach of faith. Next (no. 11) came a concession to human weakness: an expelled member who frankly and meekly admitted his error in comitia majora might be restored to his place by a majority vote if he paid all the fines due from him and also £10. After this came statutes giving effect to the clauses in the charter about a standing committee (no. 12) and to the demand for a bond from the treasurer and his election (no. 13). In consequence of damaging rumours that some physicians of the College had circulated handbills in the manner of empirics,[2] members were forbidden to print or circulate without leave of a majority of the president and censors anything relating to the medical art or to their practice, on pain of £4 for the first offence, £8 for the second and expulsion for the third (no. 7). The use of the College seal for diplomas was restricted to those of fellowship (no. 14). Arrangements were laid down for a muniment cupboard in the study of Henry Guy, Esq., and for the safe-keeping of the seal (no. 15).[3]

Such were the fifteen *statuta nova* all except one of which were

[1] The text of this statute and of no. 10 is printed from the Annals in Underwood, pp. 360–1.

[2] This must refer to the case of the licentiate Richard Brown who was charged on 14 and 21 October 1687 with so advertising his London pills and made a shuffling defence and a plea of poverty on 28 October but got off with nothing worse than threats.

[3] See above, p. 355 n. 2. Neither of these references fits the well-known Henry Guy, secretary to the treasury.

in force for many years.[1] A sixteenth was sealed with the others to put a stop to the admission of surgeons and apothecaries, and other such craftsmen. None such was to be accepted if he had practised any less liberal art or served an apprenticeship in a shop. There was a sanctimonious reference to the dignity of the College and the honour of the universities; but on the face of them the words mean that no degree of competence should be allowed to overcome a disadvantage of early education, which was nearly the same thing as a disadvantage of social origin. This bold and bad proposal was accepted unanimously for the first time.[2] It seems to have been accepted as valid for the next three years; but then Dr. Richard Blackburne proved to the comitia that a new statute was illegal, This appears to be the statute in question, for from that time in all copies of the *statuta nova* no. 15 is the statute about the custody of the muniments and seal.[3] The ground of the illegality was no doubt the duty of the College to reject only for lack of due learning and skill. The universities had to be content with the restriction of honorary fellowships which followed a few days later.[4]

The College presented the same stern face to applicants for licences to print or publish books. The printer of the *Weekly Occurrences* was told not to insert any more advertisements concerning physic or surgery.[5] Sydenham indeed, as we saw, was approved, but no one else was so fortunate, neither Dr. Crell with his *tractatus*,[6] nor Dr. Dring with his *libellus*,[7] nor the translator of Glauber's works[8] nor, apparently, the anonymous author of 'a small tract'.[9] A translation of Glauber's works by Christopher Packe, a protégé of Robert Boyle and of Dr. Edmund Dickinson, was published in folio in 1689. Packe was an empiric, practising chemical

---

[1] The *Statuta Nova* were sealed on 28 September 1687. There are five sets of them in Bodleian manuscripts, the references for which are Rawlinson Statutes, 3–6 and Gough, London, 12.   Of these the first and third follow complete sets of the statutes previously in force; the second, fourth and fifth include some later additions. The numbering in the text above follows that of Rawl. Statutes, 5. Rawl. Statutes 3 also contains as no. 15 the proposal mentioned below. The dates of the discussion of the statutes are in committee 5, 12 March 1682/3; 15 June–12 October 1687; in comitia 16 June–29 November 1687. The first four statutes in order of enactment were revivals of Elizabethan statutes which had been dropped in or before 1647.

[2] 29 November 1687.

[3] 16 October 1690. On 30 September Dr. Blackburne was fined 2s. by the president for speaking too freely and paid. It may be he who was charged with illicit practice on 7 November 1684, the year before he became an honorary fellow.

[4] 8 December 1687: see above, p. 348.

[5] Committee, 23 March 1687.

[6] 21 October, 16 December 1687: Crell appears in Munk as Crell Spinowski.

[7] 9 December 1687.   [8] 9 April 1688.   [9] 25 May 1688.

medicine at the sign of the Globe and Chemical Furnaces.[1] It is to be feared that he defied the College but the story has a fairly happy ending for his son got as far as being admitted a candidate.

Hugh Chamberlen, afterwards a more conspicuous public figure than any of his family had been, imitated his father and his grandfather by petitioning for 'a patent relating to midwifery'. His attempt seems, however, to have been stifled without difficulty at an early stage.[2] It was followed by a charge of malpractice. The censors behaved so harshly over this, and the registrar recorded their proceedings with so much care and so little respect for Chamberlen that this charge seems to have been part of an effort to put down his ambitions. He had given medical treatment to an unfortunate woman who then suffered a miscarriage and died. He was accused of refusing to consult with physicians over the case. His defence was not convincing, but the censors refused to let him see the written statements on which they relied. They fined him £10, wrote out a warrant for committing him to Newgate and sent for a constable. The prisoner pulled £10 in gold out of his pocket, but the board told him to give it to the beadle. When they met a fortnight later Mr. Chamberlen sent his apothecary with an order from the lord chancellor that they were to give him a copy of the information or affidavit against him. They told the messenger that their proceedings had been perfectly correct, but in deference to the lord chancellor they as good as gave in. In the end they seem to have got their money, but nothing more.[3]

On the first occasion when a Chamberlen tried to set up as the lawful head of the midwives' profession, the College had put up a counter-proposal for assuming some such control itself.[4] An incident now followed which may have arisen from a similar intention, but there is no proof that it was so, and it may have come about independently of these events, or of any initiative from the College. In the still unexplored records of the position of women in England there is much to show that for one reason and another their

---

[1] Was he perchance the 'Peck' who appears in the list of those who were to be sued at law, 12 October 1688?

[2] The committee decided on 22 August 1687 to oppose the application, and their minute of 28 November 1687, that a caveat is to be entered with the lord chancellor, perhaps relates to their action to this end.

[3] The entries from 16 March 1687/8 to 18 January 1688/9 are given in full in J. H. Aveling, *The Chamberlens* (1882), pp. 139 ff. A reader who looks closely will detect one discrepancy between the evidence and the record signed by the four censors.

[4] See above, p. 237.

opportunities widened in the late seventeenth century. Perhaps it is a sign of this that the best advocate of a college for midwives was now a woman, Mrs. Cellier. This and the project of a foundling hospital which she combined with it may have had no real chance of success even in the reign of James II, when she was at least sheltered by authority from persecution as a convert to popery[1]; and no doubt she would have been rebuffed if she had asked for the approval of the physicians. Very soon after the Revolution, however, their College did give its approval to another woman's attempt to improve the status of midwives on the smallest possible scale. The College deserves a mite of credit for not blocking the way. One censors' day 'Mrs. Wolveston came to have our hands to her being a Licentiate in Midwifery. She was examined and modestly and prudently answered to satisfaction'.[2]

There is little or nothing of scientific interest to record in these years. The censors refused to allow Mr. Stoughton, the apothecary, to use their names in advertising his new oil for use against the gout.[3] The committee gave its approval to Dr. Clench's proposals for amending the Bills of Mortality. Although these weekly returns from the Parish Clerks' Company were the only materials for statistics of the health of London, they were notoriously defective. Dr. Clench's proposals may have some relation to some which were drawn up much earlier by Dr. Betts and referred to the College by the court of aldermen. Neither set seems to have been adopted.[4]

There was a drive against unlicensed practitioners. More than thirty of them were accused, for the most part of the usual types. Mrs. Coleby was the only woman[5]; two foreigners absconded after failing in their examinations, the linguist Sylvanus from Hungary who did not know his anatomy,[6] and the twenty-years practitioner Salvator Winter, who owned to having no Latin.[7] 'The mountebank on Tower Hill'[8] and the Benedictine Julian Whitefield,[9] were the most picturesque. Except for one oculist charged with malpractice,[10] and one empiric who printed bills, the crimes present little of

---

[1] Mrs. Cellier's husband was a Frenchman and the idea of a foundling hospital may have been suggested by the example of St. Vincent de Paul.

[2] 6 December 1689: not, however, in Munk.

[3] 15 November, 7 December 1688.

[4] Committee 5 December 1687. The earlier proposals and the reference from the City (5 December 1676) are in Bodleian MS. Rawlinson C 406, fos. 84–85.

[5] 1, 8 March 1688/9.

[6] Nine entries from 28 October 1687 to 18 May 1688.

[7] Four entries from 16 March 1687/8 to 11 May 1688.

[8] 18 May 1688.   [9] 4, 11 May 1688.   [10] 2 March 1687/8.

interest. The persons accused behaved much like their forerunners, but perhaps there was more inclination to offer money to buy off the censors.[1] There was an unusual number of prosecutions in the courts; it is impossible to say exactly how many; but the results appear to have disappointed the censors. It may, however, have been only in consequence of temporary inconveniences caused by the confused state of College business that when they resolved on 4 October 1689 to summon all the London practising doctors who had not applied to the College,[2] they also resolve 'that practice against Quacks be taken, but prosecution suspended till time convenient'.

The new charter strengthened the College on paper against the surgeons and the apothecaries, and the College was in the mood to press this advantage. There was indeed no significant increase in prosecutions of surgeons; but several apothecaries were charged, and one was discommoned.[3] In 1687 John Badger presented himself as a Cambridge doctor. But a week before he applied the new statutes had been sealed, and he was told that in accordance with the eighth new statute he must prove that he was entirely relieved of any jurisdiction and obligation of the Society. This he never did. The College thus defeated his attempt to win the right of practice for such apothecaries as also acquired a medical qualification. When he wrote on the apothecaries' side in the next great collision of the two interests, the Society refused to pay his expenses, so that he seems to have had little personal satisfaction. But the trick by which the College defeated him was remembered against it.[4]

In the winter of 1687-8 both the Companies were on their guard. Mr. Gardiner in conversation with Dr. Charlton 'impudently bade the College not dare to meddle with the surgeons'.[5] With the apothecaries the committee was determined to meddle, and by November 1687 all was ready. The moment was not indeed propitious. The Society of Apothecaries had its own new charter and the new

---

[1] 30 March, 6 July 1688, 7 November 1690.
[2] Those named were Cary, Byfield, Salmon, Lloyd, Hicks, Grear.
[3] Richard Neger, 12 October 1688, 8 March 1688/9.
[4] The Annals for 7 December 1683 and 7 October 1687 are supplemented by Barrett, p. 17; Venn, *Alumni Cantabrigienses*, and the prefatory matter in *Statuta Collegii Medicorum* (1693). Badger matriculated from Emmanuel in December 1681, took his M.B. in 1682 and his M.D. in 1687.
[5] 23 March 1687/8.

livery was doing what the king expected of it in City elections. He received a deputation which the Society sent to thank him for his Declaration of Indulgence to religious dissenters, and he received it graciously.[1] Not only was it the wrong time to pick a quarrel; there were also weaknesses on the physicians' side. As of old there were some among the fellows who played the apothecaries' game: the committee bluntly resolved that breaches of faith and honour had caused the late difficulties of the College. It asked the president and censors to prosecute the offenders and so, incidentally, to raise some money for paying off the debt.[2] The censors singled out one fellow whom they accused of frequently violating the ninth new statute by adding Latin directions to his prescriptions. This fellow was none other than Dr. Edward Browne, a future president and the eldest son of Sir Thomas Browne. He failed to answer at a censors' day, with the inadequate excuse that he had been summoned to attend the great banker Sir Josiah Childe. For this he was fined 10*s.*, but he seems to have escaped further annoyance.[3] In the meantime the committee sent the beadle to Apothecaries' Hall with a summons to the master and wardens. They were to ordain first that none of their freemen should practise physic, upon such penalty as they should think fitting, and secondly that they would compensate anyone who complained on oath that any of their freemen had oppressed him by an unreasonable bill.[4] This was a summons to unconditional surrender, and when the December comitia assembled it must have been well known that battle was imminent.

At the comitia the censors complained that some of the apothecaries questioned their authority to search the files of bills. The standing committee, having considered the law, recommended the College to pass an order at once that any apothecary who refused them this right should be discommoned: 'but some heats arising between some of the members of the College, fitter to be forgot than registered, nothing concerning this order was done'.[5] The master and two of the wardens of the Society of Apothecaries paid a call on the president and censors, when both hosts and visitors exchanged civilities, but little of moment passed between them.[6]

[1] Barrett, pp. 106–8.   [2] Committee, 4 November 1687.
[3] 23 November; 9, 21 December 1687. No decision is recorded on Dr. Elliot's accusation that Dr. Browne misbehaved over a consultation: 7, 21 January 1687/8.
[4] Committee, 23 November 1687.
[5] 22 December 1687; Committee, 21 December.   [6] 14 January 1687/8.

Two months later there was a very different scene in Warwick Lane. The lord chancellor, Lord Jeffreys, visited the College.[1] His visitation was arranged beforehand, but the College cannot have known beforehand exactly what he intended to do. We must not heighten the drama of the occasion by supposing that all his public and personal ambitions and vices came into play; he was a lawyer, carrying out his legal duty, just as he did many other circumscribed legal duties which had nothing to do with state affairs. He had been recorder of London and standing counsel to St. Bartholomew's Hospital. But we must not divest that day of its excitement. The dreaded Jeffreys had been more responsible than anyone else for the changes of the physicians' and the apothecaries' charters. Now he had summoned all the fellows and the heads of the two Companies.

By some means or another the two Companies had obtained copies of the new by-laws passed in the previous August and each had put in a well-arranged and well-phrased petition stating its own objections to them. None of the old, familiar arguments was omitted, and there were new ones which could not be despised. Both Companies said that it was contrary to the College charters to refuse a licence to any qualified person on the ground of his being a surgeon or an apothecary. The surgeons said it was monopolistic and they added that 'within the circuit of the doctors' charter there are upwards of a million of persons, and the doctors of all sorts not many above one hundred'. Thus at last the fatal defect in the College case was nailed down in an official paper. The surgeons also said that the lord mayor and court of aldermen had lately refused an application from the College to have their beadle sworn in as a constable. The apothecaries said that the College had assumed the power to ruin any one of them without trial and had used it to gratify personal animosities.

The lord chancellor was received in the censors' room; then all except the College were excluded. He said that the occasion of his visiting was the great outcry in the town that they were injuring the surgeons and apothecaries, whose petitions he could not in justice disregard. Yet as a favour to the College he first asked them privately what they had done to disoblige the surgeons. They said

[1] He seems to have acted not as a senior visitor of the College under the new charter, which confirmed that of Charles II, but as lord chancellor. He acted at the same time in the same relation to the surgeons and the apothecaries, and under the charter two visitors had to act together.

they had done nothing except to summon Mr. Gardiner and warn him not to practise physic as a doctor. The doors to the long gallery were opened, and the surgeons came in. Mr. Hobbs, the master. spoke, but Lord Jeffreys told him that the new College statute did not mean that physicians were not to consult with surgeons, and so he dismissed the surgeons briefly as persons more afraid than hurt. Before the apothecaries were called in, the visitor had a private word for the College. He was civil enough, as he could be when he chose, and his words were moderate but they amounted to a reprimand.[1] He told them that before making statutes and putting them in execution they ought to have brought them, as they easily might have done, to him as their visitor and friend to give them his sanction. They replied, we may think tactlessly or worse, that their standing counsel Serjeant Holt had advised them there was no need to trouble his lordship. The chancellor seemed in some measure to be on the side of the apothecaries over the by-laws, and the College had to promise to submit its reasons in writing. The doors were opened for the master, Alderman Saint Amand, and his brethren, to whom the lord chancellor said that according as was fit he would do them right.[2]

This visitation was unique. Never before and never after it did any public authority assemble the three medical professions of London in order to judge of their mutual relations. From the lord chancellor's point of view it was occasioned by public feeling about a dispute between the corporations and to that extent he may be said to have acted on behalf of the community; but there was nothing in his legal position which made such action possible then but not earlier or later. It is worth asking whether there was something special to the temper of the time that favoured it, and the answer to this seems to be that we may have an example here of the good side, the paternalistic or even reforming side, of those authoritarian ideas which earned such detestation for James II.

The committee met two days later. It decided, as was proper, that the lord chancellor should be thanked for the honour he had done the College, and that papers should be drawn up about the apothecaries. It considered that it would be useful if members

---

[1] I hesitate to accept the statement of a publication of 1689 (or perhaps 1690) that Jeffreys spoke 'in great *Fury*': *Vindication of the College of Physicians from the Reflections made upon them by the Apothecaries in Parliament*, p. 2, in Bodleian MS. Rawlinson C. 419. By that time Jeffreys was down or dead and it was politic to represent him as an enemy.   [2] 28 March 1688.

would report for record excessive bills or notorious mischief perpetrated by ignorant apothecaries.[1] Whether its emotions were as calm as its minutes may be doubted. The papers were not ready until May. In the meantime the apothecaries were thought to have entered a *caveat* with the lord chancellor against the new College statutes. Two of these were defended in the papers which the College deputation handed to him. He does not seem to have replied in writing.[2] One physician at least was disheartened: Sir Thomas Witherley, the president, moved at the censorial comitia a week later 'about the apothecaries' willingness to comply &c.', which means that he wanted to negotiate. The president and the lord chancellor were both concerned in an odd little incident in which John Tivell profited from the confusion of the moment. He was the first apothecary who complied with the new statute and obtained his disfranchisement from the Society before becoming a licentiate, but his admission as a licentiate was irregular. One day in May 1688, when a pro-president was sitting in the *comitia minora*, Tivell was asked who spoke for him to the lord chancellor that he might come in as a licentiate *intra urbem*. He said it was Sir Thomas Witherley, who had given him a College seal.[3] That was true, for he produced the document at the next meeting; and Sir Thomas alleged that he had been authorized in full comitia to give seals to several persons. Several months later Tivell was balloted on and admitted, but he was told that if he dispensed physic to any patients but his own he would be expelled.[4] Whether Sir Thomas Witherley, with or without reluctance, was carrying out the wishes of Lord Jeffreys and doing all he could for apothecaries must remain uncertain. He received proposals from the Society, but he did not carry the censors with him.[5] They considered that they should be left to proceed in their own method. They were willing to yield to anything reasonable but unwilling to make any approach to the apothecaries.[6] While they held on their course the whole face of law and politics changed.

[1] Committee, 29 March 1688, on which day it was also decided to enquire from the clerk to the privy council whether the Companies were taking action in that quarter.

[2] Committee, 11 May 1688.

[3] For the word 'seal' see above, p. 104.

[4] 11, 18 May; 21 December 1688, the last entry having the text of his dismission from the Society of Apothecaries, dated 7 August 1688.

[5] During the negotiation of 1690 (R.C.P., MS. 274a) he handed over the proposals made when St. Amand was master of the Society, i.e. between August 1687 and August 1688.   [6] 18 May 1688.

Even when the new charter was received with deferential ceremony in the spring of 1687[1] the king's fortunes were waning, and
in the autumn of 1688 he faced manifest danger from his aggrieved
subjects and from the prince of Orange. He retreated from the most
high-handed of his measures, and he proclaimed that all corporations were to be restored as they were before they surrended their
charters; all officers holding since a surrender were removed from
place; all deeds of surrender were to be cancelled and returned; all
charters of incorporation granted after 1679 were to be annulled
and void.[2] Three days later he informed a special council meeting
of the intended landing of the Dutch, against whom he was resolved
to go in person. Mayors and aldermen and physicians had to take
their bearings.

The College had elected a new president immediately before the
smash, Dr. George Rogers, ex-treasurer.[3] This change may have
had nothing to do with political events. Under this new head the
comitia censoria went on with the energetic steps begun by his
predecessor, uninfluenced by the world outside. The censors, Drs.
Johnston, Griffith, Harris and Blackborne, acquainted the College
that several of its number daily transgressed the statute about
English directions, and the committee called for its immediate
enforcement. Dr. Bernard, the ex-apothecary, argued in opposition
that the nobility and gentry would not like to have the censors
viewing prescriptions made for them. To this the censors retorted
'Why not the censors as well as the apothecaries and their boys and
any they were pleased to show them to'. Besides, they added, what
they would principally look at were the Latin directions and,
venturing hardily, they said the laws of the land were not to be
annulled to please the nobility or others. The College backed the
censors up by twenty-three votes to six, and the voting was the same
on a proposal that none of the College should write prescriptions
for apothecaries who refused to let the censors see their files.[4]

On the same day the censors demanded the right to summon their
own meetings, giving the president three days notice. Before the
end of the year the beadle had served notices of these decisions on
the fellows who had been absent, and on St. Valentine's day three

[1] 12 April 1687.

[2] 17 October 1688: Steele and Crawford no. 3881; *London Gazette*, no. 2391.

[3] Munk mistakenly says that Rogers served as English consul at Padua: he was consul
for the English 'nation' in the university. He was the son of a former fellow.

[4] 21 December 1688.

fellows, each prominent in his way, were brought to book. Dr. Pitt was fined £1 for one offence. Dr. Tyson shuffled and was granted time until the first Friday in March. Dr. John Radcliffe frankly owned his offence and told the censors that if they had not come into the shop at the moment when the apothecary was dispensing his prescription it would have been hidden. He promised to obey the statute as well as he was able, but the censors fined him £2 for two offences. When March came there was a fourth defendant, Dr. Grew, and he quibbled about the form of his summons, but he had to pay £2. Dr. Tyson failed to appear and his fine was £4. It was decided to prosecute any of the four who did not pay. Dr. Tyson had other troubles on his hands, and for one reason or another the censors began proceedings against him in the courts, but the president stopped them and the censors could only protest.[2] Dr. Radcliffe, as we shall see, was an even tougher customer.

The censors had done what they could to vindicate the law; but the College was now to be convulsed by a matter of law on a larger scale. There was a division of opinion about a legal nicety. The proclamation which reversed the policy of King James II made some distinction between those old charters of which the surrender had been enrolled and those of which it had not. Dr. Rogers thought as anyone but a lawyer might well think, that since neither the new charter of the College nor the surrender of the old charter had gone through this final stage of enrolment, the old charter of Charles II was again in force. Therefore at the quarterly meeting before Christmas, when England had no king, Dr. Torlesse and Dr. Morton were present, and the fellows intruded by James II were not summoned. For the next quarterly comitia, after William and Mary were proclaimed king and queen, summonses were issued in the same way; but many of the new fellows appeared unsummoned, demanding the right to be admitted. There followed a great debate, at the end of which it was agreed that whether the old charter was surrendered or not, the new was valid. The statutory procedure was then followed: at the censor's request Sir Charles Scarburgh, a consiliarius, in the presence of the censors, the registrar, Sir Thomas Millington and Dr. Lower, admonished the president in the privacy of the censors' room and advised him to

<hr />

[2] The licentiate Dr. Richard Brown complained that Dr. Tyson refused to meet him (presumably in consultation) 'saying that he gave his own physick and was a quack' and 'that it was a quackish thing to give his own physick'. For this Dr. Tyson was fined £4: 4, 11, 18 January; 8, 10 February 1688/9.

acknowledge his errors, which he did. The party moved to the theatre where several new fellows were present, including three of the papists, but none of the four whom James II had excluded. The president repeated his confession and promised for the future to abide by the new charter. He also declared that what had been done was not his act, but the act of those that deluded him', with whom he would cabal no more. Sir Charles Scarburgh then successfully appealed for an amnesty, to keep unity among the fellows. The president announced that he had ordered a 'general college' for that day week.[1]

At this special meeting clouds gathered again. The president produced a letter signed by all four of the excluded fellows and by three of their colleagues. They had taken legal advice and they warned the College of the dangers it ran in acting under the pretended new charter. The thirty-nine fellows present at the meeting decided, it seems contemptuously, against them; but Dr. Bateman pointed out that the new charter might be accidentally included among others that were likely to be vacated. A committee was therefore appointed to consult lawyers, to attend the house of commons committee of grievances and if need were the parliament itself, and to do anything else that might be necessary in this affair.[2] Within a week the next quarterly comitia came round and the fellows present signed a petition to the committee of grievances.[3] No help came from that quarter: the petition was withdrawn. Knowing by this time the insecurity of charters, the College committee pressed on and presented a Bill to the house of lords.[4]

At the June comitia when it confirmed this action and appointed the same committee to continue in charge of the Bill, the College had before it an ominous communication from the house of lords about another matter.[5] Printed copies were going about in London of a declaration issued by the late king from Ireland to all his loving subjects in England. Some of those who circulated these were arrested, including two of King James's fellows of the College, Dr. Robert Gray and Dr. John Elliott.[6] The house of commons voted

[1] 11 March 1688/9. On 3 May following Dr. Goodall was appointed to draw up the heads of Sir Thomas Witherley's case for the new president and the censors, but any document which may have resulted does not seem to be preserved.
[2] 19 March 1688/9.   [3] 25 March 1689.
[4] For the parliamentary proceedings see *House of Lords Papers, 1689–1690* (1889), pp. 121–9, and *The Case of the College of Physicians, London,* 1689.
[5] See also 10 October 1689.
[6] N. Nuttrell, *Brief Historical Relation of State Affairs* (1857), i. 546, 551–2.

to impeach them of high treason and preparations went forward for their trial before the lords. The house of lords ordered the College to return the names of such members as were papists, and reputed papists or criminals. It sent in five names under the religious heading, the two Betts father and son, Sir William Waldegrave and Dr. Mendez; under the other Dr. Gray and Dr. Elliott. Assuming that all seven would have to be thrown overboard, it chose, to fill their place in the Bill to confirm the charter, two candidates, four honorary fellows (Dr. Burnet, Dr. Coxe, Dr. Gibson and Dr. Grew, dismissed by James) and one licentiate.[1] Soon afterwards the oaths to the new king and queen were tendered.[2] Most of the victims of James II took them, and a few of his creatures, so the College was persisting in its line of holding that both charters were valid.

As it was first drafted the private Bill promoted by the College contained clauses to confirm the privileges granted in the charters earlier than James II, to give the censors power to summon and put accused persons on oath, and also for exemption from jury service, City offices and watch and ward. As might have been expected the Barber Surgeons and the Apothecaries opposed it, but the College, through its counsel before the committee of the lords took a very reasonable line. As its counsel said, the College would be content so long as they had an Act raising their permitted number to eighty and that of the elects to sixteen. After offering a proviso to except the two companies from the operation of the bill, in the end it withdrew the clauses concerning them, so that they were satisfied. There was, however, also opposition from another quarter. The president himself, Dr. Rogers, with eleven of the ancient fellows petitioned against it, alleging that Sir Thomas Witherley and others had procured the surrender of the old charter by threats and that the new fellows had put in a petition to the house of commons which, not being liked, was withdrawn. They maintained that forty fellows were enough to govern any corporation; but the committee decided against them; the Bill was reported and sent to the commons. There it was dropped after the first reading.[3]

---

[1] 1 October 1689.

[2] 1 William and Mary c. 8; 30 July 1689. Dr. Timothy Clarke did not take the oaths until 22 December and was absent from the Michaelmas comitia.

[3] 10 December 1689, 7 February 1689/90, 22 September 1690; Barrett pp. 110–11. The lords' proceedings lasting from 7 June to 4 July 1689, with the text of the bill and amendments and notices of the petitions are given in *House of Lords Papers 1689–1690* (1889) pp. 121–9. The eleven ancient fellows were Drs. Lawson, Brooke, Torlesse,

Towards the end of the year the College made a further attempt to heal the breach among the fellows. By twenty one votes to three four of the old fellows and four of the new were set down to devise a plan.[1] They reported in writing and at a special meeting the College voted on eight questions, six of which had to do with precedence among the various kinds of fellows and honorary fellows who had to be sorted out. These we may pass over. Such puerilities still trouble the harmony of colleges (may Heaven forgive us) but we try to forget them. The remaining questions were more substantial. It was decided in answer to one of them that *pro hac vice* the statutes concerning examinations, that relating to Oxford and Cambridge and others which stood in the way should be suspended for the fellows admitted by King James's charter. None of the votes was unanimous; in most of them there were abstentions, in two the minority was nine, but in none of the others was it more than two. We cannot put names to any of these figures; but there is one further answer which seems to do everyone credit: the College would pay the expenses, amounting to £82, of the fellows who had opposed the Bill. This painful and unheroic chapter in the history of the College seems to have ended, if not with good will, at least with dignity.[2]

One chance remained of obtaining a settlement of the membership question under parliamentary sanction. The attempt to do this by private Bill had failed, but the government had also brought in a general Corporation Bill for restoring the old charters of corporations. This bill was intended to settle all the legal complications, and here the College committee saw a chance of easing the internal difficulties. It drafted a proviso which the College decided to send to the house of lords, with a view to protecting the Jacobean (and possibly Jacobite) fellows whom it wanted to retain.[3] The College also decided *nem. con.*, but with some subsequent opposition, to

J. Clerk, Fine, Morton, Browne, Tyson, Atfield, Downes and Alvey. The undated *Reasons for Passing the Physicians' Bill* (1690) is an extract from a longer document formerly in the possession of Charles Goodall, now in the Bodleian MS. Rawlinson C 406, fos. 362–3.

[1] Committee 18, 25 October; Annals 18 November 1689. The last committee minutes before these are dated 20 December 1688.

[2] 21, 26 November; 5, 17 December 1689. The indignant narrative in Brit. Mus. MS. Sloane 1815 fos. 7ᵛ ff. shows that there was still resentment among the fellows.

[3] The proviso ran that, whereas the College was in no wise concerned with electing members of parliament, the Act should not extend to disfranchising or prejudicing any of those admitted to any order or degree in it so long as they took the new oaths and made the declaration required by the Act (Committee, 9 January 1689/90).

delay putting the oaths to these fellows 'for a while till the Bill of Corporation shall passe'.[1] It never did pass: the whigs tried to turn it into a weapon for driving their old opponents out of political life, and this rashness ruined the Bill.

The house of commons no doubt had too much on its hands to legalize the enlargement of the College but the ultimate result of its deliberations opened a new era in the history of the medical profession, not a better era but one with new problems and new solutions for the old. The Revolution Settlement, without making any of them too strong for the free and sometimes boisterous play of interests and opinions, gave the Crown and parliament, the aristocracy and the corporations, Anglicans, Roman Catholics and dissenters each a firm footing to live their own life without the constant fear of oppression. The College entered at last on a period when matters of state and religion no longer interrupted its proper activities. A generation later indeed it did happen that one of the fellows, Dr. Freind, was charged with High Treason and immured in the Tower of London; but this was the aberration of an individual, and it shook the reputation of the College no more than did the nocturnal yelling of the neighbouring cats.

In the meantime what had become of Dr. Gray and Dr. Elliott? Dr. Gray escaped, but he was recaptured in an open boat on his way to Calais. After a good many months in prison he was released on bail and then both the impeachments were dropped. In 1696, at the time of the Assassination Plot against William III, Dr. Gray was again taken up for treasonable practices, but not convicted. In 1705 he became an honorary fellow of the Royal College of Physicians of Edinburgh. The more tractable Dr. Elliott, after his release faded silently out of sight.[2] So did the charter of James II. Once the problems of the membership were settled the College could get on without it. It was never enrolled, nor printed nor, it would seem, even copied out. Lawyers could have discovered many arguments against its validity and there was no need to invoke its authority in public. For the next seven years it stayed in its box undisturbed.[3]

---

[1] 22 December 1689; 9, 14 January 1689/90; Committee 7 January 1689/90.

[2] Luttrell, i. 553–6, 559, 561, ii. 13, 29, iv. 79. For the mistaken identification of Dr. Gray as the town's physician at Newcastle-upon-Tyne until he died in 1701, see Venn and J. Brand, *History of Newcastle-upon-Tyne*, ii (1789), 363. His name re-appears in the published lists of the College of Physicians in 1694, but without any address.

[3] In a return made to the select committee of the house of commons on medical education and printed in their *Report* (1834), pt. I, Appendix, p. 12 the College stated

'The Charters of James I, Charles 2, and James 2 were never accepted by the College'. What constituted legal acceptance of a charter at any of these three dates I do not pretend to know; but the proceedings described above on pp. 231, 243 and 369 prove that from the point of view of untutored common sense the College accepted those of James I and James II. Although parliament did not confirm any of them, the first two were printed in Goodall's *Royal College of Physicians founded by Law* (1684). In the negotiations with the apothecaries in 1690 (see above, p. 368 n. 5) Mr. Bradford asked whether the College renounced the charter of James II: 'We answered no.' On 8 November 1692 Dr. Bateman explained in comitia that by not publishing a list of fellows the College had avoided publicly accepting that of James II which was 'solely an act of the government, the College noways to be blamed'. I suspect that in 1696 the lawyers blessed the idea that it had not been accepted. By that time the law itself may have changed.

APPENDIXES

I The Earliest Statutes of the College

II The Statutes of 1647

III The Charter of King James II

I The Earliest Statutes of the College [1]

fo. 9

Statuta Collegii Medicorum Londini per clarissimum virum Thomam Linacrum et Collegium predictum regia authoritate incepta atque edita anno domini 1520. Et per Joannem Caium presidentem in ordinem redacta aucta et abso- luta eadem au- thoritate et Col- legio, anno 1555

fo. 10

Statuta Collegii Medicorum Londini

Quum regi nostro serenissimo Henrico euis nominis octavo visum sit et privata concessione et publicis plebisciti seu perlamenti sui decretis ut hoc nostrum Collegium in decus regni et salutem reipublicae stabili- atur, privilegiis muniatur, possessionibus ornetur, electoribus insigniatur, presidente gubernetur, statutis dirigatur, eadem condendi facultate donetur, consiliariis adiuvetur, literis perpetuetur, consultissimum etiam nobis visum est ut prescribamus, primo qui sint futuri electores, quod eorum sit officium: tum quis sit futurus presidens, quo modo eligatur et a quibus: quid fide sua et iuramento recipiet se facturum, quod eius officium et potestas, quis locus atque dignitas: dein qui consiliarii, quid illis iuramento prestandum, et quod eorum sit officium locus et potentia: Quarto qui censores literarum morum et item medicinarum sint consti-

10ᵛ tuendi, quoque officio | ex iuramento illis fungendum: postremo quid reliquos collegas decat in sui honorem et Collegii, in quid illis iurandum:

---

[1] The text is taken from Bodleian MS. Ashmole 1826. Marginal annotations in later hands are not included, nor the alphabetical index on fos. 5–8.

Sique statuta condenda, sique abroganda, quo id fiat modo: que sit comitiorum, examinationum atque admissionum forma: que sit offense habenda ratio, cum iis que in universum ad omnes eiusdem Collegii personas et negotia ex aequo spectant. Etenim nihil duraturum est quod careat ratione modo atque ordine.

De electoribus creandis

Volumus igitur et statuimus ut e numero collegarum electores octo tantum eligantur et creentur qui gravitate, literis, moribus incorruptis, et senioritate ceteris prefulgeant, doctoratusque gradu insigniantur, et natione Angli sint. Horum intererit ex authoritate Collegii et argumento nominis, postridie divi Michaelis in celebribus comitiis perpetuo officio presidentem eligere, si anni superioris presidens defuncto anno officio superfuerit. Sique autem defecerit ille, quanta fieri potest commoditate alium surrogare, ad plurimum | post dies viginti quam is defecerit.

11   Si electorum unus aliquis defecerit aut plures, electione sufficiat alius aut plures in eius aut eorum locum ex ceteris collegis qui eiusdem nationis, gradus, morum, literarum atque ordinis erunt, cuius priores erant de quibus iam ante diximus, intra dies triginta aut plurimum quadraginta, sed ita ut illis comitiis alii collegarum nulli intersint preter electores, quo liberior sit electio et morum, ingenii, gravitatis, atque litterarum iustior examinatio, quorum probitatem in electore vel maxime requirunt statuta regni. Eligatur autem ceterorum omnium electorum consensu, si fieri poterit, sin minus, per seniorem partem.

Juramentum Electoris

Jurabis te nemini daturum consensum aut suffragium tuum ut presidens aut elector creetur nisi secundum formam statuti, et nisi cuius gravitatem, literas, mores incorruptos, aetatem decentem, bonum animi affectum in Collegium et rempublicam et alacritatem ad obeunda officia, cognitam et perspectam | habeas, ita te Deus adiuvet et sancta Dei
11ᵛ evangelia.

De Presidente

Qui presidens sit futurus in annum designetur, ex numero esto electorum, et quem ceteri electores presentes, aut omnes aut eorum maior pars, pro temporis, rei et persone ratione idoneum indicaverint, et eo anni tempore quo iam ante constitutum est cum de electoribus ageremus, postridie videlicet divi Michaelis. Si paritas sit suffragiorum, ea pars vincat, in qua plures ex senioribus doctoribus fuerint. Quod si horum quoque paritas fuerit, ea obtinebit in qua vetus presidens, aut eo mortuo vel absente, presidens natus inclinabit.

Presidentem natum vocamus qui omnium primus ex iis qui pro presenti tempore superfuerint, in Collegium admissus est qui etsi presidentis nomen gerat, tamen nullam potestatem habeat condendi aut mutandi 12 statuta, administrandi fungendive presidentis munere, nisi presidente | mortuo, aut vacante officio.

Qui per se vel per alium repugnavit aut contradixerit statutis de electione presidentis et electorum, ipso facto Collegio expellatur et omni eiusdem beneficio privetur in perpetuum.

Juramentum Presidentis

Jurabis te pro viribus conaturum ut honor Collegii conservetur, statuta eiusdem pro sensu grammaticali sine fraude aut fuco ullo observentur teque studiose perlecturum statuta Collegii et annales intramenses tres ab electione tua, nisi tibi prius cognita et perspecta fuerint, omniaque acturum in salutem reipublicae et honestam utilitatem Collegii, ita te Deus adiuvet et sancta Dei evangelia.

Juramentum deferet seu ministrabit presidenti novo superioris anni aut presidens si adfuerit, aut consiliariorum alter, senior potissimum, si adsit.

De Presidentis Admissione

12ᵛ Qui iuramentum detulit, idem porrigat | virtutis insignia, pulvinar nempe honoris et caduceum, dicatque: damus tibi presidendi authoritatem, tradimusque pulvinar honoris, librum cognitionis et caduceum gubernationis et prudentiae: ut intelligat tua excellentia et ceteri college universi, cognitione et prudentia collegium nostrum stare et permanere. Quamobrem ne id memoria excidat tua, in solemnioribus processionibus, pompis et officiis funebribus aliisque temporibus atque locis opportunis gestari curabis ante te per accisum librum et caduceum, in cognitionis et prudentiae signum, ut quod virtus postulat, id usus confirmet.

De Ratione Ponendi Officium

Defuncto officio, presidendi munus depositurus presidens finita quam velit prefatione, ita dicat: depono presidendi authoritatem inque tuas manus (alterius videlicet consiliariorum, senioris potissimum) omnium nomine restituo, ut integrum omnibus sit quibus eligendi potestas sit 13 quem velint substituere. Reddo igitur tibi pul | vinar honoris, librum cognitionis, et caduceum prudentis gubernationis praecorque Collegio et vobis omnia fausta. Quo facto, cui delegata potestas est, proponat eligendum quem in id officii maxime idoneum fore noverit et eum aliumve qui pro statutorum ratione electus est, clare et nominatim pronunciet electum iubeatque ut omnes eum pro presidente habeant.

Tunc electum iurare faciet in verba Collegii, ut est ante comprehensum, et cetera rite peragat, ut in admissione presidentis est statutum.

De Presidentis Loco et Dignitate

Eius locus primus esto, ut et dignitas prima, sed in Collegio tantum. Extra Collegium nullum arrogabit sibi locum aut dignitatem eximiam preter ceteros nisi pro ratione gradus et senioritatis observato semper doctores licentiatis, seniores iunioribus in suo gradu atque ordine et intra Collegium et extra preferendos. Collegium vocamus non solum comitiorum ordinarium locum, sed ipsos conventus et comitia | etiam collegarum funeris, processionis aut convivii solemnioris causa celebrata: ut et senioritatem, non quam aetas aut longi temporis gradus fecere, sed quam admissio in Collegium. Aeque et licentiatos appellamus, non candidatos, sed quos baccalaureos fecit aliqua universitas, aut facultatem tantum donavit exercendi medicinam sine gradu aliquo.

De Presidentis Officio

Illi officium esto ut comitia indicat, sed qua ratione tum dicemus cum de comitiis statuemus: tum ut causas comitiorum proponat: singulorum sententias excipiat, pro maiori parte decernat, aut aliter pro statuti ratione: factiones excludat, quod decretum est in libros actorum seu pandectas primo referat, et presens legat, post, finito anno memoratu tantum digna in annales transferat, ad eam formam que per omnem librum observata prius est. Electores, consiliarios, literarum, morum et medicinarum censores cum ceteris, quorum intererit, eligat. In collegis admittendis suam sententiam | ferat et aliorum accipiat, lites inter collegas dirimat, graviorum offensarum penas infligat: sed id communi consilio et sententia consiliariorum seorsum a reliquis adhibitorum. At horum altero dissentiente ascitis duobus ex electoribus qui eo graviores videbuntur, cum maiori eorum parte decernat, dato his prius iuramento ut omnem seponant affectum. Componat etiam litem si que oriatur consiliariis aut inter se aut cum alio quopiam, adhibito omnium seniore electore, aut eo qui consiliarii vices pro eo tempore gerat pendente enim lite ut suus sit in officio iudex consiliarius, aequum non est: ut autem locus interim vacet commodum non est. Quare in id tempus tantum, et is deponat officium, et alius surrogetur. Curet praeterea ut sigillum commune in archa communi reservetur. Omnia ipse obsignabit in que reliqui college pro ratione, officio aut statuto consenserint. Siqui libri Collegio donentur reponat in bibliotheca, et exacto anno suo eorum rationem reddat novo presidenti, et singulos nominatim perstringendo ex indice eidem ostendat. Si quis sit redditus seu fructus annuus Collegii ex | fundis, si quid donetur Collegio, si quid aliis nominibus accedat, in communi arca seu cista presidens et consiliarii conservabunt, cuius ipse clavem unam, consiliariorum singuli unam habeant: rationem acceptorum et expensorum anni superioris exigat, et sui reddat: atque inprimis ut statuta observentur curet. Si abfuerit uspiam extra urbem, in suum locum propresidentem substituat, qui usque eo eius vicem gerat dum redeat tantum. Officium autem nulli nisi electoribus resignet. At si in urbe fuerit nec poterit tamen interesse comitis alicuius vel magnatis cura vel aliis negotiis necessariis detentus, licebit aliquem ex electoribus in suum locum substituere, sed pro illis saltem comitiis concessa authoritate. Curet demum quantum in se est per Collegii literas adhoc in annalibus anni 1555 prescriptas, ut non urbs solum Londini sed omnis etiam per omnem Angliam respublica indoctis impostoribus repurgetur: prelegatque statuta penalia singulis comitiis ordinariis collegis omnibus presentibus, nisi gravis aliqua causa impediat.

De Propresidente

15   Licebit etiam presidenti sibi multitudine negotiorum Collegii oppresso propresidentem eligere. Is vero presidens natus esto si commode per aetatem negotia aut valetudinem fieri potest. Sin minus ex electoribus aliquis qui ratione, gravitate rerum iudicio et experientia, diligentia et agendi alacritate prestet, pro presidentis voluntate.

Jurabit se integre curaturum negotia Collegii sibi commissa, et sedulo acturum omnia in honorem et commoditatem Collegii et presente et absente presidente, nihilque gesturum nisi consilio presidentis aut consiliariorum, si presidens absit, ita eum Deus adiuvet et sacra Dei evangelia.

Officium esto supplere locum presidentis in omnibus Collegii negotiis gerendis et administrandis si quando abfuerit etiam adiumento sit ubi adfuerit etiam, sique negotia urgeant que commode per presidentem obiri nequeant, ita tamen ut nihil nisi presidentis aut consiliariorum si presidens absit iuditio et consilio faciat. Duret officium pro negotio. Sit
15ᵛ locus pro gradu et senioritate, nisi | cum presidens abfuerit tum presidentis locum occupet sed in Collegio tantum loco videlicet comitiorum ordinario.

De Consiliariis

Postridie divi Michaelis in comitis ordinariis statim a presidentis electione iidem electores ex suo ordine duos qui ad id officii idonei fuerint in consiliarios eligant assentientibus vel omnibus vel maiori electorum numero. Si paritas suffragiorum fuerit, ea pars preponderabit in qua plures fuerint ex senioribus doctoribus. Si hi quoque numero pares fuerint tum ea in quam presidens inclinaverit.

Jurabunt presidenti se integre et aeque omni seposito affectu officio suo functuros sic ut illos Deus adiuvet et sancta Dei evangelia.

In officio his esto semper in comitiis presto esse presidenti opera et consilio ubi ea postulaverit adesse, nunquam abesse nisi gravis aliqua causa (cuius in reditu suo iuramento fidem faciant) obstet. Quare ne locus vacet substituat loco suo alium electorem usque dum redierit, qui etiam ille iurabit ut prius | est constitutum consiliariis. Sique sit controversia inter presidentem et collegas ambigua decernant illi et ipsis inter se dissentientibus maior pars electorum. Sin eorum aliquis aut moriatur aut aliter defecerit antequam annum expleverit, alius intra dies quindecim surrogetur. His ille locus sit in Collegio et extra quem gradus et senioritatis ratio dedit nulla officii ratione habita.

De Censoribus

Post electum presidentem et consiliarios mox iisdem comitiis postridie divi Michaelis per eosdem electores eligantur ex doctis et gravibus sive electoribus sive collegis Anglis censores literarum, morum et medicinorum quatuor eo modo et ratione quibus ante in electione presidentis et consiliariorum constitutum est.

Jurabunt presidenti se neminem unquam in Collegium admittendum decreturos nisi quem omni seposito affectu indicabunt et literis et moribus idoneum, neque pretio, prece vel gratia aut quemquam hominum approba-|-turos, aut quicquam medicamentum, inque ceteris suo officio probe se functuros sic ut Deus eos adiuvet et sancta Dei evangelia.

Horum officium esto de omnibus medicinam exercentibus, sive nostrates sint sive advene, per urbem Londini, suburbia atque adeo per omne regnum Anglie inquirere, eos examinare, corrigere, gubernare et lite, si opus, persequi, eorum medendi rationes discere, medicinas indicio perstringere, pharmacopolarum officinas scrutari, de pharmacis iudicare, vitiata comburere aut proiicere et si pharmacopole obstent ad presidentem et Collegium rem referre, omniaque hec in honorem Collegii et salutem reipublicae agere. Sit his locus qui gradus et senioritas.

De Comitiorum Ratione atque Tempore et de Caduceatore

Ante triduum quam futura sunt comitia aut pridie eius diei si res urgeat monendum est authoritate presidentis per | accisum seu bedellum aut presidentis ministrum collegas omnes ut intersint comitiis futuris die, hora et loco prescriptis. Quo ubi conventum est accumbant singuli eo ordine quo ante constitutum est cum de presidentis loco proposuimus. Comitia vocamus conventus seu (ut rex Henricus in diplomate suo nominat) congregationes collegarum. Ratio autem admonitionis talis esto. Dominus presidens orat tuam excellentiam (doctor eximie) ut comitiis cras intersis hora et loco consuetis. Subscribat dein ad hunc modum: A. v. B. id est authoritate vestra bedellus.

Sit caduceator vir honestus qui nec honestatis leges preterire nec fide fallere aut corrumpi didicit.

Juret se diligenter et fideliter inserviturum presidenti et Collegio in omnibus Collegii negotiis et gerendis et referendis sine fuco et fraude sine pretio premio aut gratia in quenquam ita eum Deus adiuvet et sancta Dei evangelia.

Huius officium erit schedulas admonitionis scribere, collegas omnes ad comitia accersire, in eorum adventum omnia parare | munda politaque, omnia conservare, in comitiis non abesse, res in Collegii usus a presidente acceptas fideliter transportare et reportare, quoscunque sive medicos sive empiricos impostores medicine invenire et eorum nomina presidenti et censoribus [referre et eos iubente praesidente][1] summonere, vitiata pharmaca comburere, funeribus et conviviis interesse et cetera peragere que ministro par est et ex officio incumbit. Sed redeamus ad comitia.

De Temporibus Ordinariis Comitiorum

Ea ordinarie quidem per quatuor anni tempora equidistantia celebrentur, prima postridie divi Michaelis nam ea precipua sunto, secundo divi Thomae apostoli, tertia postridie festi palmarum, quarta postridie nativitatis divi Johannis Baptiste. Extraordinarie vero pro ratione rerum et personarum. In his presidens conventus causam exponat, quid singuli suo ordine dicant expectant excipiatque. Nec ante discedat quisquam nisi data prius | venia quam preses comitia conceptis hisce verbis dissolverit: dissolvimus hec comitia.

Summa agendum hic modestia est, summa gravitate, ne qua lis aut convitium oriatur, quod per hec statuta vel maxime prohibetur, turpius in nobis hoc vitium fore rati ut qui ex disciplinis honestos civilesque mores hausisse iudicamur quam in imperita multitudine. Turpe certe convitium est in privatis congressibus sed turpissimum in publicis. Nihil hic agatur publice nisi Latine.

Cum varia sint medicorum negotia nec ullo stato tempore comprehensa, ut paucissimas lucri sui occasiones per Collegii occupationes amittant, statuimus ut nisi urgens aliquod negotium cogat semel tantum trimestri spatio comitia fiant. In his tantum ordinarie electiones fiant, examinationes et admissiones novorum collegarum. Quod si quis extra illa comitia cupit examinari, cum collegis de opera conveniat. Licet enim presidenti preter comitia illa ordinaria etiam alia indicere extraordinaria, pro necessitate aut dig-|-nitate incidentis cause, de quibus si dubitetur per presidentem et consiliarios decernatur.

---

[1] These omitted words are supplied from the text of the Statuta Vetera (see above, p. 173).

De Statutis Condendis et Abrogandis

Statuta in posterum condenda paucissima sunto, sed que iureiurando vel [et *deleted*] mulcta confirmentur. Sit mulcta lenis sed irremissibilis. Minima mulcta drachme argentee esto. Id aequat hodie quinque quos vocant denarios.

Ad statutum aliquod condendum sufficiant comitia duo, sed ad abrogandum non nisi tria.

Illud pro statuto habebitur, in quod omnes college presentes consenserint, vel duo omnium partes, vel saltem maior pars si pauciores sint quam sex. Quod ita est statutum atque ratum rescindendum non est nisi consensu aut omnium collegarum totius Collegii aut trium eorum partium, aut saltem maioris partis si pauciores sint quam octo. Neque id unius diei deliberatione concludatur, sed trium per dierum aliquot intervalla succedentium. Quod si in statuto aliquo condendo aut rescindendo | in comitiis ultra tres non fuerint non esto id ratum nisi postea reliqui per presidem accersiti aut omnes aut maior pars subscribat.

De Statutis Moralibus seu Penalibus

Statuimus ut college omnes quum in urbe fuerint singulis intersint comitiis. Quod si quis in urbe existens premonitus non accesserit, solvat in usus Collegii sedecim denarios, ni fuerit aut egritudine aut carcere detentus.

Qui abfuerit a comitiis eo die quo presidens et consiliarii eligendi sunt nisi gravi de causa a consiliariis et consiliariis[1] approbata aut intra mensem a reditu approbanda, solvat in usus Collegii tres solidos et quatuor denarios.

Si qua lis aut convitium ex ordine et gravitate et modestia (quae in comitiis observari prescripsimus) parum observatis oriatur, arbitrio presidentis et consiliariorum qui deliquerit puniatur.

At si presidens contra statuta quid admiserit declaretur quidem per consiliarios coram collegis in comitiis non tamen | privetur aut anno suo aut insequentium aliquo ob id delictum tantum tribuimus presidentis honori et authoritate.

Ratio reddatur annis singulis acceptorum et expensorum per presidentem coram octo electoribus aut maiori eorum parte tum presentibus in Collegio, ipso electionis die si vacet aut quidem longissime ex octo insequentibus diebus aliquo quem ipse novus presidens indixerit.

Si elector aliquis presidentis officium cum ei deferatur recusaverit, mulcta esto quadraginta solidorum nisi regius medicus fuerit.

---

[1] *Sic :* in margin 'presidente' before 'consiliariis' first time; the second time is an obvious mistake for 'censoribus'.

Nisi consiliarii se paratos exhibeant cum eorum consilium presidens exigat solvent singuli viginti denarios ni urgens aliqua causa, de qua cum proxime redierit iuramento presidenti fidem faciet, impediverit.

Nemo collega recuset officium censoris seu iudicis literarum, morum et medicinarum sub pena quadraginta solidorum.

Ne quis revelet aut propalet quicquam quod in Collegio dictum sit nec cum aliis a collegis id communicet sub pena trium solidorum et quatuor denariorum.

20 | Nullus collega alterum apud alienos vel ignorantie vel maleficii nomine accusabit, publicene contumeliis afficiet sub pena decem solidorum Collegio solvendorum. Quod si quid offendatur seorsum agat cum eo animo reconciliandi, aut ad presidentem et consiliarios rem referat quo sibi aliqua ratione satisfiat.

Nullus collega qui secundus ad alicuius medici curam ab egro vocetur priorem medicum repelli faciat nec prius quicquid innovet nisi res urget que illum convenerit sub pena trium solidorum et quatuor denariorum; postea tamen ex egri sententia vel solus vel cum priori medico administrare licebit · solvatur mulcta Collegio.

Cum multi curationis gratia convenerint de conditione egri deliberandum statuendumque summa modestia est, et non nisi seclusis omnibus arbitris alienis alioqui mulcta esto iij^s iiij^d in usus presidentis.

Nullus adhibebit sibi in curationibus ex iis quenquam qui iuxta
20^v publicum saltem regni statutum examinati non sunt et | approbati, sub pena sex solidorum et octo denariorum Collegio solvendorum.

Nemo collegarum pacisceretur cum egro aut alio quovis egri nomine de pretio restituende sanitatis, sed contentus esto honesta pro conditione egri et laboris sui mercede sub pena trium solidorum et quatuor denariorum Collegio solvendorum: nisi egrotantes, facultatum suarum nulla habita ratione nec honoris, parce nimis et illiberaliter agant cum medicis · cum talibus licebit in posterum pacisci. Reservata tamen potestate domino presidenti et consiliariis et in absentia eorum quatuor ex electis pro sua prudentia corrigere si quid iniquius partum sit et emendare.

Nemo collega exercebit omnino alchymiam nec in curationibus utetur quinta quam vocant essentia.

[Here seven lines are erased.]

21   Ne quis doceat populum medicamenta aut ei apperiat medicinarum nomina ne abusu laedatur populus, sub pena iij^s iiij^d solvendorum in presidentis usus.

Qui paciscetur cum aromatariis de aliqua pretii parte ex medicamentis que illi scribet percipienda aut preciosiora medicamenta ideo pharmacopole scribet quo favorem eius in procurandis curis demercatur periurus esto solvatque decem solidos Collegio.

Nullus collega frequentabit eos aromatarios qui aut ipsi exercent medicinam aut iis medicis inserviunt qui examinati et approbati non sunt secundum statuta huius regni, sub pena quinque solidorum quoties hic offenderit Collegio solvendorum.

Nemo mulctam sibi pro delicto secundum statuta inflictam solvere recusabit, sub pena violati iuramenti Collegio prestiti.

Cum ex collegis quempiam aut alicuius uxorem mori contigerit (nisi peste obierit) unusquisque collega et funus sequi suo ordine et exequiis interesse teneatur, sub pena duodecim denariorum · misse item eiusdem funebri sub pari pena Collegio solvenda.

21ᵛ Volumus preterea in honorem Collegii ut | presidentis sedile in ecclesia tapete et pulvinare serico ornetur tantisper dum officia funebria aut alia officia celebrantur.

Ne college ostendant statuta cuique qui collega non sit interdicimus sub pena quinque solidorum.

Si collegarum quisque se religioni aut sacerdotio manciparit postquam in Collegium cooptatus fuerit ne vocetur ad Collegium ne videamur ad medicinae usum revocare eum quem religio ecclesiasticaque lex a medicine functione ablegat, neve honestum putemus clerico inter cetera tractare res morbosque muliebres. Quod si clericorum aut religiosorum quisquis admitti cupit multo minus assumatur ideoque propter easdem causas.

Si quis criminis alicuius gravis atque publici reus sit aut vitio aliquo insigni infamis sit ablegetur e Collegio ne si retineremus videamur virtutem contemnere aut eodem morbo laborare. Ne autem talis collega non existens cooptetur in Collegium, et aliis statutis est prohibitum et isto prohibemus.

22 Quod hoc omnia que proposuimus rite | observata ad decus et honorem Collegii atque adeo collegarum omnium pertinent faciuntque plurimum et contra non observata graviora sunt quam ut ferrri debeant primo quoque tempore solvat qui deliquerit quod est descriptum pro offensi ratione; secundo duplicetur, tertio triplicetur, quarto etiam gravius pro arbitrio presidentis et consiliariorum tractetur, quorum severitatem in hoc casu magnopere exigimus. Quod si eorum iudicio non paruerit sed reclamet resistatve, periurus esto.

At qui periurus est excludatur Collegio, privetur eiusdem privilegiis, ulteriusque puniatur prout presidenti et consiliariis visum fuerit donec satisfecerit pro delicto et in obedientiam gratiamque Collegii supplex redierit.

De Examinationum Forma

Si quis ignotus examinandus fuerit aut notus sed is tamen cuius eruditio prius perspecta esse debeat quam admittatur, quater ed per trimestria intervalla examinandum censemus ita ut periculum fiat primo
22ᵛ in cognitione rei medice, quam specu|lationem vocant, secundo in signis

quibus utitur medicus, causis et symptomatibus, tertio in medendi ratione, quarto in materia medica, quinto et potissimum in usu exercitioque medicine. At si notus sit sique omnium iudicio peritissimus habitus est, in usu exercitioque medendi omnino examinandum volumus moresque expendendos. Quod si Oxoniensi aut Cantabrigiensi Academia in priorum trium generum aliquo publice legerit, in eo genere ut examinetur opus non est; in quarta tamen ille curiosius examinandum iudicamus. Examinationis autem forma talis esto.

Presentibus collegis presidens ex Galeni libris ad hoc (ut dicemus infra) destinatis colligat non studio sed forte quaestiones tres ex tribus locis diversis, exhibitatque ei qui examinandus est, eumque loco aliquo concludat ubi eadem Galeni opera sunt sed sine indice horis aliquot ad expendendas retractandasque questiones concessis. Quibus elapsis reversusque collegis coram legat ille clare et aperte que invenerit loca questionum integra aperiat observato interim ex distinctione an que legat
23 intelligat. Quod si recte invenerit, bene legerit, | distinxerit et intellexerit preterque quod licebit collegis si volent aliquid in eis questionibus in dubium vocare et disputare, sique in re videbitur dubitare vel herere tamen sat esto in presens probeturque, maxime si probe accomodateque responderit. Quo casu ne se morosos prebeant et difficiles disputando college cupimus.

Ea ratio servetur secunda tertia et quarta examinatione, sed petitis e suis cuiusque examinationis (ut dicitur) libris questionibus tribus aliis et a prioribus et inter se diversis ex totidem diversis locis. Illud interim ignorare non oportet neque ex epilogis sumendas questiones nec si is qui examinandus est ex epilogis tantum eas invenerit atque ex eis legerit probatum iri. Si aliis in locis licet non suis invenerit explicationes, si (ut ante diximus) recte legerit, distinxerit, intellexerit et responderit, etiam probatus esto. At in prima examinatione nisi questiones et earum loca invenerit, prima illa vice reiiciatur, cum eo ut admoneatur paratior instructiorque accedat ad secundam examinationem. Qua si doctius se
23ᵛ non gesserit, nec quesita invenerit, nec | bene legerit, distinxerit nec adversanti college periculumque facienti an intelligat apposite responderit, ne sit amplius collegis molestus. Nam qui trimestri spatio non suffecerit neque ut in tertia examinatione sufficiat spes est.

Quod si ex tribus questionibus duas tantum invenerit et eas probe legerit et distinxerit, tertie vero non iuncte recte et scienter responderit, per hanc non stabit quo minus approbetur. Contra, si non recte nec intelligenter tertie responderit proba lectio et distinctio duarum primarum non faciet ut eis comitiis admittatur.

Rursum si unam tantum invenerit sed nec accomodate legerit aut responderit aut duas quidem sed eas male et legerit et distinxerit quorunque modo duabus illis inventis responderit nullum id esto, dimittaturque aliud comitiorum tempus.

Questiones ducantur ex Galeni libris,

In prima examinatione, de

Elementis
Temperamentis
Naturalibus potentiis
Anatomicis
Usu partium

24 et cetera naturali medicine parte:

In secunda ex eiusdem libris de

Arte medicinali
Locis affectis
Causis morborum et symptomatum
Febribus
Pulsibus, ex Hippocratis libro de
Prognosticis

In tertia ex libris de

Sanitate tuenda
Medendi methodo
Ratione victus in morbis acutis
Simplici medicina

In quarto ex libris de

Crisibus
Aphorismis Hippocratis
et id genus aliis.

At preterea in his que ad medendi usum spectant utque cautio purgando sit aut venam secando, quo tempore, morbo, persona, medicamine aut vena, quid etiam soporiferorum seu narcoticon usus et cautio est, quis locorum internorum positus aut situs ut ad ea pervenire possit medicamina aut secus et qua ratione. Quis clysterum usus, | genus et mensura.

De Admissionibus

Qui ad hanc formam examinatus fuerit indicabitur satisfecisse partibus docti viri vel non per maiorem partem collegarum presentium, qui pauciores quinque omnino non sunto. Judicium autem fiat per suffragia coniectis calculis pisis aut aliis id genus rebus accomodatis in urnas duas quarum altera probationis altera condemnationis erit, ea lege ut si plures calculi in urnam probationis coniecti fuerint admittatur, sin minus repudiatur.

Hic illud obiter admonendum severitate in examinationibus vel maxime opus esse (si modo severitas vocanda sit que paucorum librorum cognitione circumscripta sit et trimestribus spatiis intermissa, quibus quivis vel familiarissimos sibi eos Galeni libros facere posset) tum ne alioqui ambientium multitudine oneretur Collegium, tum quo omnibus constet neminem huius Collegii fore collegam qui medicine et cognitione et
25   usu non sit plane doctus, quique aut non | legerit publice in aliqua academia aut minime annos quatuor non exercuerit medicinam. Quare per sacrosanctum illud iusiurandum quod prestiterunt collegas hortamur atque obtestamur ut severius agant neque quenquam in gratiam personarum preter rationem admittant, sed ad honorem et perpetuitatem Collegii omnia decernant que sola honestate et eruditione collegarum fulcitur.

Latis suffragiis qui admittendus est primo iuramento fidem faciat cuius sit patrie, ut si forte vocetur a rege, tum literas testimoniales veras et authenticas eius academie proferat unde doctoratus gradum susceperit maxime si alterius nationis fuerit, alioqui ne admittatur quidem. Dein solvat ante admissionem in usus Collegii peregrinus quatuor libras, Anglus quadraginta solidos. Ac preterea iij^s iiij^d uterque in usus proprios presidentis pro literis testimonialibus scribendis et obsignandis et in augmentum salarii accisi iij^s iiij^d.

In quid Iurandum Cooptato

25^v Tum recipiatur, iuretque in hec verba. | Observabis statuta condita et tuo tempore condenda, pro sensu grammaticali, adniteris pro viribus ut status Collegii perpetuetur, parebis presidenti in iis que ad honorem Collegii et perpetuitatem spectant, non dabis que abortum faciunt aut conceptum adiuvant aut impediunt, nec ad pernitiem venenum, imo ne docebis quidem ea ubi aliqua mali doli suspitio est, neminem decernes in Collegium cooptandum nisi quem omni affectu seposito iudicabis idoneum scientia et moribus, non indicabis verbo aut signo per se aut alium loca questionum in examinationibus, paratus eris ad examinationem eorum qui petunt examinari atque admitti, dices vere ac bona fide patriam tuam, leges intra annum omni studio et diligentia quinque primos libros de simplici medicina et octo de usu partium, sciens non loqueris nec ages contra Collegium, preciosiora medicamenta non scribes pharmacopole quo favorem eius in procurandis egris demerearis, persequeris omnibus modis honestis indoctos empiricos et impostores, et presidenti aut censoribus eos nominabis. Jurabis item te exercuisse
26   medicinam ad annos quatuor aut legisse publice | in aliqua academia, ita te Deus adiuvet et sancta Dei evangelia.

At si doctor non fuerit iuret se intra biennium aut summum triennium in universitate aliqua futurum doctorem. Quod si fidem iusiurandumque statuto tempore fefellerit, solvat in usus Collegii primo quadraginta solidos, secundo anno tres libras, tertio anno quatuor libras et sic de ceteris insequentibus augendo annis singulis libram unam usque dum insignitus fuerit.

De Candidatis

Atque hec quidem de collegis examinandis et admittendis dicta sunto. De candidatis vero iam pauca statuere expedit. Quod constitutum prius est ne quis in collegam admittatur qui non sit egregie doctus et medicinam exercuerit ad annos minimum quatuor, statuimus ut examinentur quidem qui dudum in urbem aut regnum venerint ad eam formam quam ante prescripsimus etsi non exercuerint medicinam per annos quatuor ne quid preter legem admittant docti aut proceribus et plebi iniuriosi sint indocti, non tamen admittantur in Collegium | ante annos quatuor, ut in altero illo statuto constitutum est. Hi si docti fuerint et probi viri facultate quidem donentur exercendi medicinam (maxime si doctores fuerint) ad quartum usque annum tantum inclusive, sed ita ut alios doctos experientes medicos e Collegio sibi adiungant quo tuto fiant omnia que in omnibus rebus sua est infantia. Hos ex argumento candidatos vocamus. Solvant hi Collegio ante concessam licentiam viginti solidos si Angli, quadraginta si exteri fuerint, ac preterea uterque iij^s iiij^d in proprios usus presidentis pro literis testimonialibus scribendis et obsignandis et iij^s iiij^d in incrementum stipendii accisi.

Cum licentia donentur iurent quot annos exercuerint medicinam, tum ut in futurum Collegio faveant, presidenti pareant et omnibus modis honori Collegii studeant, id verbo et opere defendant, nihil temere, nihil precipitanter sed summa cura, studio, diligentia et religione medendis egris omnia agant, nihil insalubre, nihil nociturum ministrent, aut ministraturis re aut verbo suggerant, sibique cum res urget et difficultas inopiaque consilii subest, ex Collegio quemque accersant ut | illos Deus adiuvet et sancta Dei evangelia.

Quod si doctores non fuerint iurent se ante quartum annum fore.

Accedant hi ad Collegium singulis comitiis ordinariis si vocentur aut sepius si visum fuerit presidenti cognituri novum presidentem suo tempore, rationemque reddituri suorum operum foeliciter aut secus gestorum. Solvant acciso et onera sustineant Collegii ut college solent. Exacto anno quarto eius rei presidentem moneant, rogentque ut college fiant. Tum examinentur rursum, solvantque ut college consuerunt et admittantur in Collegium si et literis, etate provectiori, gravitate et moribus digni videantur. Alios iuvenesque doctos moribusque probatos admittamus licet ad practicandum sed non in Collegium. Non admittantur in Collegium qui exteri sunt et hoc regno minime nati sed ad practicandum tantum. Dein habeant literae testimoniales collegarum, fruanturque Collegii privilegiis, quod candidatis minime est concessum.

Admissis pro ratione singulis, suas habeat quisque literas admissionis et probationis testimoniales sigillo Collegii obsignatas. Sed collegarum 27ᵛ literae non solum facultatem exercendi | medicinam sed fructum etiam et commoditatem privilegiorum que Collegio concessa sunt contineant. Candidatorum vero facultatem exercendi tantum. Utrarumque formam subscribemus.

Forma Literarum Testimonialium Collegarum

Patent universis nos N. medicine doctorem, presidentem Collegii medicorum Londini una cum consensu collegarum dicti Collegii authoritate nobis a Rege et parlamento concessa examinasse, approbasse atque in Collegium nostrum cooptasse 22 Decembris anno domini 1556 doctum et probum virum dominum N. Norvicensem in florentissimis Academiis Cantabrigiensi et Patavina artium et medicine doctorem eique concessisse et dedisse liberam facultatem et licentiam exercendi et practicandi scientiam et artem medicinale iuxta formam statutorum ad hoc editorum, largitosque preterea esse usum ac fructum omnium commoditatum, preeminentiarum, libertatum et privilegiorum que Collegio nostro authoritae predicta et concessa iam sunt et in futurum concedenda. In cuius 28 rei fidem et testimonium sigillum nostrum commune | presentibus apposuimus. Datum Londin in Collegio nostro 24 die mensis Novembris anno domini 1556.

Forma Literarum Testimonialium Candidatorum et Exterorum

Sciant universi per presentes nos N. medicine doctorem, presidentem Collegii medicorum Londini, consentientibus collegis dicti Collegii, authoritate nobis a rege et parlamento concessa, examinasse et approbasse 22 Aprilis anno domini 1556 doctum et probum virum dominum N. Eboracensem in florentissima Academia Oxoniensi artium et medicine doctorem eique concessisse et dedisse liberam facultatem et licentiam exercendi et practicandi scientiam et artem medicinalem iuxta formam statutorum ad hoc editorum ad annos quatuor a die approbationis sue proxime insequentes. In cuius rei fidem et testimonium sigillum nostrum commune presentibus apponi fecimus. Datum Londini in Collegio nostro 17 die Aprilis anno domini 1556.

He litere etiam exteris subservient si annorum quatuor tempora subducas que etiam addentur si candidati fuerint.

28ᵛ | *De Conviviis*

Quod ex honestis congressibus mutuus amor alitur atque animi studiosorum impendio recreantur volumus ut omnes admissi, sive college sive candidati fuerint, teneantur presidentem et collegas omnes

in urbe existentes frugali honesto et sufficienti convivio excipere xl⁸ quo
tempore presidens indixerit. Indicet autem per trimestria spatia ipso
comitiorum die aut quo die visum fuerit ex quindecim proxime insequentibus festum divi Michaelis, nativitatis Domini, pascha et nativitatis
divi Johannis Baptiste. Quod si ampliori liberalitate velit uti augebit ea
favorem et benevolentiam erga eum presidentis et collegarum. Eo convivio
peracto licebit etiam eo in loco exclusis alienis arbitris comitia celebrare
et Collegii negotia tractare si res id postulet et necessarium presidenti et
consiliariis visum fuerit.

De Coercendis Empiricis per Senatores et per Senatores Urbis Londini

9   Cum tanta imperitorum turba sit quae | rempublicam premit, nobisque
ex precepto regis et plebisciti ut populi securitate et saluti consulamus
incumbit, stautimus in commodiorem talium extirpationem ut quos
indoctos et inhonestos re esse comprobavimus, non solum carcere et
mulcta puniamus sed etiam senatores et prosenatores cuiusque urbis
provincie seu custodie ubi tales impostores habitant certiores per literas
faciamus eos non esse medicos, ac proinde tractandos suo iure ut ceteri
cives. Forma autem literarum talis esto, sed vulgari lingua.

Vos certiores facimus (egregii viri) N. Flandrum vestre provincie
urbane empiricum in vice N. commorantem quia indoctus imperitusque
medicine sit nostri non est Collegii. Quamobrem vobis liceat pro iure
vestro eum aliosque omnes quibus nostrum sigillum commune non est
per nos concessum in omnia urbis vestre idonea officia fungenda cooptare
et eligere, cogereque caetera agere et prestare que authoritate vestra
potestis imperare. Hec ideo scribimus ne sub medicine nomine et
pretextu privilegia vestra fallant imperiti. E Collegio nostro N. die
November anno 1557.

per me N. presidentem.

v | ### De Commissionibus

Statuimus etiam ut omnes quibus commissiones concedientur contra
empiricos sint boni viri et graves, quique iuramento astringant fidem
suam verbis conceptis se non lucri aut private utilitatis causa sed rempublicam imperitis medicis purgandi gratia eas aut petituros aut habituros,
ita eos Deus adiuvet et sancta Dei evangelia; utque presidens pro com-
missionibus obsignandis et scribendis habeat sex solidos et octo denarios.

De Lectione Statutorum bis annis singulis

Statuimus etiam ut bis annis singulis in comitiis paschalibus et Sancti
Michaelis statuta omnia publice legantur. Ut quivis intelligat cetero anno
quemadmodum se habeat.

Si ad has normas Collegium recta ratione, consilio et electione prim-
orum collegarum hoc est presidentis, consiliariorum et ceterorum
electorum (apud quos omnis est potestas preterque in admissionibus
collegarum et candidatorum, que res communis sit in reliquis collegis)
30 | gubernetur debito et obedienti ceterorum officio honestetur, et extermi-
natis indoctis profligatisque doctrina decoretur, dubii nihil est, et florentissimum fore Collegium in perpetuum et sanam recteque curatam rempublicam.

II The Statutes of 1647[1]

Statuta Collegii Medicorum Londinensium

Quum regis serenissimi, Henrici octavi, privata gratia, et publicis parliamenti decretis, sancitum sit; ut Collegium Medicorum Londinensium, in decus regni, et salutem reipublicae stabiliatur; privilegiis muniatur; possessionibus locupletetur; electoribus insigniatur; praeside et censoribus gubernetur; statutis dirigatur; illaque de novo condendi facultate donetur; consiliariis adjuvetur; et literis perpetuetur; consultissimum etiam nobis visum est, ut praescribamus; primo, qui sint futuri electores; quodque eorum sit officium: tum quis sit futurus praeses; quo modo et a quibus eligendus; qua lege obstringendus; quodnam ejus officium; et potestas; denique quis locus, atque dignitas: deinde quinam futuri sint consiliarii quid illis, fide data, sit praestandum; quodque eorum sit officium, locus, et potestas: qui censores literarum, morum, itemque medicamentorum sint constituendi; quoque officio, ex juramento illis sit fungendum; quodnam sit officium thesaurarii, regestarii, et bedelli: postremo quid reliquos deceat, in sui honorem, et collegii decus; et qua sponsione teneantur: si quae statuta condenda, si quae abroganda fuerint, quomodo id facere oporteat; quae sit comitiorum, examinationum, atque admissionum forma; quae sit offensae habenda ratio; cum aliis, quae universim ad omnes Collegii personas, et negotia, ex aequo spectant. Enim vero nihil durabile est, quod ratione, modo, atque ordine careat.

Caput 1

De Electoribus Creandis

Statuimus igitur, et ordinamus; ut, e numero sociorum, octo tantum electores creentur; qui gravitate, literis, moribus, et aetate caeteris praefulgeant; doctoratusque gradu insigniantur; et natione sint Angli. Horum officium erit ex authoritate collegii, postridie Divi Michaelis, (si commode fieri potest; at vero, si ob gravia quaedam impedimenta, id non licebit, tunc alio die ad eam rem magis idoneo; modo sit intra septimanam a tempore praestituto) in celebribus comitiis, praesidem e numero electorum eligere; si anni superioris praeses, defuncto annuo officio, superfuerit: sin autem defecerit ille, quam primum commode fieri poterit, alium surrogare; ad plurimum intra dies viginti, postquam is defecerit. Deficere autem praesidem, vel electorem, intelligimus; si vel mortuus

---

[1] The text is taken from a late copy: Royal College of Physicians MS. 291. The table of contents is at the end on p. 417.

fuerit, vel e Collegio sit expulsus, vel cum pannis (ut aiunt) a civitate discesserit, et per integrum annum abfuerit, nisi sit in ministerio principis. Si electorum unus, aut plures ita defecerint, electione nova sufficiatur alius, aut plures, in ejus, aut eorum locum, ex caeteris sociis, qui ejusdem nationis, gradus, morum, doctrinae, atque ordinis erunt; intra dies triginta, aut saltem quadraginta.

Sed ita, ut illis comitiis soli electores intersint; quo liberior fiat electio, et morum, ingenii, gravitatis, ac doctrinae, justior examinatio; quas omnes virtutes in electore vel maxime requirunt statuta regni. Qui eligendus est, prius examinabitur ab electoribus; prout cautum est per statuta regni; tum eligatur omnium eorum consensu, si fieri poterit; sin minus, per majorem partem; at si paria fuerint suffragia, per seniorem partem.

Si autem propter pestis saevitiam, vel aliam ob causam, electores abfuerint ab urbe, ita ut certus dies statui nequeat; tunc licebit praesidi, quo tempore et loco comode poterit, electores convocare.

Si quis ex numero electorum, civitatem reliquerit, et cum familia sua in alio aliquo loco, ultra septem ab urbe milliaria, per annum integrum commoratus fuerit; is (nisi medicus regius, aut aliter principis ministerio detentus) inter electores locum amittet, aliusque per praesidem, et electores surrogabitur. Volumus tamen, ut suum in Collegio societatis locum, et dignitatem retineat; si interea temporis praesidem de absentiae suae causa certiorem fecerit.

Dabit fidem, se nemini daturum consensum aut suffragium, ut praeses, aut elector creetur; nisi secundum formam statuti, et nisi ejus gravitatem, eruditionem, mores integros, aetatem decentem, sincerum animum in Collegium et rempublicam, et alacritatem ad obeunda officia, cognita et perspecta habuerit.

Caput 2

De Praeside, et ejus Officio

Qui praeses futurus est, in annum designetur: sitque e numero electorum; et quem caeteri electores praesentes, aut omnes, aut plurimi, pro temporis, rei, et personae ratione, idoneum judicaverint. Idque eo anni tempore fiat, quo jam ante constitutum est, cum de electoribus ageretur; postridie nempe Divi Michaelis (si commode fieri potest &c.) ut supra, in cap. de electoribus creandis cautum et statutum est. Si paria fuerint suffragia, ea pars vincat, in qua plures ex senioribus fuerint; quod si hi quoque pares fuerint, ea praevalebit, in quam vetus praeses, aut eo mortuo, vel absente, praeses natus inclinaverit. Praesidem natum vocamus, qui senior ex electoribus fuerit. Qui, etsi praesidis nomen gerat, nullam tamen potestatem habeat condendi aut mutandi statuta: administrandi vero, fungendive praesidis munere,

APPENDIX II 395

caeteris in rebus ad Collegii negotia pertinentibus, sit ei plena potestas, secundum verum sensum statutorum.

Si elector aliquis, praesidis munus ei delatum recusaverit; mulctabitur quadraginta solidis; nisi fuerit medicus regius.

Sponsio, sive Fides a Praeside Data

Dabit fidem se pro viribus conaturum, ut honor Collegii conservetur; statuta ejusdem, sine fraude, observentur; omniaque acturum, in salutem reipublicae, et honestam Collegii utilitatem.

Fidem a praeside novo postulabit superioris anni praeses, si adfuerit; aut consiliariorum alter, senior potissimum, si adfuerit; aut his absentibus, senior ex electoribus praesentibus. Qui fidem postulavit, is porrigat virtutis insignia: pulvinar nempe honoris, librum, et caduceum. Dicatque, Damus tibi praesidi auctoritatem, tradimusque pulvinar honoris, librum scientiae, et caduceum gubernationis, ac prudentiae, ut intelligat excellentia tua, caeterique collegae omnes; scientia et prudentia Collegium nostrum firmiter stabiliri. Quamobrem, ne id memoria tua excidat, in solennioribus conventibus, officiis funebribus, aliisque temporibus et locis opportunis, curabis gestari ante te per bedellum, librum et caduceum; in scientiae, ac prudentiae signum: ut, quod virtus postulat, id usus confirmet.

Ratio Deponendi Officium

Defuncto praesidendi officio, munus depositurus praeses, finita, quam velit, praefatione, dicat:

Depono praesidendi auctoritatem, inque tuas manus (alterius videlicet consiliariorum, senioris potissimum, aut, his absentibus, senioris electoris praesentis) omnium nomine restituo. Ut integrum sit, quibus eligendi potestas est, quem velint eligere et substituere. Reddo igitur tibi pulvinar honoris, librum scientiae, et caduceum prudentis regiminis; precorque Collegio, et vobis omnibus omnia fausta. Quo facto, cui delegata potestas est, proponat eligendum, quem ad id officii maxime idoneum fore iudicaverit. Eligatur autem eo modo, quo sub initium huius capitis ordinatum est. Et eum, qui pro statutorum ratione electus est, clare et nominatim pronuntiet electum in praesidem.

Iubeatque, ut omnes eum pro praeside habeant. Denique fidem ab eo postulabit, eadem formula, qua supra dictum est.

Praesidis officium esto, ut comitia indicat (qua autem ratione, postea dicetur, cum de comitiis statuemus) tum ut causas comitiorum proponat; singulorum sententias accipiat; pro majori parte decernat; factiones, et partium studia excludat; electores, consiliarios, literarum, morum, et medicamentorum censores, cum caeteris, quorum ea res intererit, eligat. In collegis eligendis, aliorum suffragia primum accipat, dein suum ferat, et pre majori parte decernat. Lites inter collegas dirimat, sed id communi consilio, et sententia electorum et censorum seorsim adhibitorum: eoque modo, quo postea in capite de Consiliariis dicetur plenius. Curet praeterea ut sigillum commune in arca tuto custodiatur. Omnia ipse obsignabit, in quae reliqui socii, pro officio et statuto consenserint.

Si qui libri Collegio donentur; curabit, ut reponantur in bibliotheca; et, exacto anno, eorum ratio reddatur novo praesidi, ostendanturque ei nominatim ex indice. Si quis sit redditus, seu fructus annuus ex fundis Collegii: si quid donetur Collegio; si quid aliis nominibus accedat; procuret, ut in communi arca conservetur: cujus ipse clavem unam, consiliariorum singuli itidem unam habeant: rationem etiam acceptorum, et expensorum anni superioris exigat a thesaurario, caeterisque officiariis Collegii, in praesentia reliquorum electoris tunc temporis in urbe praesentium: quos omnes admoneri volumus, ut putandis rationibus praesto sint, si modo commode poterint.

Inprimis autem videat, ut statuta diligenter observentur; et in Collegio legantur: vel ab ipso, vel a regestario, vel ab alio aliquo, prout illi videbitur: eo nimirum modo, quo postea in statutis provisum, et constitutum est.

Caput 3
De Pro-Praeside

Licebit praesidi, vel ministerio principis, vel magnatis alicujus cura detento, vel multitudine aliorum negotiorum oppresso, pro-praesidem eligere, et sibi substituere. Is vero praeses natus sit, si commode per aetatem, negotia, aut valetudinem fieri potest: sin minus ex electoribus aliquis, qui gravitate, rerum judicio, experientia, diligentia, et agendi alacritate polleat; pro-praesidis voluntate, et arbitrio. Hujus officium erit, supplere locum praesidis absentis, in omnibus Collegii negotiis gerendis, et administrandis, quae commode per praesidem obiri nequeant.

Sit ei locus, et dignitas, pro gradu et senioritate; nisi cum praeses abfuerit: tum enim praesidis locum occupabit, sed in Collegio tantum: loco nimirum Comitiorum ordinario. Abesse autem praesidem intelligimus, non modo si extra urbem et suburbia fuerit: sed etiam si morbo aliquo, aut gravioribus negotiis in urbe detentus, adesse nequeat. Sed in his casibus volumus, ut absentiam suam vel per literas propria manu subscriptas vel per Collegii bedellum notum faciat.

Duret Officium pro Negotio

Dabit fidem, (si electores aequum judicaverint) se pro virili curaturum negotia Collegii sibi commissa, et sedulo acturum omnia, in honorem et utilitatem Collegii: nihilque facturum, nisi judicio et consilio praesidis, aut consiliariorum, eorumque sociorum, quorum per statuta intererit.

Caput 4

De Consiliariis

Postridie Divi Michaelis, (si commode fieri potest, &c.: ut supra in cap: de electoribus creandis, in comitiis ordinariis) statim a praesidis electione, iidem electores, ex suo ordine, duos, qui ad officium hoc idonei fuerint, in consiliarios eligant, assentientibus, vel omnibus, vel majori saltem electorum praesentium numero.

Si paria fuerint suffragia, ea pars praevalebit, in qua plures fuerint ex senioribus: si hi quoque numero pares fuerint, tum ea, in quam praeses propenderit.

Dabunt fidem, se probe, et aeque; ut viros bonos decet, seposito omni affectu, officio suo functuros.

Horum officium esto, praesidi semper in comitiis majoribus adesse: eundem opera et consilio, ubi opus fuerit, juvare; nunquam abesse, nisi gravis aliqua causa cogat. Et ne tunc temporis locus vacet; qui abfuerit, substituat loco suo alium electorem, donec redierit; cum consensu tamen praesidis, aut (eo absente) pro-praesidis.

Si quae lis, aut controversia, de re ambigua, aut genuina interpretatione alicujus statuti; aut hujusmodi aliquod dissidium inter collegas oriatur; totum id negotium volumus quiete, placideque componi per praesidem, consiliarios, et censores; aut per majorem eorum partem. Similiter, si inter praesidem et collegas, controversia aliqua orta fuerit; rem totam decerni volumus, per consiliarios, et censores; aut per majorem illorum partem. At si ne sic quidem componi potest; tunc volumus, illis arbitris praedictis, reliquos etiam electores adjungi; ut horum omnium, vel majoris partis suffragiis, tota illa controversia dirimatur.

Atque hanc regulam observari volumus, in omnibus collegarum rixationibus decenter compescendis. Hac nempe ratione futurum speramus (quod maxime optandum est) ut rixosa jurgia, ac contentiones evitentur, et fraternus amor cum suavi animorum et voluntatum consensu quotidie coalescat, ac in perpetuum confirmetur.

Si consiliariorum alter aut moriatur, aut aliter defecerit, antequam annum expleverit; alius intra dies quindecim surrogetur. Nemo recuset officium consiliarii, sub poena quadraginta solidorum; nisi sit medicus regius.

Quoties eorum consilium praeses rogaverit, paratos se praestent; sin minus, solvant singuli tres solidos et quatuor denarios; nisi urgens aliqua causa impedierit: de qua cum proxime redierint, praesidem certiorem facient.

Caput 5

De Censoribus

Post electum praesidem, et consiliarios, mox, in iisdem comitiis, statuimus, et ordinamus, ut singulis annis quatuor viri docti, et graves eligantur; sive ii electores fuerint, sive socii: quos censores Collegii Londinensis, sive gubernatores, nominari volumius.

Horum electio sit, per suffragia praesidis, et totius societatis; aut majoris partis, occulte accepta.

Horum officium esto, de omnibus medicinam exercentibus cognoscere; sive nostrates fuerint, sive advenae; per vrbem, suburbia, et intra septem milliaria in ambitu eorundem: eos examinare, corrigere, gubernare, et lite (si opus sit) una cum praeside et thesaurario, persequi; eorum medendi rationes inquirere; medicamenta judicio perstringere; pharmaco-polarum officinas scrutari; de pharmacis judicare; vitiosa comburere, aut alio pacto destruere: et si pharmacopolae obstiterint, ad praesidem et Collegium rem referre: omniaque haec in salutem Reipublicae et Collegii honorem agere.

Censorum Juramentum

Jurabunt, coram praeside, se neminem in collegium admittendum decreturos; nisi quem omni seposito affectu, judicaverint et literis et moribus idoneum. Nec pretio, prece, vel gratia, aut quenquam hominem, aut quidquam medicamentorum approbaturos; inque caeteris suo officio probe functuros: sicut Deus eos adjuvet, et sancta Dei Evangelia.

Nullus socius recuset officium censoris, sub poena quadraginta solid-orum: nisi sit medicus regius.

Caput 6

De Comitiorum Ratione, atque Tempore; et de Caduceatore, sive Bedello

Triduo, antequam futura sunt comitia solennia; aut pridie ejus diei, si res urgeat; auctoritate praesidis, monendi sunt omnes collegae, per bedellum, aut praesidis ministrum; ut intersint comitiis futuris, die, hora, et loco praescriptis. Quo ubi ventum est, sedeant singuli eo ordine, quo postea dicetur. Comitia vocamus, conventus; sive ut Rex Henricus in suo diplomate nominat, congregationes collegarum. Et ea comitia solennia, sive majora, legitima judicamus; quibus ut intersint omnes collegae, in urbe, per bedellum admonentur: et in quibus duodecim socii, ut minimum adsunt, praeter praesidem.

Modus autem admonitionis, talis esto: dominus praeses orat excellen-tiam tuam (doctor eximie) ut comitiis intersis, mense, die, hora, et loco a praeside praescriptis. Subscribat dein ad hunc modum: A.V.B. i.e. authoritate vestra bedellus.

Sit bedellus vir probus: detque fidem se fideliter, et sedulo inserviturum praesidi, et Collegio, in omnibus Collegii negotiis, sine fuco et fraude.

Promittat insuper, se nec pretio, nec prece, nec gratia, secreta Collegii cuipiam vulgaturum.

Hujus officium esto, schedulas admonitionis scribere: collegas omnes ad comitia accersere; in eorum adventum omnia parare; munda politaque conservare: a comitiis non abesse: res in Collegii usum a praeside acceptas fideliter ferre et referre: quoscunque sive medicos sive empiricos, et impostores indagare; eorumque nomina praesidi, et censoribus indicare: atque illis, jubente praeside, aut censoribus, diem indicere; improba pharmaca comburere, aut aliter destruere: conviviis et funeribus adesse: virtutis insignia gestare: et caetera peragere, quae ministro, ex officio, incumbunt; bedello stipendium duodecim librarum a thesaurario annuatim solvetur.

Volumus etiam, ut a singulis candidatis et permissis, quatuor solidi quotannis pro mercede ipsi erogentur.

In omnibus praeterea admissionibus, et mulctis, quae viginti solidos excedunt; et anatomiis; tres solidi et quatuor denarii illi persolventur.

De Collegis Admonendis ad Comitia

Statuimus, ut collegae omnes, qui in vrbe, aut suburbiis fuerint; singulis comitiis majoribus, sive ordinariis, sive extraordinariis, intersint; nisi grave aliquod impedimentum obstiterit. Quod ad minores illas congregationes attinet, quae singulis mensibus, aliisque temporibus habentur; liberum erit caeteris collegis, (praeter sex illos, quos postea in cap: de temporibus ordinariis comitiorum nominabimus) vel adesse, vel abesse, pro arbitrio; nisi praesidis aut pro-praesidis monitu adesse jubeantur.

Quod si quis praemonitus, per bedellum ipsum, vel per schedulam ab eo domi suae relictam, non accesserit; solvet, in usus Collegii, duos solidos; nisi per valetudinem excusatus fuerit, aut abfuerit ab urbe duobus minimum milliaribus.

Qui abfuerit a comitiis eo die, quo praeses et Censores eligendi sunt; nisi gravem ob causam a praeside, aut pro-praeside, aut consiliariis et censoribus approbandam; solvet, in usum Collegii, tres solidos et quatuor denarios. Imo solidum solvet, qui ante auditam tertiam non accesserit. Quoniam autem complures legitime a praeside, per bedellum, admoniti, comitiis praedictis interesse vel negligunt, vel aspernantur; quo fit ut saepe irriti fiant conventus; reliquique socii praesidis monitis obtemperantes, frustra negotia sua privata negligant; propterea statuimus, et ordinamus; ut, si quis socius, praedicto modo admonitus, ad stata comitia majora accedere recusaverit, quaterque hoc pacto deliquerit; nec, interea temporis, absentiae suae causam praesidi aut pro-praesidi cum consiliariis et censoribus approbandam reddiderit; alius (quamprimum commodum videbitur Collegio) in ejusdem locum sufficiatur.

Omnia statuta in tres partes, sive sectiones dividantur. Prima pars, ea omnia comprehendet, quae pertinet ad electores; ad praesidem; et propraesidem; ad consiliarios; ad censores; ad comitia; aliaque, donec ventum sit ad cap: nonum, quod tractat de officio thesaurarii.

Secunda pars complectetur ea statuta, quae pertinent ad thesaurarium; et regestarium; ad numerum sociorum, et candidatorum; ad eorundem examinationes, electiones, et admissiones: ad permissorum ordinem, et officia: et reliqua, usque ad caput vicesimum secundum, quod agit de statutis paenalibus, sive moralibus.

Tertia pars, continebit statuta paenalia, sive moralia. Atque secundum hanc triplicem statutorum partitionem, perlegantur in comitiis majoribus omnibus, praeterquam die comitiorum Divi Michaelis, quo tempore electiones officiariorum instituuntur. Lectioni statutorum intersint socii, candidati, et permissi, quotquot adesse poterunt. Atque haec nostra statuta ad praedictum modum perlegentur, vel ab ipso praeside, aut propraeside, (si ipsis placuerit) vel a regestario, si adfuerit: at si forte regestarius, sive negotiis districtus, sive morbo detentus, sive alia aliqua gravi causa impeditus, non adfuerit: tunc pro arbitrio praesidis, propraesidis, alius aliquis e sociis pro illo tempore designetur, qui illam statutorum partem perlegat.

Cautum tamen interea volumus, atque provisum; ut si graviora quaedam negotia illis comitiis pertractanda fuerint, liberum sit praesidi, aut propraesidi, pro arbitrio, hanc statutorum lectionem, pro tempore, vel penitus omittere, vel ejus partem duntaxat aliquam legere, aut legendam praecipere.

Caput: 7

De Temporibus Ordinariis, et Extraordinariis Comitiorum; et reliquis, ad Comitiorum rationem pertinentibus

Ordinata, sive stata comitia, per quatuor anni tempora aeque distantia celebrentur: prima, postridie Divi Michaelis (si commode fieri potest &c.: ut supradictum est) secunda, postridie Divi Thomae, (si commode &c.) tertia, postridie festi Palmarum, (si commode &c.) quarta, postridie nativitatis Divi Joannis Baptistae, (si commode &c.:) atque haec omnia sunt ordinaria, sive stata comitia: quae etiam solennia, et majora licebit appellare. Ac praeter stata ista, sive ordinaria, licebit etiam praesidi alia quoque solennia sive majora comitia extraordinaria convocare, pro necessitate aut dignitate incidentis rei.

Atque in omnibus istis solennibus comitiis, volumus, ut duodecim, ad minimum, socii adsint, praeter praesidem, aut pro-praesidem. At si urgens aliqua necessitas (ut saevitia pestis, &c.:) aut grave aliquod negotium, per principis mandatum, expediendum, inciderit: idque eo forte tempore, quo tot socii in civitate non adfuerint; tunc quidem necessitati parendum est: talique casu res tota relinquenda praesidis aut pro-praesidis prudentiae, et judicio: ut, quot fuerint in vrbe, eos omnes per bedellum admonendos curet, ut intersint comitiis.

Atque in istis majoribus comittiis, volumus, ut ordinariae fiant electiones, et admissiones novorum sociorum, candidatorum, et permissorum. Quod vero ad sociorum, candidatorum, et permissorum examinationes attinet; eae recte peragi possunt, sive in majoribus istis comitiis, sive etiam in aliis minoribus conventionibus; pro praesidis, aut pro-praesidis arbitrio.

In omnibus comitiis, praeses, aut pro-praeses, conventus causam exponat: quid singuli ordine dicant, expectet; accipiatque suffragia. Nec quicquam discedat, (nisi impetrata prius venia) antequam praeses, aut pro-praeses, comitia disertis hisce verbis dissolverit: Solvimus haec comitia.

Sunt etiam alia comitia, quae minora dicuntur; qualia singulis mensibus, aliisque temporibus, pro ratione rerum, et personarum habentur: prout occasio aliqua subitanea postulaverit. In his, admittendi in Collegium examinantur: res item agyrtarum, et impostorum, omniumque medicinam male factitantium, a praeside et censoribus excutiuntur: ipsique pro merito puniuntur: aliaque id genus negotia tractantur.

In minoribus istis comitiis, non requirimus, ut tot adsint socii, quot in majoribus et solennibus requiruntur. Suffecerit, si in his dominus praeses, quatuor censores, et regestarius adfuerint. Necesse autem est ut omnes censores intersint, secundum statuta regni; modo legitime admoniti fuerint per bedellum. Quare ne reliqui frustra conveniant, absentem censorem decem solidis mulctandum statuimus; nisi praesidem antea de absentiae suae causa certiorem fecerit.

Summa in omnibus comitiis agendum est modestia, summa gravitate: ne-qua lis, aut convitium oriatur. Turpe certe jurgium in privatis congressibus; sed turpissimum in publicis: praesertim inter eos, qui ex bonis disciplinis honestos mores hausisse judicantur. Proinde nemo proponat, aut dicat aliquid publice in Collegio, nisi capite aperto, veniaque prius a praeside impetrata: ad quem solum oratio dirigenda est. Quod si plures simul loqui inceptent, cedat junior seniori. Unusquisque breviter, et graviter, sine prolixa dicacitate loquatur: et praesidis monitu sileat: neminique liceat loquentem interturbare; nisi praesidi, aut pro-praesidi, aut praesentium censorum seniori: cujus etiam munus esto, quemlibet sui officii admonere. Vnusquisque autem ad rem propositam semel tantum, suoque ordine, sententiam dicat; nisi iterum impetrata a praeside venia. Reliqui socii attenti sint, nec privatis confabulationibus, susurris, strepituve, loquentem, vel auditores interturbent: et semper ad praesidis nutum fiat silentium. Qui contra fecerit, duobus solidis, statim solvendis, plectetur.

In rebus dubiis, et magni momenti, elegantur delegati, pro-praesidis arbitrio; qui rem undequaque discutiant, referantque ad collegium.

Singulis comitiis, postquam praeses conventus causam exposuerit; regestarius, quae novissimis acta comitiis, clara voce recenseat: ut (expunctis, si quae fuerint emendanda) demum inscribantur Libro Annalium. Suffragia colligenda nemo proponat, nisi praeses, aut pro-praeses.

In omnibus electionibus, tacite et occulte, per pisa aut fabas, ferantur suffragia. In aliis Collegii negotiis, prout visum fuerit praesidi, aut pro-praesidi.

Caput: 8

De Statutis Condendis, et Abrogandis, et de Mulctis Irrogandis

Statuta pauca sanciantur; eaque vel fide data, vel mulcta confirmentur. Sit mulcta levis, sed inevitabilis. Minima mulcta, sit duodecim denariorum.

Ad statutum aliquod condendum, sufficient comitia duo: sed ad abrogandium, non nisi tria.

Statuimus et ordinamus; ut omnes mulctae, quae a praeside, aut propraeside, et quatuor censoribus, vel a majori parte sociorum quomodocunque infliguntur; cedant duntaxat in usum Collegii; non autem in ullius privati emolumentum: exceptis tamen illis pecuniarum solutionibus, quae per statuta Collegii, officiariis aliter conceduntur. Volumusque, ut hae mulctae ilico solvantur: aut saltem data hypotheca, qualem praeses expetierit, sibi caveant de praesenti pecunia.

Caput 9

De Officio Thesaurarii

Collegii redditus, et emolumenta, quae annuatim accrescunt Collegio, recipiet, et in custodia sua tuto conservabit, in usum Collegii:

Collegii utensilia, aliaque necessaria, quoties opus fuerit, procurabit. Ejusdemque bona, libros, supellectilem, caeteraque ornamenta ad decus pertinentia, quantum poterit, tuto et decenter conservabit.

Si quid reparandum fuerit in Collegii aedificiis; curabit, ut id tempestive fiat.

Lites Collegii, et causas juridicas, ipse una cum praeside, aut propraeside, et censoribus prosequetur.

Collegii officiariis, sua cuique salaria, sive stipendia ex statutis debita, quatuor usitatis anni temporibus, persolvet.

Computi rationem bis quotannis, praesidi, et electoribus reddet: modo ad hoc postulatus, et praemonitus fuerit.

Intra mensem, post festum Divi Michaelis, perfectam computi rationem, pro integro elapso anno, reddet; eo nempe die, quem praeses illi assignaverit; totamque pecuniae summam, quae tunc temporis supererit, caeteraque Collegii bona, supellectilem, utensilia, quae in ipsius custodia fuerint, praesidi, et electoribus restituet. Syngrapha praesidi et societati obligabitur, eodem die quo admittitur ad officium, ut stipendia Collegii officiariis debita, intra septimanam, post plenam computi sui rationem pro illo anno redditam, fideliter solvat.

In reparandis Collegii aedificiis, rebusque necessariis in usum Collegii coemendis, non impendet ultra quadraginta solidos, sine praesidis, aut pro-praesidis voluntate, aut consensu.

Thesaurario, pro stipendio, solventur annuatim, ex Collegii redditibus, quadraginta solidi.

Statuimus praeterea, et ordinamus; ut a singulis in Collegii societatem admissis; itemque a singulis, qui vel in candidatorum ordinem, vel in permissorum numerum admittentur: accipiat sex solidos et octo denarios, tempore admissionis illorum.

Dabit fidem, se perfuncturum officio suo fideliter, secundum statuta: omniaque acturum, in honorem et utilitatem Collegii: et computi rationem fideliter redditurum, monitu praesidis.

Caput 10

De Regestario

Officium regestarii hujusmodi esto: singulis Collegii comitiis, sive majoribus sive minoribus, legitime et tempestive admonitus per Collegii bedellum, sive praesidis, aut pro-praesidis ministrum, ipsemet coram adsit, sub poena decem solidorum.

Quicquid ibi actum, ratum et sancitum fuerit, consentientibus praeside, et sociorum praesentium majori parte (nisi sit res levioris momenti et notatu indigna) id omne fideliter adnotet; et initio comitiorum proxime sequentium perlegat: ac postea (correctis, si quae emendanda fuerint) in Librum Annalium Collegii referat.

Sin autem, per valetudinem, aut graviora negotia impeditus fuerit, quo minus adesse possit: tunc ei licebit, socium aliquem pro tempore substituere: qui et absentiae ejus causam praesidi significet, et locum ipsius diligenter suppleat.

Formulas literarum ad Collegium, vel a Collegio scriptarum; et reliqua omnia acta, Libro Annalium inserat.

Pro annuo stipendio, regestario quotannis solventur, ex Collegii redditibus, quadraginta solidi; eidem per aequales partes, quatuor usitatis hujus regni terminis, a thesaurario annumerandi.

A singulis, qui vel ad praxin in medicina permittuntur, vel in candidatorum ordinem adsciscuntur; vel in sociorum numerum admittuntur; ipso vel permissionis, vel admissionis tempore, regestario solventur sex solidi et octo denarii; et quinque insuper solidi, pro illorum nominum inscriptione in Librum Annalium.

Quotiescunque contigerit, aliquem ex sententia praesidis, aut pro-praesidis, et censorum, mulctari aliqua pecuniae summa notabili Collegio persolvenda, a singulis ita punitis, tres solidi et quatuor denarii regestario solventur. Si quis aliqua pecuniae summa in usum Collegii solvenda mulctatus, non simul et semel totam mulctam solverit; sed solutionem imperatam ad dies aliquot distulerit, adeoque eam partitim solverit: singulis istis solutionibus sic divisim factis, tres solidi et quatuor denarii regestario persolventur: quippe officium ejus molestum onus judicamus. Dabit fidem, se officio debite perfuncturum, secundum statuta, in honorem et utilitatem Collegii: omniaque fideliter libro annalium, quae fuerint acta vel in majoribus, vel minoribus comitiis sine fraude inscripturum.

Caput 11

De Candidatis

Statuimus, et ordinamus; ut numerus candidatorum non excedat duodecim: volumusque, ut nemo admittatur in illorum ordinem, qui non sit in medicine doctor, et natione brittannus, et medicinam exercuerit per quadriennium.

Quod si doctoratus gradum in extera aliqua academia adeptus fuerit; volumus, ut antequam admittatur ad examen, diploma, sive literas testimoniales veras et authenticas illius academiae proferat, et ostendat Collegio; et praeterea, ab alterutra nostrarum academiarum incorporationis suae testimonium habeat, et adducat. Volumus praeterea, et ordinamus; ut singuli candidati et permissi, antequam admittantur, omnes Collegii socios bis, gratiae impetrandae ergo, conveniant; nimirum primo, ante examinationem ullam: secundo autem, finito examinationum curriculo.

Fides a Candidatis postulata

Dabis fidem, te observaturum statuta Collegii; et, pro viribus, conaturum, ut honos ejus sartus tectus conservetur. Nec unquam consilium, aut familiaritatem inibis cum aliquo, qui studet verbo, vel facto Collegii statutum labefactare; sed in omnibus, quae ad honorem, et utilitatem Collegii spectant, consilio, ope, et auxilio juvabis. Dabis etiam fidem, te, in omnibus licitis et honestis, morigerum futurum domino praesidi, aut pro-praesidi, et electoribus.

Seniori in Collegio (secundum statuta) locum cedes, eundemque honore debito prosequeris. Accedes ad Collegium, ex mandato domini praesidis, aut pro-praesidis, vel censorum; quoties fueris per bedellum admonitus, et accersitus.

Intereris singulis anatomiis; nisi gravi detinearis impedimento, approbando a praeside, et censoribus. Nec pretio, nec prece, neque ulla alia causa, medicamenta, quae abortum faciunt, vel venena cujusvis generis, in pernitiem, aut malum usum dabis: nec ea quempiam docebis, quem suspicaris velle illis abuti. Neminem, qui admissus est in Collegium, vel ignorantiae, vel maleficii nomine accusabis, aut publice contumeliis afficies.

Persequeris omnibus modis honestis, indoctos, empiricos, et impostores, eorumque nomina ad praesidem, aut censores referes; nec te empiricis, aliisque per Collegium non licentiatis, familiarem reddes: neque eorum conventiones, ad Collegii detrimentum vel infamiam, ullo modo frequentabis. Secreta Collegii nemini extra Collegium divulgabis. Dabis fidem, te neque literis a magnatibus, nec pretio, nec ullo alio modo illicito, Collegii societatem ambiturum: omniaque in arte medica pro viribus facturum, ad honorem Collegii, et reipublicae utilitatem.

Statuimus et ordinamus; ut permissi, sive licentiati, itemque candidati, statuta et decreta nostra diligenter observent: praesidi, electoribus, et censoribus morem gerant: mulctasque ab iis ob delicta inflictas prompte persolvant.

Praeterea non recusabunt, medicamenta illa sua, quae secreta, sive arcana appellant, solentque in sua praxi usurpare, plane et nude exponere; quoties a praeside, et censoribus, ad id faciendum requiruntur. Qui pertinaciter contra fecerit, pro arbitrio praesidis, et censorum poenas luet.

Unusquisque candidatus solvet, tempore admissionis suae, quatuor libras, in usum Collegii: et decem solidos, in proprios usus praesidis: thesaurario vero sex solidos, et octo denarios: itemque regestario pro debito salario, sex solidos et octo denarios: eidemque insuper quinque alios solidos, pro insertione nominis in librum annalium: praeterea bedello Collegii tres solidos, et quatuor denarios.

Quoniam multi huc confluunt quotidie ad exercendam praxin; e quorum numero complures sunt, qui ante debitum tempus ex academiis suis emigrantes, ad transmarinas oras volitant, ut in exteris regionibus breviori spatio, et minori impendio ad doctoratus gradum perreptent, quam domi in academiis nostris assequi poterant, idcirco statuimus, ut quicunque vel in Collegii societatem, vel in candidatorum ordinem, vel in permissorum numerum admittetur; si doctoratus gradum apud exteros susceperit; is admissionis tempore, duplo plus solvat Collegio, praesidi, thesaurario, regestario, aliisque Collegii officiariis; quam iam solvere solent, qui in nostris academiis doctores creantur.

Item quicunque doctor creatus fuerit in nostris academiis; si tamen festinantius ad gradum illum subvolando, quam par est, tempus illi dignitati debitum anticipaverit; id est, si doctor fiat, priusquam vel in artibus integros septem annos rexerit, vel per quinquennium baccalaureus in medicina praeextiterit: is duplos plus olvet Collegio, praesidi, caeterisque praedictis Collegii officiariis, quam illi solvent, qui secundum laudabiles leges et consuetudines nostrarum academiarum, tempore praefinito, et maturiori cum judicio ad doctoratus gradum ascenderunt.

Volumus, ut omnes candidati, et permissi a bedello admoniti, singulis nostris comitiis intersint; ut, si quos congnoverint illicite et inscienter praxin exercentes, eorum nomina praesidi et censoribus significent; tum etiam ut statutorum praelectionem audiant.

Solvant etiam, si occasio fuerit, et necessitas Collegii postulet, ut socii: modo ad id requirantur.

Exacto anno, candidati praesidem ejus rei moneant; rogentque, ut in sociorum numerum adsciscantur; si modo id commode fieri potest, salvis Collegii statutis.

Caput 12

De Sociis

Statuimus, et ordinamus; ut numerus sociorum non excedat triginta: volumusque, ultra hunc certum et determinatum numerum, regis, reginae, et principis medicos ordinarios, tanquam medicos honorarios, supernumerari, et admitti.

Volumus praeterea, ut nemo admittatur in Collegii societatem, qui non prius fuerit per annum integrum de candidatorum numero, aut publice in aliqua britanniae academia medicinam per triennium praelegerit; aut doctor cathedrae, ut ajunt, in aliqua hujus regni academia praextiterit; aut regius medicus fuerit ordinarius.

Singuli socii tempore admissionis suae, solvent Collegio, praesidi, thesaurario, regestario, et bedello, prout de candidatis antea statutum est: omnes item solutiones duplicabunt; conditionibus iis, quae supra dictae sunt.

Statuimus etiam, ut omnes socii, tempore admissionis, literas habeant patentes sigillo Collegii munitas: et hac data fide obstringantur:

Adniteris, pro viribus, ut status Collegii perpetuetur; statuta collegii observabis: parebis praesidi in iis, quae ad honorem, et perpetuitatem Collegii spectant. Non dabis quae abortum faciant, aut conceptum adimant, vel impediant; nec venena in malum finem; imo vero nec ea docebis quidem, ubi aliqua doli mali suspitio est. Neminem decernes in Collegium cooptandum, nisi quem, seposito omni affectu, judicaveris scientia et moribus idoneum. Leges diligenter intra annum, quinque primos libros Galeni de simplici medicina, et omnes de usu partium. Persequeris omnibus modis honestis, indoctos, empiricos, et impostores; eorumque nomina praesidi, aut pro-praesidi, vel censoribus deferes. Dabis etiam fidem, te medicinam exercuisse per quadriennium; aut legisse publice in aliqua academia. Item, dabis fidem, te statutum de publica corporis humani dissectione, summa diligentia quando-cunque a praeside, aut pro-praeside admonitus fueris, observaturum. Dices denique vere, et bona fide, quaenam sit patria tua.

Literae Admissionis

Sciant omnes, nos I: C: medicinae doctorem, et praesidem Collegii Medicorum Londinensium, una cum consensu sociorum ejusdem, auctoritate nobis a domino rege, et parliamento concessa, examinasse, approbasse, et in Collegium nostrum cooptasse, doctum et probum virum R: M: Cantuariensem, in florentissima academia (Cantabrigiensi vel Oxoniensi) medicinae doctorem: eique concessisse liberam facultatem, et licentiam exercendi scientiam et artem medicam: juxta formam statutorum ad hoc editorum: largitosque praeterea usum ac fructum omnium commoditatum, libertatum, ac privilegiorum, quae Collegio nostro auctoritate praedicta et jam concessa sunt, et in futurum concedenda. In cujus rei fidem, et testimonium, sigillum nostrum commune praesentibus apponi fecimus. Datum Londini in Collegio nostro 7º die mensis Maii, Anno Domni 1647.

Si collegarum quispiam se sacerdotio addixerit, postquam in Collegium cooptatus fuerit, nolumus illum denuo vocari ad Collegium. Quod si quispiam clericus, aut sacris initiatus, admitti cupit in Collegium, aut permitti ad praxin: multo minus id illi concedetur.

Statuimus, et ordinamus; ut si quis criminis alicujus gravioris ac publici reus, aut vitio aliquo insigni infamis fuerit, ablegetur a Collegio: ne, si retineremus talem, videremur aut virtutem contemnere, aut eodem morbo laborare. Ne autem talis, collega non existens, admittatur in Collegium; et aliis statutis prohibitum est, et istis prohibemus.

Caput 13

Literae testimoniales practicantium per universum Angliae Regnum

Sciant omnes, nos, J: C: medicinae doctorem, et praesidem Collegii medicorum londinensium; una cum consensu F:P: B:H: et R:M: praedicti Collegii sociorum, et electorum; auctoritate nobis a domino rege, et parliamento concessa, examinasse, et approbasse 17 die Augusti, aº. 1647. probum virum T: W: ex comitatu B: in florentissima academia (Oxoniensi vel Cantabrigiensi) magistrum artium, et in civitate Eboracensi, bene in praxi medica exercitatum: eumque dignum judicamus, que admittatur ad praxin medicinae, juxta formam statutorum ad hoc editorum. In cujus rei testimonium, sigillum nostrum commune apposuimus, et nomina adscripsimus. Datum Londini in Collegio nostro, die et mense. &c.

Si quis a praeside, et tribus electoribus, modo praedicto ad praxin idoneus judicabitur: is nomen suum regestario indicabit, ut id Libro Annalium inscribatur.

Caput 14
De Coercendis Empiricis

Cum magna sit imperitorum turba, qui rempublicam affligunt; nobisque ex praecepto regis, et parliamenti incumbat, ut populi saluti et securitati consulamus: statuimus, et ordinamus, in commodiorem talium extirpationem; ut quos indoctos, et inhonestos esse reipsa comprobaverimus, non solum mulcta, et carcere puniamus; sed etiam senatores, et prosenatores cujuslibet vrbis, provinciae, sive custodiae, ubi tales impostores habitant, certiores per literas nostras faciamus; eos indignos medicorum nomine censendos, proindeque tractandos ut caeteros cives. Forma autem literarum, talis esto (sed lingua vernacula).

Formula Literarum ad Senatores

Vos certiores facimus (egregii viri) H: M: vestrae provinciae empiricum, in vico s. morantem, esse virum indoctum, et imperitum medicinae, nostrique nequaquam esse Collegii: quamobrem vobis licet, pro jure vestro, eum, aliosque omnes, qui literas testimoniales sigillo nostro munitas non habent, ad omnibus urbis vestrae idoneis officiis fungendum cooptare et eligere: cogereque caetera agere, et praestare, quae auctoritati vestrae imperare conceditur. Haec in eum finem scripsimus, ne sub medicinae nomine et praetextu, privilegia fallant insubidi isti plebis impostores. Datum e Collegio nostro.

Caput 15
De Permissis, sive Licentiatis ad Praxin

Quoniam complures in hac civitate medicinam faciunt, quos inidoneos omnino censemus, ut in numerum sociorum, aut candidatorum, adoptentur; vel quod natione non sint Brittanni; vel doctoratus gradum non adepti fuerint; vel non satis docti, aut aetate et gravitate provecti sint; vel alias consimiles ob causas: et tamen reipub. inservire, et saluti hominum prodesse possent, saltem in nonnullis curationibus.

De his ordinamus, et statuimus; ut post examinationes debitas, et approbationem praesidis, et censorum; permittatntur ad praxin, quamdiu se bene gesserint.

Volumus, ut omnes, qui solummodo permittuntur ad praxin, eadem fide, qua candidati, obstringantur. Praeses igitur, tempore permissionis, his verbis utetur. Ego J: C: praeses Collegii Medicorum Londinensium, auctoritate per leges mihi concessa, permitto te A: B: ad praxin medicinae in civitate Londini, et per septem circumcirca milliaria: quamdiu te bene gesseris, statuta Collegii observaveris, et solutiones debitas praestiteris. Ita facienti, precor omnia fausta.

Volumus, ut permissi, sive licentiati, solutiones omnes usitatas praestent Collegio, praesidi, thesaurario, regestario, et bedello; quas modo candidatis praestandas assignavimus.

Volumus praeterea, ut primo permissionis anno, solvant Collegio sex libras: nisi ob causas, a praeside et censoribus approbandas, mitius cum iis agere aequum censebitur: solvent utcunque quatuor minimum libras. Sequentibus autem annis, quamdiu permissi fuerint, solvent in usum Collegii quadraginta solidos.

Statuimus, et ordinamus; ut nemo ad praxin medicinae exercendam permittatur, intra urbem, suburbia, septemque circumcirca milliaria; nisi prius ter (totidem diebus ad id constitutis) examinatus fuerit, a praeside et censoribus, et ab iisdem approbatus, et ad medicinae praxin permissus fuerit.

Quod si quis intra spatium, sive ambitum praedictum, facultatem medicinae exercuerit; nec tamen se examinandum praesidi, et censoribus ultro obtulerit: is primum admoneatur per bedellum, idque praesidis nomine, ut omnino a medicinae praxi abstineat, donec praesidis et Collegii approbationem obtinuerit; utque stato et praefixo tempore, se coram praeside et censoribus sistat; eorum examinationem, atque approbationem expectaturus.

Bedellus autem admonitionis schedulam vel ipsi in manus tradet, vel domi illius relinquet; in haec verba: nos, praeses et censores Collegii Medicorum Londinensium, te admonitum volumus, ut 14° die Junii, coram nobis in propria persona tua compareas; idque post meridiem, inter secundam et tertiam horam ejusdem diei, in aedibus Collegii: ibidem responsurus ad ea, quae tibi de arte medicinae, ejusdemque praxi obiicientur. Datum in aedibus Collegii nostri. 10 die Junii. Anno Domini 1647. Quod si praedicto modo admonitus, non comparuerit; pro refractario habendum, et secundum regni statuta plectendum judicamus. Cum autem nullo modo (nisi examinatione prius habita) nobis constare possit, quam sit quilibet idoneus, ut secundum regni leges ad medicinae praxin admittatur:

Statuimus etiam, et ordinamus; ut si quis medicinam Londini, aut intra limites prae dictos exercens, praesidis jussu ad examen vocatus,

28

comparuerit quidem, sed illi tamen et censoribus respondere, et scientiae suae in medicina facienda, experientiaeque rationem reddere recusaverit; pro ignaro et refractario habeatur, atque ob praxin ita institutam, a praeside et censoribus, secundum regni statuta puniatur.

Statuimus etiam, et ordinamus; ut si quis a praeside et censoribus examinatus, eorum judicio non satis peritus aut idoneus censebitur, qui ad medicinae praxin admittatur; is statim ab iisdem praxi interdicatur: quod si post hujusmodi prohibitionem, medicinae tamen facultatem exercuerit, vel cuipiam medicamentum aliquod, intra eandem civitatem vel circuitum praedictum, exhibuerit; prout regni statutis cautum est, puniatur.

Aequum autem censemus, ut censores, et socii, examinatos omnes, quotquot tam doctrina quam moribus idoneos repererint, ad medicinae praxin admittant: ne Collegium nostrum monopolii accusetur: modo tamen statutis Collegii morem gesserint.

Caput 16

Forma Examinationum Sociorum et Candidatorum, eorundemque Admissionis

Antequam quispiam vel in sociorum, vel candidatorum ordinem admittatur; ter examinetur in legitimis comitiis, sive majoribus, sive minoribus, pro arbitrio praesidis. et censorum; ut antea dictum, et ordinatum est in cap: de comitiis.

Forma autem examinationis hujus modi esto

Primo examinetur in parte physiologica, ipsisque medicinae rudimentis. Atque in hac examinatione proponantur quaestiones ex libris de elementis: de temperamentis: de usu partium: de rebus anatomicis: de naturalibus potentiis et facultatibus; et de caeteris naturalis medicinae partibus.

Secundo, examinetur in parte pathologica, sive de morborum causis, differentiis, symptomatibus, et signis, quibus utuntur medici ad essentiam morborum cognoscendam. Atque in hac examinatione, proponantur quaestiones ex libris de arte medicinali: de locis affectis: de morborum, et symptomatum differentiis: de febribus: de pulsibus: de libris prognostic: Hippocratis. &c.

Tertio, examinetur de usu exercitioque medicinae, sive medendi ratione. Idque fiat ex libris de sanitate tuenda: de methodo medendi: de ratione victus in morbis acutis: de simplici medicina: de crisibus: de aphorismis Hippocratis: et id genus aliis, quae ad medendi usum spectant. Exempli gratia: Quae cautio observanda sit, in purgando? quaenam, in sectione venae? nempe, quo tempore, quo morbo, in qua persona, quali medicamine, in qua vena, ista fieri debeant? Similiter, quis sit usus narcoticorum, et soporiferorum, et quae cautio in illis observanda? Quis sit locorum internorum positus, sive situs: et quibus viis ad ea loca pertingant medicamenta? Quis sit clysterum, quis vomitoriorum usus, periculum, genus, et mensura? Omnes has examinationes fieri volumus a praeside, et censoribus. Licebit tamen cuilibet socio pro arbitrio disputare, et periculum facere, quantum examinandus in re medica valeat. In istis autem examinationibus, cupimus, ut socii candide se gerant, et suavi quodam sermonis temperamento utantur; nequaquam morosos se praebeant aut difficiles in disputando. Si doctoris gradum in aliqua nostrarum academiarum susceperit, honoris causa sedeat, decenter examinandus: ne quid indignum pati a nostra examinationum forma, mater academia videatur.

Qui ad hunc modum examinatus fuerit, si se virum doctum praestiterit, moresque etiam honestos et amabiles habuerit (de quibus insignem curam haberi cupimus) admittatur per majorem partem sociorum praesentium, modo non pauciores illis comitiis adfuerint, quam duodecim, praeter praesidem, aut pro-praesidem:

Formula Admissionis talis esto :

Admittendus, flexis genibus, manus invicem applicatas tradat in manus praesidis; qui dicat, ego J: C: praeses hujus Collegii; admitto te A: B: in societatem nostri Collegii: (vel in ordinem candidatorum, vel in numerum permissorum) quibus peractis (si socius fuerit) singulis sociis praesentibus, exhibita manu, gratias agat. Quod si constet, eum qui examinandus est, in aliqua e nostris academiis per triennium fuisse publicum medicinae praelectorem regium, et doctorem cathedrae, ut aiunt: vel, ob singularem scientiae famam, ad aulam vocatum, atque regis, aut reginae medicum esse; non erit necesse ut examinetur: sed pro arbitrio praesidis, aut pro-praesidis, et majoris partis sociorum praesentium, potest admitti absque ulla disputandi ceremonia. Quicunque, vel censor, vel socius, quaestiones proponit in examinationibus; detecto sit capite, perinde ac doctor ille, qui istuc, ut examinetur, accessit.

Caput 17
De Loco, et Dignitate Praesidis, et omnium Sociorum

Praesidis locus primus esto, ut et dignitas prima: non solum in collegio, sed et aliis omnibus locis.

Medicorum regiorum ordinariorum, qui assignatum stipendium, literasque patentes sub magno regni sigillo habuerint, locus et honos proxime post praesidem esto. Unicuique locus esto pro senioritate; ita ut seniores junioribus, non modo in Collegio, sed et extra illud, ubique praeferantur. Senioritatem autem vocamus, non quam aetas, aut dignitas,

28*

aut ubicunque suscepti gradus tempus fecere, sed quam admissio in Collegium.

Cap: 18

De Anatomica Administratione

Statuimus, et ordinamus; ut singuli Socii, admissionis tempore, fidem dent; se corpus humanum publice, Collegii sumptu, anatomice administraturos, eo anno quem praeses indixerit: idque vel in Collegio, vel alio loco, judicio praesidis, et electorum assignando: potissimum, si quis anatomices peritus iis videbitur. Quod si quis onus impositum recusaverit, atque ipsemet ad eam rem minus idoneus illorum judicio habeatur; solvet quatuor libras in usum Collegii. Sin autem munere hoc debito defungi pervicaciter negaverit: is, pro libito praesidis, et majoris partis sociorum praesentium, mulctabitur; modo tamen poena haec viginti libras non excesserit.

Statuimus etiam, et ordinamus; ut nullus socius, aut alius collega, alibi quam in Collegio, aut loco a praeside et electoribus assignato, publice corporis humani administrationem suscipiat, aut profiteatur, sub poena quatuor librarum: nisi locus ille ab urbe septem minimum milliaribus abfuerit.

Volumus tamen, ut integrum sit cuilibet collegae, publice anatomiam exercere in aula chirurgorum; dummodo communitatis chirurgorum magister, et Domini guardiani, veniam illi prius impetraverint a praeside, aut propraeside. Quippe aequum et rationi consentaneum arbitramur; ut qui per collegam aliquem proficiunt, ii Collegio ipsi aliquod grati animi officium praestent.

Statuimus praetera, ut omnes socii, et candidati, singulis publicis anatomicis dissectionibus in Collegio factis intersint, toga, et pileo decenter vestiti, pro honore collegii et artis; qui contra fecerit, tribus solidis et quatuor denariis plectetur.

Caput 19

De Ornatu, et Vestitu Medicorum

Statuimus, juxta Hippocratis consilium, ut socii omnes vestitu decoro amiciantur, quoties ad Collegium accedunt, aut in publicum prodeunt: ne artis praestantia et dignitas, ob immunditiem, male apud vulgus audiat, et contemptui habeatur.

Quare statuimus, et ordinamus; ut praeses, pro-praeses, electores, censores, reliquique omnes socii, in omnibus comitiis majoribus, collegarum conviviis, funeribus, et anatomicis administrationibus, toga, reliquoque vestitu decenti induantur; sub poena quinque solidorum, Collegio solvendorum, quoties deliquerint.

Caput 20
De Exequiis

Si ex collegis quempiam mori contigerit, (nisi peste obierit) unusquisque collega, per bedellum legitime praemonitus, funus suo ordine sequi, et exequiis, reliquisque divinis officiis, interesse tenebitur; sub poena trium solidorum et quatuor denariorum, Collegii usibus solvendorum. Volumus praeterea, in honorem Collegii, ut praesidi sedile in templo, tapete sive aulaeo, et pulvinari decenti ornetur; tantisper, dum funebria officia, aliaeque divinae solennitates celebrantur.

Caput 21
De Conviviis

Quoniam ex honestis conventibus mutuus amor alitur, atque animi studiosorum recreantur: volumus, ut omnes qui in Collegii societatem admissi fuerint, praesidem, et socios omnes in urbe praesentes, frugali, honesto, ac sufficienti convivio excipiant: idque tempore a praeside prius indicto. Indicat autem ipsorum comitiorum ordinariorum, sive majorum, die; aut quo die visum fuerit, ex quindecim proxime insequentibus festum Divi Michaelis, Nativitatis Domini, Paschalis, aut nativitatis Divi Joannis Baptistae.

Peracto convivio, licebit eodem in loco, exclusis alienis arbitris, comitia celebrare, et Collegii negotia tractare; si res id postulaverit, et necessum praeses et consiliarii judicaverint.

Si autem aliquando contigerit, ut is, cujus est convivium apparare, id commode praestare nequeat, ac propterea ob justam aliquam et honestam causam, a praeside et majori societatis parte approbatam, petierit a societate, ut benigne legibus his solvatur, illoque onere liberetur: rem totam praesidis et societatis prudentia moderandam relinquimus. Quicunque tamen collega gratiam hanc obtinuerit, ut a convivio adornando immunis sit, solvet nihilominus Collegii usibus decem, aut viginti libras; prout aequum videbitur praesidi et majori parti sociorum.

Caput 22
De Conversatione Morali, et Statutis Poenalibus

Si quae lis aut controversia, ex ordine, gravitate, et modestia (quae in comitiis observari praescripsimus) parum observatis, oriatur: arbitrio praesidis aut pro-praesidis, et censorum, quicunque deliquerit, puniatur.

At si praeses contra statuta quid admiserit: admoneatur quidem, per consiliarios, coram sociis in comitiis; non puniatur tamen, nisi ob grave aliquod crimen (quale est peculatus, sive dissipatio bonorum Collegii, et similia) tale judicatum per majorem partem sociorum praesentium: inter quos, volumus, ut quatuor sint ex electoribus; qui una cum reliquis super ea re sententiam ferant. Tantum tribuimus praesidis honori, et auctoritati. Ne quis revelet, aut propalet quidquam alicujus momenti, quod in Collegio dictum sit; sub poena decem solidorum.

Nullus collega alterum, vel ignorantiae, vel malae praxis, vel alicujus sceleris, aut ignominiosi criminis nomine accusabit; vel publice contumeliis afficiet. Si quem contra fecisse, praesidi et censoribus innotuerit; prima vice solvet in Collegii usum quatuor libras: secundo duplicabitur mulcta; quod si tertio quis similiter offenderit, expelletur e Collegio; nec denuo restituetur, priusquam Collegio decem libras solverit.

Nullus medicus, qui secundus ad aegrum vocabitur, priorem medicum repelli faciet: nec quicquam prius innovabit (nisi res urgeat) quam illum convenerit. Et, ne quis fraudi locus sit; quicunque ad aegrum accersitur, ab illo, vel astantibus, an quis medicamentum aliquod praescripserit, percunctabitur: sub poena viginti solidorum.

Postea tamen, ex aegri sententia, vel solus illi medebitur; vel cum priori medico, aut alio aliquo, rem administrabit. Dabit tamen operam, quantum poterit, ut priorem secum in praxi retineat. Quod si aegroti, vel amicorum consensu, id fieri nequeat; priorem tamen medicum nullo modo vituperabit; nec vultu, gestu, suspitioso silentio, vel ullo alio modo illius acta apud aegrum vel astantes traduces sed eum laudabit potius; neque id dolose, honestatis et probitatis nomine; sed (quod ad rem maxime attinet) periti et intelligentis medici: memor semper, ut alterius famam apud alios eo loco habeat, quo suam mutatis vicibus esse cuperet. Nempe, ad artis, quam profitetur, honorem et dignitatem.

Consultandi Formula

Si plures, curationis gratia, convenerint; de conditione aegri deliberaturi; consultandum est summa modestia, et non, nisi seclusis arbitris alienis: latine autem res transigatur; alioquin mulcta esto quinque solidorum, in usum Collegii.

Tunc primum, sedulo inquirendum in morbi speciem, causam, et symptomata: deinde remedia proponenda, ad morbum profligandum, et symptomata mitiganda maxime convenientia.

Incipiat junior medicus, concludat senior. At si senior aliquis primo accersitus fuerit, enarret ille primum rem totam reliquis; nempe, quid egerit, et quo successu: deinde fiat, ut dictum est.

Si saepius ad eundem aegrum visendum convenerint; nemo quidquam praescribat, imo ne innuat quidem quid agendum sit, coram aegro, vel astantibus, priusquam conjunctis consiliis privatim inter ipsos medicos conclusum fuerit: ne quis ambitiose nimium videatur praxin praeoccupare, et reliquis liberam praescribendi ansam praeripere; nisi subita et urgente aliqua occasione (eaque approbanda a praeside, et censoribus) coactus fuerit solus praescribere.

Si medici in diversas eant sententias, ita ut in eandem praxin inter se consentire nequeant; summa tamen prudentia et moderatione sic se gerant, ut eorem discordia in artis praejudicium non cedat; nec aliis, si fieri possit, innotescat.

Si duo tantum medici fuerint, junior cedat seniori; vel tertium advocent, cui res referatur: si plures, vincat pars major: si dissidentes numero pares fuerint, concludatur cum majori parte seniorum. Sic honori et dignitati artis providebitur; quae alioquin, per medicorum discordiam, facile contemptui habebitur: qui contra fecerit, mulctabitur quadraginta solidis.

Ne qua lis aut controversia inter medicos, propter officiosas visitationes, praeoccupationes, et insinuationes, oriatur; statuimus et ordinamus; ut cum ad medicum quemlibet alii medici consultandi gratia advocati fuerint; ac secundum formulam, a nobis praescriptam, de morbo et remediis inter eos convenerit; senior medicus, aut alius aliquis, referat aegro, aut astantibus, quae approbata et praescripta communi consensu fuerint; eorundemque executionem caeteri ordinario medico relinquant; nec denuo visitabunt aegrum, nisi a medico ordinario, aut ab aegro, ut id faciant, expresse rogati fuerint. Nullus medicus, sive socius, sive candidatus, sive permissus, consilium ineat cum empirico, aut rejecto a Collegio, et a medicinae praxi prohibito, aut alio aliquo, sine admissione, aut permissione, medicinam exercente: nisi urgente aliqua causa, a praeside aut propraeside, et censoribus, aut majori parte illorum approbanda, sub poena quadraginta solidorum.

Quilibet medicus contentus esto honesta pro conditione aegri, et laboris sui, mercede. Nemo pasciscetur cum aegro, aut alio quovis aegri nomine, de pretio sanitatis restituendae. Verum si quis aegros susceperit curandos, qui sibi aliter satisfactum non putabunt, ni pactionem ineant cum medico: aut in eos incidat, qui facultatum suarum, aut honoris nulla habita ratione, parce nimis et illiberaliter agunt cum medicis; cum talibus licebit pacisci. Reservata tamen potestate domino praesidi, et censoribus, atque in eorum absentia, quatuor ex electoribus pro ipsorum prudentia corrigere, si quid iniquius pactum sit, et immutare.

Ne quis doceat populum medicamenta, aut horum nomina illi indicet; (praesertim si fuerint medicamenta vehementiora, veluti purgantia, opiata, vel narcotica, abortum facientia, vomitoria, aut quidquam aliud majoris momenti ac periculi) ne abusu eorum laedatur populus: sub poena quadraginta solidorum, quoties offenderit.

Qui pasciscitur cum pharmacopolis de aliqua pretii parte ex medicamentis praescribendis percipienda; mulctabitur quadraginta solidis, quoties ita deliquerit.

Nullus socius, candidatus, aut permissus, eorum pharmacopolarum opera utetur; qui aut ipsi medicinam exercent; aut iis medicis crebro inserviunt, qui examinati et approbati non sunt secundum statuta hujus regni: sub poena decem solidorum, quoties offenderit, collegio solvendorum: modo ea de re, a praeside, aut pro-praeside, et censoribus praemonitus fuerit.

Nemo mulctam, sibi pro delicto secundum statuta inflictam, solvere recusabit; sub poena violatae fidei Collegio praestitae.

Quoniam pharmacopolae, et chirurgi, saepe ad medicos urinas aegrotantium deferunt; petuntque, ut ab urinarum inspectione aliquid aegris suis praescribant; ac deinde, sub hoc consultationis praetextu, reliquam curationis telam, ipsimet pro arbitrio pertexunt: quicquid inde quaestus, sive lucri est, id omne sibi arripientes; medicis vero nihil, praeter exilem illam et jejunam urinarum spectandarum mercedem, offerentes: idcirco statuimus, et ordinamus; ut nemo, sive socius, sive candidatus, sive permissus, consilii quidquam impertiat istiusmodi veteratoriis impostoribus, super urinarum nuda inspectione: nisi simul ad aegrum vocetur: ut ibidem pro re nata, idonea medicamenta, ab honesto aliquo pharmacopola componenda, praescribat.

Volumus praeterea; ut singulis schedulis, sive receptis (ut vocant) diem mensis, et nomen aegri, suumque quisque adscribat. Ridiculum quidem est, et insulsum, ex urinarum solummodo inspectione, sive de morbi genere et natura, sive de aegrotantis statu ac conditione, aruspicum et conjectorum more, velle quidquam certi solidique divinare. Monemus igitur omnes medicos, ut hac in re multo cautius in posterum se gerant, quam antehac a plerisque factitari solitum. Et hanc ob causam, omnibus medicinam exercentibus interdictum volumus, ne idiotis istis et mulierculis, aegrotantium matulas circumferentibus, aliquod medicamentum praescribant; nisi aut ipsum aegrum prius recte noverint, aut saltem ab iis, qui consilium petunt, de morbo, ejusque circumstantiis, et plane, et plene instructi fuerint. Quippe hac ratione, et dignitatem medicinae melius tuebimur, et multo aptius certiusque remedia periclitantibus profutura excogitabimus.

Denique, statuimus, et ordinamus; ut, quicunque admittuntur in societatem Collegii, subscriptis nominibus polliceantur, se statuta omnia praedicta diligenter observaturos; aut mulctas, contra facientibus inflictas, non invito animo persoluturos.

Si ad hanc normam, Collegium prudenti consilio praesidis, electorum, et censorum, gubernetur; debito et obedienti caeterorum officio honestetur; et exterminatis indoctis, profligatisque odiosis impostoribus, scientia decoretur; certissimum est, et florentissimum futurum hoc nostrum Collegium in perpetuum, et universae etiam reipublicae (quantum nostra officia attinet) recte provideque consultum iri.

Quare per fidem illam Collegio datam, socios omnes hortamur, et obtestamur, ut quoquoversum diligenter prospiciant, et providenter agant: nec quenquam, respectu personarum habito, admittant in societatem Collegii: sed ad laudem, decus, honorem, et perpetuitatem societatis omnia decernant. Quoniam certum est, Collegium nostrum nulla re firmius stabiliri posse, et continuari; quam bonis legibus, probis gubernatorum moribus, et collegarum singulari virtute atque eruditione.

Finis.

Index Capitum

III : THE CHARTER OF
KING JAMES II

JAMES THE SECOND By the grace of God of England Scotland France and Ireland King defender of the faith &c To ALL to whom these presents shall come greeting WHEREAS our most noble and renowned predecessor Henry the Eight late King of England by his Letters Patents bearing date at Westminster the twenty third of September in the tenth yeare of his reigne did erect found and establish a perpetuall Colledge Comonalty and Incorporacion of Phisitians in the Citty and Suburbs of London and for seven miles every way in distance from the same with power annually to elect a president of the same Colledge or Comonalty and did thereby give and grant unto the sayd Colledge or Comonalty divers liberties priviledges immunities powers and authorities as well for the advantage of the said President Colledge or Comonalty and their successors as for the suppressing and restrayning of illiterate persons from being practizers in the said faculty as by the same Letters Patents remayning of record amongst other things therein conteyned more plainly and fully doeth and may appeare which said Letters Patents and every article grant and thing therein conteyned were by Act of Parliament made in the Parliament begun at London in the fourteenth yeare and prorogued to Westminster in the fifteenth yeare of the reigne of our said noble predecessor King Henry the Eight approved ratified and confirmed And by severall other Acts of Parliament divers other priviledges powers & authorities are and were afterwards given granted and confirmed to the said President Colledge or Corporacion of Phisitians and their successors as by the same severall Acts of Parliament thereof made more fully and at large also it doth and may appeare And whereas neverthelesse our royall grandfather James the first of ever blessed memory late King of England perceiving abuses not then sufficiently provided for did dayly encrease through the unskilfulnesse and fraud of phisitians apothecaries druggists and such like by his Letters Patents under the Great Seale of England bearing date at Westminster the Eighth day of October in the fifteenth yeare of his reigne over England did ratify allow approve and confirme unto the said President Colledge or Comonalty of Phisitians and their successors the said Letters Patents of our said noble predecessor King Henry the Eight herein before mencioned and every grant article and the thing therein conteyned and not altered by the said Letters Patents of our said royall grandfather And further our said royall grandfather did by his said Letters Patents give and grant unto the said Colledge or Comonalty

and their successors divers other liberties powers priviledges abilities
and authorities not onely for the benefitt of the aforesaid President and
Colledge or Comonalty and their successors but also for the more certaine
speedy and easy discovery punishment and restraint as well of illiterate
and unskilfull practizers of the faculty of phisick as likewise the frauds
and deceipts of apothecaries druggists and others as by the same Letters
Patents remaining of record amongst other things therein conteyned doth
and may appeare AND whereas our dearest brother Charles the Second
late King of England of ever blessed memory in his great wisdome and
prudence finding the many and great liberties powers and priviledges
aforesaid unto the said President Colledge or Comonalty given granted
and confirmed by the said Letters Patents and Acts of Parliament in-
effectuall for the purposes intended was graciously pleased to the end
that all frauds abuses and defects might be more easily remedied and
supplied by his Letters Patents bearing date at Westminster the twenty
sixth day of March in the fifteenth yeare of his reigne to give and grant
unto the said President and Colledge or Comonalty that they from thence-
forth forever should be continue and remaine on perpetuall body corporate and politick in deed fact and name by the name of the President
Colledge and Comonalty of the Kings Colledge of Physitians in the Citty
of London And by the same Letters Patents did likewise give and grant
unto the said President Fellowes or Comonalty divers liberties priviledges
and immunities powers abilities and authorities as well for the good
government of the said Colledge or Comonalty as for the surveying
restrayning and punishing unlicenced and unskilfull practizers in the
faculty of Physick and all dealers in corrupt medicines and druggs or
other things to be used in physick as in and by the said Letters Patents
of our said royall brother remayning of record amongst many other
things therein conteyned more fully and at large it doth and may appeare
KNOW YEE that wee graciously designeing and zealously affecting nothing
so much as the safety and honour of our Kingdome and the publique
good and comon benefitt of all our loving subiects and seriously intending
to remedy and prevent the great abuses frauds enormities frequently
practized and comitted by divers apothecaries druggists and others in
the said Citty of London and to punish and suppresse all ignorant
unskilfull and unlicenced empiricks who have in open defyance and
contempt of authority dared publickly to professe and practize physick
and have yett evaded the just and condign punishment provided &
intended by the Charters and Acts of Parliament aforesaid for such
presumptuous offenders and to give all due encouragement to the judicious
learned and experienced professors of so noble and necessary a faculty
of our especiall grace certaine knowledge and meer mocion at the humble
peticion of Sir Thomas Witherley Knight now President of the said
Colledge or Comonalty one of our Physitians and of divers other learned

doctors of the said Colledge or Comonalty HAVE willed ordeyned given granted and confirmed And by these presents do for us our heires and successors will ordeyne give grant and confirme unto the said President Colledge or Commonalty that they from henceforth forever herafter shall bee continue and remaine one perpetuall body corporate and politick in deed fact and name by the name of President Colledge or Comonalty of the Faculty of Physick in London and that they shall have perpetuall succession and a comon seale to serve and use for all the affaires causes and things whatsoever of them and their successors And that they shall be capable by the said name of President Colledge or Comonalty of the Faculty of Physick in London of purchasing having holding alening and disposeing lands tenements goods and chattells and of impleading and being impleaded answering and being answered in any Court before any person or persons and in any suits causes or demands whatsoever and Wee have further of our like speciall grace certaine knowledge and meer mocion willed ordeyned given granted ratified allowed and confirmed and by these presents do for us our heires and successors will ordeyne give grant ratify approve allow and confirme unto the aforesaid President Colledge or Commonalty and their successors forever the said Letters Patents of our sayd noble predecessor King Henry the Eighth of our sayd royall grandfather King James the First and of our sayd dearest brother King Charles the Second herein beforemencioned and all and singular the articles clauses gifts grants franchises liberties priviledges immunities powers and authorities therein mencioned or conteyned and not hereby altered in as full and ample manner as if the same were herein perticulerly and att large recited and granted And the sayd President Colledge or Comonalty and their Successors by the name of President Colledge or Comonalty of the Faculty of Physick in London shall and may forever hereafter have receive take retayne keepe use exercise and enioy all and singular rights titles liberties priviledges immunities abilities powers authoritys and other things as by the said Letters Patents or by any Acts of Parliament are or were given granted or confirmed or were thereby mencioned or intended to bee given granted or confirmed Notwithstanding the not useing misuseing abuseing or surrender of the same or any of them AND that these presents and the aforesaid Letters Patents and every article and clause therein conteyned shall bee adiudged taken and construed most benignely and favourably to and for the best benefitt and advantage of the aforesaid President Colledge or Comonalty and their successors Any ordinance custome usage or other matter or thing to the contrary in any wise notwithstanding And for the better execucion of our will and pleasure herein declared WE HAVE named constituted and appointed and by these presents do for us Our heires and successors name constitute and appoint Our trusty and welbeloved subject Sir Thomas Witherley

Knight Our Physitian Sir George Ent Knight Sir Charles Scarburgh Knight Our Chief Phisitian Dr. Walter Charlton Dr. George Rogers Dr. Thomas Burwell Dr. Jonn Betts Dr. Peter Barwick. Dr. Samuel Collins Dr. Nathaniel Hodges Sir Thomas Millington Knight, Dr. John Lawson Dr. Humphrey Brooke Dr. John Bidgood Dr. Nicholas Stanley Dr. Edmund Dickenson Phisitian to Our household Dr. John Attfeild Dr. Henry Paman Dr. William Walgrave Physitian to Our dearest consort the Queen Dr. John Downes Dr. Charles Conquest Dr. Robert Peirce Dr. Robert Brady Our Physitian Dr. William Stokeham Dr. Richard Griffith Dr. Ferdinando Mendez Phisitian to Our dearest sister Katherine the Queen Dowager Dr. Walter Needham Dr. Richard Lower Dr. Edward Browne Dr. William Johnson Dr. Phineas Fowke Dr. Edward Hulse Dr. Samuel Morrice Dr. Edward Baynard Dr. Charles Goodall Sir John Gourden Dr. Theodore Colladon Dr. Andrew Clench Dr. Thomas Alvey Dr. Edmond King Dr. William Johnson Dr. Walter Harris Dr. Richard Blackborne Dr. William Briggs Dr. Charles Frazier Our Phisitian Dr. Francis Bernard Dr. Robert Grey Dr. Richard Smith Dr. Frederick Slare Dr. William Dawkins Dr. George How Dr. Christopher Love Morley Dr. Lancelot Harrison Dr. Walter Mills Dr. Edward Tyson Dr. Richard Robinson Dr. Richard Carre Dr. John Elliott Dr. William Dawes Dr. Joshua Leffeure Dr. Thomas Walsh Dr. Richard Darnelley Dr. Thomas Gill Dr. Christian Harrell Dr. Robert Pitt Dr. John Harrison Dr. John Bateman Dr. John Hungerford Dr. John Ratcliffe Dr. Edward Betts Dr. Thomas Palmer Dr. Hans Sloane Dr. Richard Feild Dr. Martin Lister Dr. Cornelius Callow Dr. Richard Blackmore Dr. Tancred Robinson and Dr. Simon Welman to be the first and present fellowes of the said Colledge or Corporacion And the said Sir Thomas Witherley Knight the first and present president and the said Dr. George Rogers and the first and present vicepresident and the said Sir George Ent Sir Charles Scarburgh Dr. Walter Charleton Dr. George Rogers Dr. Thomas Burwell Dr. John Betts Dr. Peter Barwick Dr. Samuell Collins Dr. Nathaniel Hodges Sir Thomas Millington Dr. John Lawson and Dr. Humphrey Brooke the first and present Elects And the said Dr. John Betts Dr. Edward Browne Dr. William Briggs and Dr. William Dawkins the first and present censors And the said Sir Thomas Millington the first and present treasurer and the said Dr. Burwell the first and present register of the same Colledge AND OUR will and pleasure is and wee do hereby for us our heires and successors direct grant and comand that the president vicepresident elects fellowes treasurer register and censors shall not exceed in the whole the number of fourscore at any one time And that the president vicepresident elects and censors and the treasurer register and other officers of the said Colledge shall respectively continue and bee and shalbe from time to time nominated and chosen and have being and continuance as such respectively for such times and in such manner and forme to all intents and purposes and they and all other the members of the said Colledge of any other order or denominacion be subject to the same government oversight correcion and punishment as in and by the aforesaid Letters Patents of our said royall brother King Charles the Second of ever blessed memory or in and by the Private Acts Bylawes Orders or Ordinances of the said Colledge is specified mencioned declared and appointed and likewise that the said present treasurer and all succeeding treasurers of the said Colledge & Corporacion which shall from time to time be chosen & elected by the said president & fellowes or in the absence of the president by the vice-president and fellowes as aforesaid shall att or before his or their entring upon the said office of treasurer give sufficient security to the said President Colledge or Comonalty in the presence of three witnesses at the least not being members of the said Colledge or Corporacion for his or their true and faithfull discharge and performance of the said office AND OUR further pleasure is and Wee do by these presents for us our heires and successors grant constitute appoint & require that every person whatsoever not formerly a member of the said Colledge and Corporation or not in and of the same rank Order or degree wherein hee is hereby ordeyned and constituted of and in the said Colledge or Corporacion who now is or hereafter at any time shalbe ordeyned constituted chosen or admitted into any of the said orders shall pay at the time of his constitution or admission all the fees and payments due and payable to the said Colledge and Corporacion by vertue of late usage or the Statutes and Bylawes or any Orders or Ordinances of the said Colledge or Corporacion And also that all and every fellow and all and every other member of what degree or order soever of and in the said Colledge or Corporacion which now are or hereafter shalbe who have not already made and paid his and their respective subscripcions towards the building of the said Colledge or hall of the said Colledge or Comonalty or towards the payment of the great debts heretofore contracted and still owing by the said President Colledge or Comonalty or their predecessors shall forthwith discharge make and pay unto the said President Colledge or Comonalty such subscriptions which of late have been ordered and appointed by the said Colledge and Corporacion And have been made by them or any of them or ordinarily made and paid by others of the same degree and order towards the dischargeing and payment of the debts of the said Corporacion or building of the said Colledge which said subscripcions shalbe made at the time of their admission into the said Colledge and Corporacion and continued by all and every fellow and other member of the said Colledge and Corporacion of what degree or order soever untill the said debts now due & oweing shalbe fully paid and discharged AND WEE do hereby will and require and by these presents give full power and authority to the said President

Colledge and Comonalty to expell amove and discharge all and every of the said fellowes and other members of the said Colledge or Corporacion now being or which hereafter shalbe who shall refuse or deny to discharge make and pay his their or any of their respective subscripcions fees and other late customary payments before mencioned or who shall deny or neglect to pay any mulct or penalty which by the Statutes Orders or Ordinances of the said Colledge or Corporacion now are or hereafter at any time shall be made or imposed upon him them or any of them respectively and to choose appoint and admitt others in his and their stead AND OUR WILL and pleasure is and wee do by these presents ordeyne appoint and declare that every person so expelled and amoved as aforesaid shall from and after the time of his expulsion and removall bee noe longer reputed deemed or taken to bee a member of the said Colledge or Corporacion nor shall enioy any privilege or imunity granted or belonging to the members of the said Colledge or Corporacion and shall bee lyable to all such punishments forfeitures and penalties as if hee had never been a member of the same And that if any member of the said Colledge or Commonalty shall presume to consult or advise for any patient with any person soe expelled as aforesaid itt shall and may bee lawfull for the said president and censors or the greater number of them to impose such amerciaments and penalties upon such offenders as are or hereafter shalbe directed by and agreeable to the Orders Ordinances or Bylawes of the said Colledge which said president and censors shall acquaint the fellowes and comonalty of the said Colledge or Corporacion with such their proceedings at their next quarterly meeting or convocacion And the sayd president fellowes or comonalty or the maior part of them being present shall have hereby full power and authority or amove and expell such offenders from their severall and respective places in the said Colledge or Corporacion and choose others in their stead if they shall thinke itt convenient soe to doe AND TO the end the government estate and affaires of the said Colledge or Corporacion may bee administered carryed on and managed with the greater care circumspecion and security in time to come Wee in our princely wisedome have thought fitt and doe these presents will and require and doe for us our heires and successors grant unto the said President Colledge or Comonalty and their successors that such persons as have election of the censors of the said Colledge shall and may in such sort as the said censors are elected within one moneth next after the date hereof and afterwards at such time and in such manner as the said censors have been usually chosen elect and choose tenn of the said fellowes of the said Colledge and Corporacion whereof the President alwaies to bee one to bee a comittee who shall assemble and meet togeather as often as they shall thinke fitt and they or any five of them have full power and authority to consider of and make enquiry into all such matters and things whatsoever as may conduce to the interest welfare and advantage of the said Colledge and Corporacion and shall make their reporte from time to time of all their proceedings to the president and other the fellowes of the said Colledge or Comonalty att their next quarterly meeting and convocacion AND WEE do further for us our heires and successors will and require ordeyn and strictly comand that noe person or persons whatsoever shall att anytime from and after the expiracion of a certein Act of Parliament now in force made in the fourteenth yeare of the reigne of our said royall brother King Charles the Second Intituled An Act for Preventing Abuses in Printing Seditious Treasonable and Unlicenced Bookes and Pamphletts and for Regulateing of Printing and Printing Presses revived and continued by a certaine Clause in another Act of Parliament made in the first yeare of Our reigne intituled An Act for Reviving and Continuance of severall Acts of Parliament therein mancioned either print or publish or cause to bee printed or published any bookes pamphletts writings papers or other significacions or intimacions whatsoever of or concerning phisick or chirurgery or the practice thereof or in any wise relateing thereto nor in the meanetime from and after the date of these presents print or publish or cause to be printed or published any bookes pamphletts writings papers or other significacions or initmacions whatsoever of or concerning phisick or chirurgery or the practice thereof not mencioned or comprized in the before mencioned Act of Parliament nor thereby appointed to be otherwise licensed unles the same bookes pamphletts papers, writings significacions and intimacions before mencioned and every of them together with all their titles epistles prefaces proems preambles introduccions and tables and all other matters and things thereunto annexed or in any wise apperteyning or belonging be first licensed authorized and appointed to be printed or published by the president and censors of the said Colledge for the time being AND WEE do further of our especiall grace certeine knowledge and meer mocion for us our heires and successors give and grant unto the said president and censors of the said Colledge and Corporacion for the time being from and after the expiracion of the said Act of Parliament beforemencioned full and sole power priviledge liberty and authority of licenceing and appointing and to license authorize and appoint to bee hereafter printed reprinted written or published all and singuler bookes pamphletts papers writings significacions and intimacions whatsoever in any wise relating to phisick or chirurgery or the practice thereof And in the meantime from and after the date of these presents all and singuler books pamphlets papers and writings significacions & intimacions whatsoever in any wise relating to phisick or chirurgery or the practice thereof as aforesaid not mencioned or comprized in the said act of Parliament concerning printing nor thereby appointed to be otherwise licensed PROVIDED alwaies neverthelesse and Our will and pleasure is and wee do hereby declare Our royall intent and meaning to bee that itt shall and may bee lawfull to and for us our heires and successors at any time and at all times hereafter by any Order or Orders of Councell of Us Our heires or successors to amove or displace the president or any the fellows elects censors or other officers or members of the said Colledge and Corporacion of any order or denominacion whatsoever which now are or hereafter shall bee when and as often as itt shall seeme meete to us our heires or Successors AND WEE do by these presents for us our heires and Successors give and grant unto the said Sir George Ent Sir Charles Scarburgh Dr. Walter Charleton and Dr. George Rogers or any one or more of them full power and authority to give and administer unto the said Sir Thomas Witherley an Oath for his duely executing the office of president of the said Colledge and Corporacion And also full power and authority unto the said Sir Thomas Witherley he being first sworne as aforesaid to give and administer unto all and every the persons above-named hereby constituted the first and present elects and fellowes and censors of the said Colledge and Corporacion the usuall and accustomed Oath on the holy Evangelists well truly and faithfully to attend and execute his and their severall and respective offices or places which said Oath Wee will and require all and every the fellowes of the said Cor-poracion for the time being And also the president elects fellowes and censors abovenamed severally and respectively to take and also that the said Oath shall att all times hereafter bee taken given and administred by and before such person and persons and in such manner as by the said Letters Patents of our royall brother is directed and appointed in that behalfe ALTHOUGH Expresse mencion of the true yearely value or certeinty of the Premisses or any of them or of other guifts or grants by us or by any of our progenitors or predecessors heretofore made in these presents is not made or any Statute Act Ordinance Provision Proclam-acion or Restriccion to the contrary thereof heretofore had made enacted ordeyned or provided or any other matter Cause or thing whatsoever in any wise notwithstanding IN WITNESSE whereof Wee have caused these Our Letters to bee made Patents WITTNES OURSELFE att Westminster the Eleaventh day of March In the Third yeare of our Reigne.

By Writt of Privy Seale PIGOTT